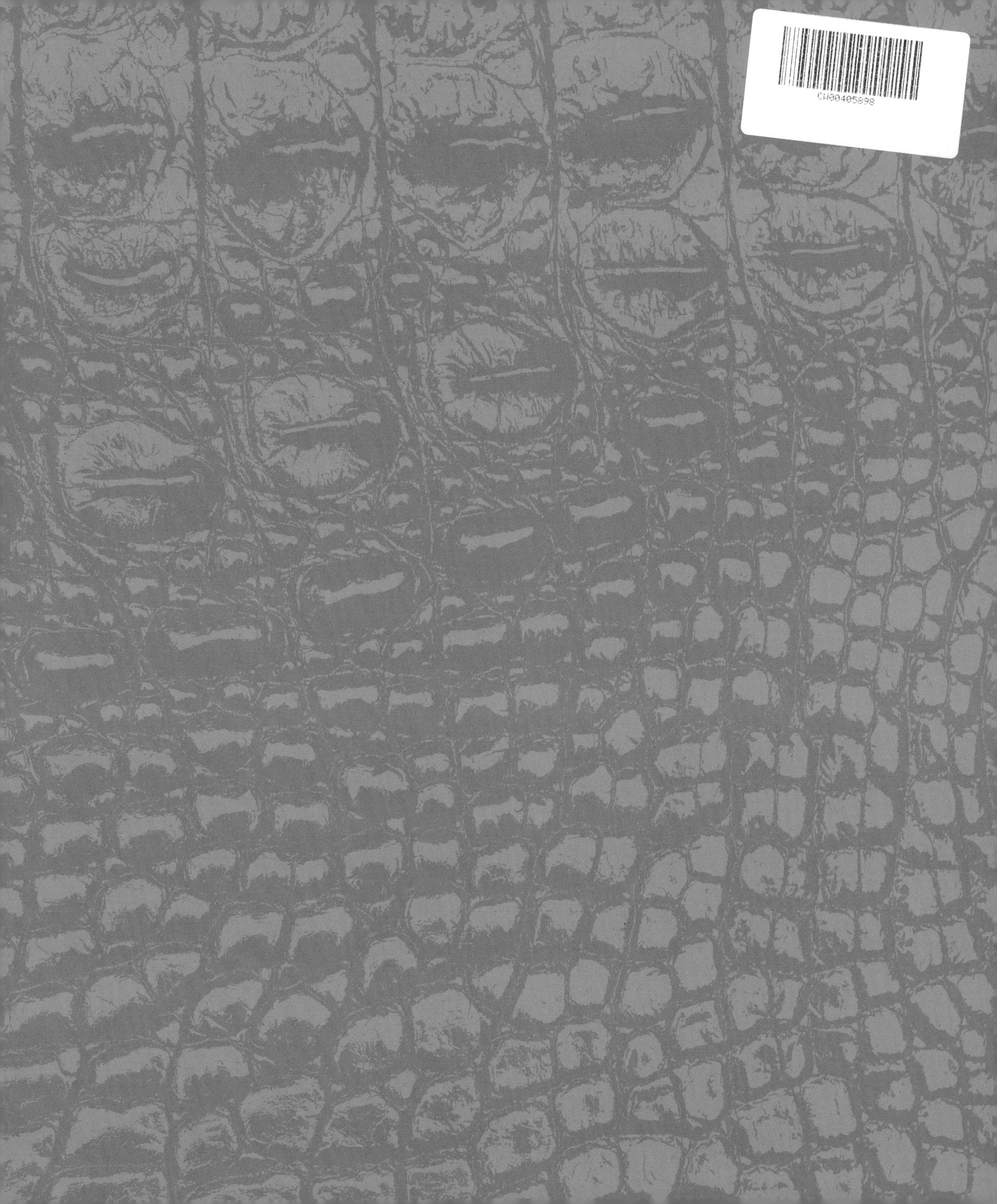

Australian Geographic

AUSTRALIA GONE WILD

Australian Geographic

AUSTRALIA GONE WILD

An anthology of the best nature stories from Australian Geographic

◆

Edited by

Chrissie Goldrick, Joanna Hartmann and Geordie Torr

The short-beaked echidna, or spiny anteater, is that most peculiar of things: an egg-laying mammal. Along with platypuses, echidnas are the only egg-laying mammals still in existence, and each shares a common ancestor.

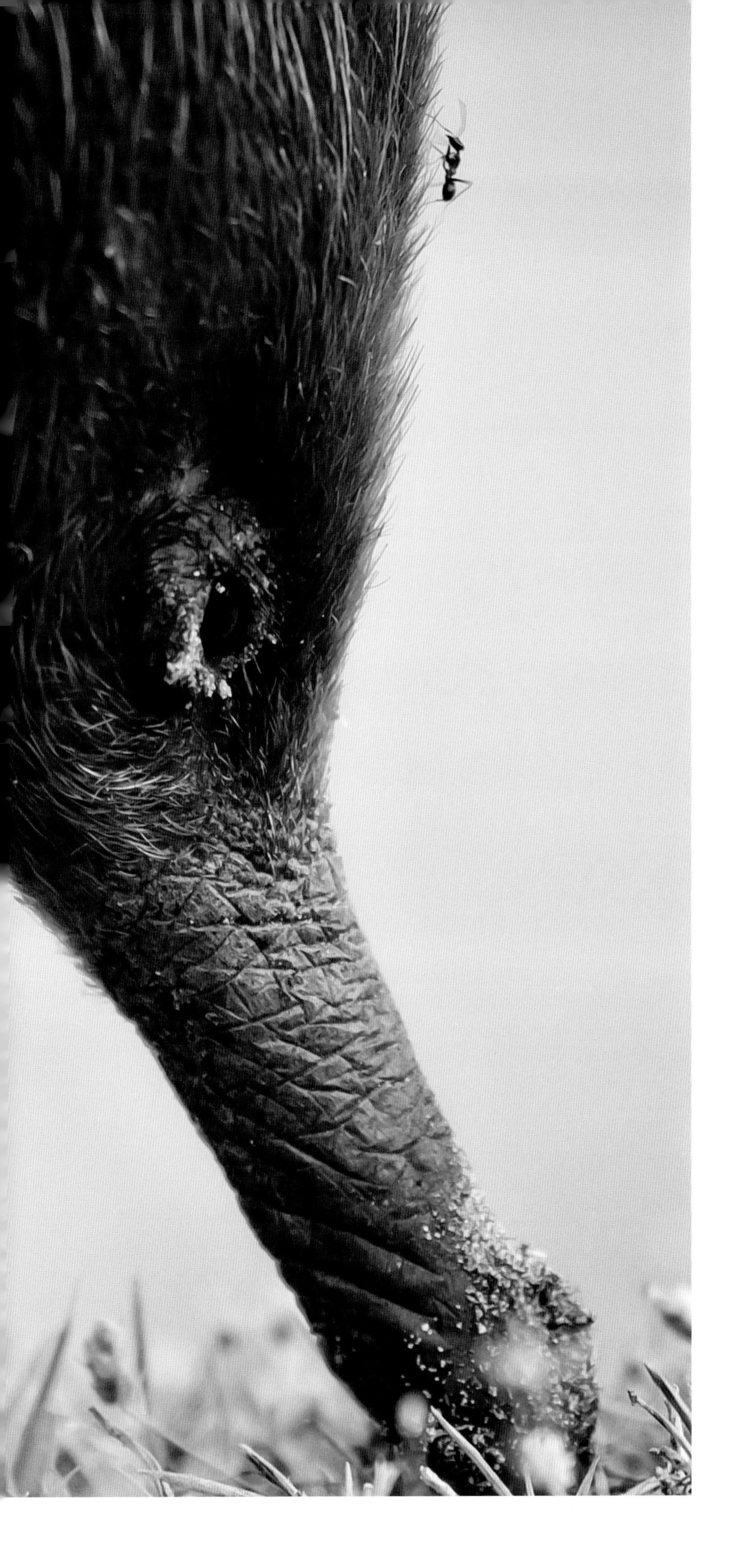

Contents

The stories included here date from 1986 to 2017 and reflect the times in which they were written. They may also contain facts, figures and values that were correct at the time of original publication.

Encrusted in corals, sponges and other invertebrates, the wreck of the *SS Yongala*, south-east of Townsville, hosts an extraordinary abundance and diversity of marine life and is regarded as one of the world's greatest artificial reefs.

Introduction

I WONDER WHAT IMAGES the word Australia first conjures up for people who have never visited the place. Could it be a packed Bondi Beach on a sizzling summer's day, complete with Aussie surf life-savers? Maybe it's Sydney's Opera House or Harbour Bridge? Perhaps it's the grandeur of Uluru as the setting sun paints its ramparts burnt orange?

I suspect it's more likely to be a bounding red kangaroo, like the one emblazoned on the tail of the national airline, or a docile koala chomping on gum leaves with a cute joey clinging to its back – the classic postcard shot. It's the very strangeness of our native creatures that prompts that instantaneous connection between beast and country. And it's almost certainly our unique fauna that symbolise Australia to the world more than anything created by humankind.

After the Australian continent broke free from Antarctica – 45 million years ago, during the last major Gondwanan continental plate split – its plants and animals evolved independently from the rest of the world. The legacy of such splendid isolation is a multitude of unusual and remarkable creatures, many of which are found nowhere else on the planet. Add to this those species we share with our near neighbours and the visitors that fly to our shorelines and swim in our waters, and what emerges is an epic, ancient story of extraordinary biodiversity that, until recent history, was largely unknown and untouched by the world beyond our shores.

It's the sharing of this story that has been at the heart of Australian Geographic's mission since the launch of the *Australian Geographic* journal in 1986. Back then, the term climate change had only recently been coined, although fears about the hole in the ozone layer and the build-up of atmospheric greenhouse gases were gaining momentum. Set against the backdrop of the '80s, which came to define excess, *Australian Geographic* was founded during a period of unprecedented growth in expert knowledge of our natural environment and of recognition of the accumulation of human impacts on it.

From its outset, *Australian Geographic* has sought to inform, educate and inspire readers about the fauna, flora and landscapes of our native land, with a particular focus on Australia's native birds, reptiles and mammals. For the first 20 years, each of the journal's covers featured an original illustration of a native species, beginning in 1986 with the stylised platypus nicknamed Banjo, an image that came to be regarded as the symbol of the organisation. A year later, the Australian Geographic Society was established to channel funds from the commercial business back into

Banjo the platypus, illustrated by wildlife artist Rod Scott, adorned the launch issue of *Australian Geographic* in 1986 and quickly became symbolic of the organisation.

the kinds of research programs that informed many of the stories being covered. It's a grant-giving program that still annually commits more than $250,000 to conservation and adventure.

During the subsequent 30 years, there's hardly a native species that hasn't had the forensic eye of an AG reporter and long lens of an AG photographer fully trained on it.

In this book, we have chosen more than 50 of the best nature stories from the first 139 issues of *Australian Geographic*. Each has been carefully edited to fit the book's format, in most cases by the original writers. The stories range in age from Andy Park's Tasmanian tiger story from issue 3 in 1986 to Tim Low's recent exposé of native Australian species creating havoc abroad, which ran in July 2017. Taken together, the narratives presented here represent a squawking, humming, snarling, growling, trilling, whistling carnival of weird and wonderful wild Aussie creatures. They range from national icons such as the red kangaroo, platypus, koala and wombat to their lesser-known relatives the tree kangaroos, hairy-nosed wombats, numbats and yellow-footed rock-wallabies.

You'll read of the birds that form an especially conspicuous part of Australia's natural bounty, including those that share our backyards such as raucous rainbow lorikeets, clever magpies and, increasingly, the comical brush turkeys making a big comeback in Sydney's not-so-outer suburbs.

You'll meet species teetering on the brink of extinction and the committed scientists working hard to save them, as well as a host of feral animals that often evoke conflicting emotions depending on which side of the fence – sometimes quite literally – that you stand.

You'll learn about the rhythm of life in a wide range of ecosystems and the boom-bust cycles that define life on the margins of existence in the harsh environments of the continent's arid heart.

Perhaps our greatest natural treasure isn't a single species at all, but a living topographical feature that extends for more than 2300km off the Queensland coast. The Great Barrier Reef is rightly a source of wonder and pride and ought to be the urgent focus of multi-agency and multidisciplinary efforts to preserve its remarkable biodiversity. And yet our custodianship of it continues to raise questions. In 1993 an Australian Geographic team was among the first to witness and document the mass spawning that occurs there after the first full moon of each November.

Running like a golden thread through this entire book is the passion of the researchers and volunteers working together to learn more, and educate others, about particular species. What becomes clear is the link between in-depth knowledge and action. There is hardly a story here that doesn't resound with the voices of those dedicated to saving their beloved animals – from the largest animal ever to have lived on earth, the blue whale, down to the tiniest frog the size of a fingernail, and everything in between.

These creatures, great and small, are universally connected by the same cocktail of human-induced threats – climate change, habitat loss, feral predation and the other consequences of a rapidly growing global human population. This could make for a depressing read, but the message that comes through loud and clear in this book is, resoundingly, one of hope.

It's probably too late to undo what's been done and to save those things already lost for good. But we can still act to safeguard what's left, and there's no time to lose. ■

Chrissie Goldrick
Editor-in-chief

Found across the continent, emus have extended their range since European colonisation owing to greater availability of human-made watering points in arid areas. At its fastest, a sprinting emu can reach speeds of 70km/h.

CHAPTER ONE

MAMMALS, MARSUPIALS & ICONS

Australia is the only continent that's still home to all three of the major groups of mammal: monotremes, marsupials and placental mammals. A total of 386 mammal species have been described from Australia, almost 90 per cent of which are found nowhere else.

This high level of endemism reflects the incredible length of time that Australia was isolated from the other continents, which amounts to more than 40 million years. During that time, Australia's mammals evolved independently from those in the rest of the world.

As the land that would go on to become Australia began its lonely journey across the Indian Ocean, its only mammalian passengers were marsupials and monotremes. Those animals radiated out to fill the various ecological niches that elsewhere were filled by placental mammals, so instead of cats and dogs we have quolls and Tasmanian devils, instead of deer and goats we have wombats and kangaroos, instead of sloths and monkeys we have possums and koalas, and instead of shrews and hedgehogs we have numbats and echidnas.

The most striking characteristic of our non-placental mammals is their reproduction. In both marsupials and monotremes, the young go through a very short gestation and begin life while still in an essentially embryonic form – tiny, pink and hairless – growing to eventual independence inside their mother's pouch, a specially developed fold of skin that protects the developing joey. In the monotremes, this process has an added level of oddness, with the young first hatching out of a soft-shelled egg.

In a country populated by singular animals, the platypus stands out – surely one of the most unusual creatures to have walked the Earth, an animal so bizarre that when the first skins were sent back to Europe, many considered them to be some sort of elaborate hoax; an aquatic, venomous, egg-laying mammal that uses electroreceptors to find its prey. Australia's other monotreme, the echidna, is only marginally less peculiar. It has one of the shortest spinal cords of any mammal, which is thought to make it flexible enough to wrap itself into a ball, presenting those hard, sharp spines to its harasser. Like the platypus, it's equipped with electroreceptors that it uses to hunt its prey, which it catches using a long, sticky tongue that can protrude up to 18cm outside the rubbery snout, bend through 180° and flick in and out as rapidly as 100 times a minute.

But it's the marsupials that make up the lion's share of Australia's mammal fauna, and Australia has the lion's share of the world's marsupials – close to 70 per cent of the global total. They range in size from the red kangaroo, which can reach a height of more than 2m, to the long-tailed planigale, which weighs about as much as a teaspoon of sugar.

The levels of endemism within the terrestrial placental mammals – rodents, microbats and mega-bats (blossom bats, tube-nosed bats and flying-foxes) – are much lower than for the marsupials. This is largely due to the fact that they arrived much more recently – less than 4 million years ago for the rodents and about 2.6 million years ago for the flying-foxes (no-one's too sure about the microbats) – both groups having made their way down from South-East Asia.

Among the most familiar of these creatures are the flying-foxes, thanks to their habit of gathering together during the day in noisy, squabbling, screeching groups known as camps that can number in the thousands and are often located in our capital cities. Eight species of flying-fox have been recorded from Australia, although only four live on the mainland (and one is considered to be extinct). At dusk, they take to the sky en masse, flapping their leathery wings, which can span more than 1m, as they disperse across the landscape in search of fruit, nectar and pollen, sometimes flying as much as 100km in a night. ■

Previous page: Competing male red kangaroos appear to 'box' as they try to knock each other off balance. If the bout escalates, they'll sit back on their tails and whack each other with their hind legs.

Among the world's largest burrowing animals, common wombats use their powerful limbs, short, broad feet and flattened claws to dig extensive tunnel systems.

By vigorously licking its forearm, this kangaroo works its saliva into a lather that evaporates, drawing heat from the blood flowing just below the skin. The cooled blood then circulates around its body.

STORY BY MITCH REARDON

KANGAROOS

Our beloved national symbol may appear ungainly when at rest, but it leaps along at speeds of up to 65km/h with dazzling agility. And while the largest kangaroos are well known, many species are rarely, if ever, seen by most Australians.

Issue 25 ◆ Jan–Mar 1992

THE KANGAROO stood bolt upright, transfixed by the spotlight's strong, steady beam. After manoeuvring his four-wheel-drive ute into position, David Croft, a senior biology lecturer at the University of NSW, grabbed a .22 rifle, steadied it against the window and fired.

The shot that echoed through the night was not intended to kill, only confuse, and the effect was dramatic. Dazzled by the light and bewildered by the crack and rush of air as the bullet passed close to its head, the disorientated animal took a few wobbly hops before pulling up abruptly. Four shadowy figures that, moments before, had quietly climbed from the back of the ute charged through the darkness, on either side of the beam, towards their quarry.

Graeme Moss and Steve McLeod, postgraduates who have been studying red kangaroos for the past three years, led the charge. Close behind was Debbie Ashworth, whose investigations into the euro (or common wallaroo) were the reason for the exercise – it was a euro (*Macropus robustus*) we were after. I blundered along in the rear. The 40m dash across the broken foothills of the Barrier Range in western New South Wales had me hurdling shrubs, boulders and gullies. I was thoroughly hooked on the thrill of the chase, but my inexperience showed. Stumbling into a bush, I came crashing down and the noise of my plight alerted the euro. It turned to escape but before it could pick up speed, Steve grabbed it with a classic flying tackle.

As we crowded around, the struggling creature stared at us with wild, frightened eyes. Debbie swiftly injected a tranquilliser to reduce heart and muscle stress. Then, growling with displeasure, the euro was wrestled into a weighing sack.

At 25kg, our young male still had some growing to do – he could eventually reach 45kg. Once his weight and body measurements had been recorded, numbered ear tags were attached. Finally, after about 25 minutes, his ordeal was over. Released from the sack, he disappeared into the night without a backward glance and with no apparent ill effects.

These curious goings-on were all in the name of science. 'Stunning' a kangaroo is one way to capture it alive and is part of a research program by the University of NSW at its 39,200ha Arid Zone Research Station at Fowlers Gap, 1280km west of Sydney. Once part of pastoralist Sir Sidney Kidman's cattle empire, this harsh property of rugged sandstone ridges and saltbush-studded plains →

Professional roo shooter Chris Bryant takes aim from inside his vehicle. Each year, more than a million kangaroos are culled across the country to protect endangered grasslands and wildlife.

A bridled nailtail wallaby is caught mid-groom at dusk. Thought to be extinct, the species was rediscovered in 1973 and is now found in three isolated populations in central QLD.

functions as a working sheep station and field laboratory for scientists studying kangaroos – creatures so strange that Charles Darwin remarked that they seemed to belong to a separate creation.

"We've looked at grazing competition between sheep and kangaroos," Sydney-sider Graeme Moss told me. "Now we're exploring the question of how kangaroos make a living, how far they wander and how many the land can support." I was riding pillion on Graeme's trail bike on one of his twice-weekly surveys to track the movements of 22 radio-collared red kangaroos (*Macropus rufus*). He stopped frequently and held his antenna aloft to get a bearing on the source of the signals. Suddenly he pointed: "There he is!"

It was a red buck, the largest marsupial on Earth. Rearing up on his powerful hind legs and balancing with his massive tail, he stood taller than a man and twice the size of the blue doe that accompanied him. With his heavily muscled shoulders and his forepaws held daintily in front of his chest, he looked the weirdest, most enchanted creature imaginable.

"Meet male 1480," Graeme said with obvious affection. His favourite study animal, it was dressed in a bright-yellow collar with its own frequency, and red ear tags for identification.

"I've been tracking him for a year and he's proved to be highly mobile, with a range of about 1600ha." Graeme explained that 1480, who weighs about 80kg, sometimes travels 5km in a night and sometimes just 50m. Mobility is the key to survival in these hostile environs, where plant growth is as erratic as the rainfall. By moving to areas where showers have produced a flush of the young grasses they prefer, then retreating in times of drought to vegetation along watercourses, red kangaroos make the most of what's available.

Fowlers Gap is in the heart of the plains that lie to the west of the Great Dividing Range – the region most affected by the loss of kangaroo species following European colonisation. Of Australia's 48 species, six subsequently became extinct, four are endangered and 13 are vulnerable. Those most at risk are small, shy and nocturnal – and consequently easily overlooked.

"The extinct species were literally eaten out of house and home by an invasion of sheep, cattle and rabbits," said project supervisor Dr David Croft. "Their food supply disappeared along with the tall grasses they relied on for shelter, which made them easy prey for introduced foxes and feral cats."

"Eastern hare-wallabies once abounded in these parts but they were one of the first to slip into extinction. Bridled nailtail wallabies were also plentiful and widespread but they were reduced to a single, isolated population in central Queensland."

David's rollcall of casualties included tiny kangaroos such as the burrowing and brush-tailed bettongs, which today cling precariously to existence in a few small refuges in Western Australia. "It's too late to undo what's been done," he said. "The job now is to save what remains."

YOU'RE looking at one of the rarest animals in the world," Laurie Pitt said. Framed in the spotlight, an elegantly patterned creature returned our stare. Bright white cheek and shoulder stripes contrasted boldly with its grey fur. It was a bridled nailtail wallaby, feeding in one of its last refuges on Earth, the 11,449ha Taunton Scientific Reserve, near Dingo in central Queensland.

"I think of it as a zombie species because, in a way, it's returned from the dead," said Laurie, officer-in-charge at Taunton. Bridled nailtails once abounded from western Victoria through central NSW to the Darling Downs in eastern Queensland. But this habitat-sensitive species declined rapidly after 1880 due to competition from and predation by introduced animals, as well as pelt and bounty hunting. By the early 1930s it was believed to be extinct.

Then, in 1973, a fencing contractor working at Taunton recognised one from an illustration in a magazine. Zoologists wasted no time in confirming that, after missing for 40 years, the bridled nailtail had indeed returned from the abyss of extinction.

After the rediscovery came the next step – ensuring that the safety of the survivors led to the recovery of the species. Peter Tierney, a senior zoologist with Queensland's Department of Environment and Heritage told me that when he began a three-year study of bridled nailtails he guesstimated their population at about 500. "Counting wallabies in thick scrub is a frustrating business – you miss more than you see – but we kept at it. In recent years we've seen a very encouraging increase."

Fitted with radio-collar and ear tags, Graeme Moss's favourite study animal, male 1480, is about 10 years old and in the prime of life. Reds are the largest of all kangaroos and adult males can weigh up to 90kg.

On a night drive with Laurie, I was pleased to find them surprisingly plentiful. As we approached they bounded away in their distinctive style, with backs arched, heads low and forepaws thrust downwards and outwards in typical 'tough guy' stance. When they hopped, their forepaws appeared to describe circles in the air which, Laurie explained, was how they got their old name: organ-grinder.

Laurie, solid, easygoing, weathered by years on the land, takes a proprietary interest in his charges and was a fund of information. "The 'bridled' part of their common name comes from the white stripes curving down the back and behind the forepaws – that's the bridle. 'Nailtail' refers to the horny spur at the tip of the tail, which is dragged on the ground when cornering at speed and acts as a stabiliser."

Back at Laurie's homestead I was amazed at the array of wallabies and tiny, darting rufous bettongs feeding on his lawn. This was my first chance to get a good look at a bettong, a nest-building, scaled-down member of the kangaroo family. This spritely, engaging creature represents an early stage in kangaroo evolution – its flexible tail is a holdover from its distant, tree-dwelling past. Watching the bettongs and wallabies, I felt I was witnessing a scene from earliest Australia. Whether we continue to enjoy such scenes depends on our efforts to conserve them. There's a long way to go, but Taunton – where there's now a real chance to reverse the fortunes of a creature that was staring extinction in the face – is a fine example of what's possible. ■

Why do kangaroos hop?

TRAINING a kangaroo to hop up and down on a treadmill might sound like a circus stunt, but that's exactly what Terry Dawson, Professor of Zoology at the University of NSW, has done.

"I was intrigued by the fact that not only are kangaroos the only marsupials that hop, but they seem to represent the only instance in evolutionary history of any animal weighing more than 5kg that bounces about like a living pogo stick," he explained.

Terry and his colleagues measured their treadmill-pounding subject's oxygen consumption and thus the energy cost of hopping. These measurements, together with field observations, indicate that at moderate to high speeds (between 15 and 65 km/h) kangaroos use less energy than similar-sized animals.

"Their powerful hind legs act as finely tuned springs, storing an increasing amount of energy in their tendons to provide propulsive force for the next hop," said Terry. Hopping also causes their innards to flop to and fro, pumping air in and out of the lungs and saving on muscle effort.

If hopping is so energy efficient, why is it so rare in large animals? Terry believes that the answer probably lies in the kangaroo's method of getting around at speeds below 6km/h. "They use an odd gait we call 'penta pedal' [five-footed], because the tail acts as a fifth leg, helping the forelimbs support the kangaroo while the hind legs move forward together." It's a clumsy way of moving and requires a great deal of energy. Kangaroos apparently use it because it would require even more energy to hop at slow speed.

Kangaroos probably developed their hopping gait because of their low metabolic rate. They use less saliva or sweat when cooling off and require less protein, so they can subsist on poor-quality food – both extremely useful adaptations for an animal that lives in an arid, infertile country – but a poor diet could also limit their ability to sustain maximum energy output. Hopping overcomes this problem through the efficient use of energy.

Koalas

The cuddly, laid-back appearance of our best-loved marsupial belies its remarkable resourcefulness.

Story by **Tony Lee** Photography by **Jim Frazier**

Issue 23 Jul–Sep 1991

A koala's strong, sharp claws allow it to virtually run up the side of a gum tree. They can also be employed as fearsome weapons, should the koala be forced to defend itself.

IN YEARS OF studying koalas, I've never met anyone who has failed to be captivated by them. With an almost human face and a rotund, cuddly appearance, the koala (*Phascolarctos cinereus*) is one of the most endearing creatures in the world.

My first encounter with a koala was as a child in 1942, when I visited a koala park in Sydney. What captivated me most was a specimen jar containing a koala's metre-long appendix, called a caecum. Having had my own much smaller appendix removed two years earlier, I was intrigued that such a small animal could have such a complicated digestive system.

The size of the caecum is what really sets the koala apart from other animals. It's up to 2m long, 10cm in diameter, holds 2L and is the key to the koala's ability to survive on a nutritionally poor diet. Koalas feed almost exclusively on eucalyptus leaves – eating up to 1kg a day – and obtain sufficient water from them except during the hottest weather.

They chew each leaf meticulously into tiny diamond-shaped pieces that pass into the stomach and small intestine, where nutrients are digested and absorbed. The coarser bits of leaf then pass into the large intestine and are excreted, but the smaller particles and fluid go into the caecum, where they can remain for up to eight days while bacteria 'ferment' the plant cells, releasing valuable bonus nutrients that the koala absorbs.

During the early 1970s, when I was associate professor of zoology at Monash University in Victoria, I noticed that many of the swamp gums that lined the creeks in Walkerville, 150km south-east of Melbourne, were dying because koalas were systematically stripping them of their leaves. Grey streaks in the lush hills that rose behind the little beach showed that swathes of swamp gums were dead or dying. The koalas were eating themselves out of house and home, even though there were healthy stands of two other eucalypts – narrow-leafed peppermint and messmate – all around them.

I was intrigued and wanted to learn more about their feeding behaviour. I enlisted research assistant Roger Martin to study the animals. Roger made monthly visits to Walkerville to monitor the koalas. The 2000ha study area was bounded by the sea on one side and by land cleared for pasture on the other three sides, and it was fairly easy to spot koalas during a systematic search of the 10–15m-high trees.

Extracting a koala from a tree to check its condition is quite an art. Roger would slip a noose over the koala's head using an extendible aluminium pole. While I tightened the noose to prevent the koala climbing higher, he would attach a flag to the top of the pole and wave it above the koala's head. At the sight of the flag flapping, the koala would retreat down the tree, often at a gallop. Once on the ground, captured koalas lose all trace of their usually sleepy disposition. Suddenly they're all fight as they roll onto their backs and lash out with their claws, and it usually took two people to hold down the koala while Roger carried out his inspection.

We captured Orange-Blue-Red, named after the colour combination of her ear tags, on an early expedition. Roger checked her vital statistics and raised the entrance to her pouch to peer in. As with many of the females at Walkerville, her teats were small, indicating that she hadn't bred recently. He then prised her jaws apart to inspect her teeth, from which he judged that she was four or five years old. Finally, we eased her into a hessian bag and weighed her, using a spring balance. Then, we released her at the base of a tree.

During the three years of Roger's study, the swamp gums became increasingly sickly and the koala population fell from 40 in 1978 to just six in 1981. Some died, but most left the site and settled in the strip of coastal reserve near Walkerville – some 10–15km away.

ROGER'S FINDINGS SERVED as a timely warning of the consequences of destroying forest and confining koalas to small patches of habitat. However, they didn't explain why koalas are such finicky eaters.

Postgraduate students Kath Handasyde and Mark Hindell accepted the challenge to examine the koala's diet in more detail. Kath spent six months in 1980 studying koalas on Phillip Island, 70km south of Melbourne, where there are manna, swamp and Tasmanian blue gums. After around-the-clock observations, she determined that they generally ate the leaves of the trees they sat in during the day, and noted →

At Lone Pine Koala Sanctuary, Brisbane, baby Frazier, named after photographer Jim Frazier, ventures out of his mother Cindy's pouch for the first time at 27 weeks and one day of age.

Frank Carrick bids farewell to Otto shortly before returning him to the wild in late 1990. Otto spent nearly 18 months at Moggil Farm with what Frank described as the worst case of pinkeye he has ever seen.

that although the manna gums were the most popular, some preferred the other species.

Mark carried out a longer study in Brisbane Ranges National Park, about 60km west of Melbourne, from December 1981 to August 1983. He chose a 40ha study site that had six eucalypt species and, having noted the location of each of the 6500 trees, visited the site every fortnight to see which the koalas were using.

Like Kath, he found that they preferred the manna gums, but during a drought he noticed that many of them moved to the swamp gums lining a creek. "Their leaves would have contained more water, which probably made them more attractive," he told me.

THE MORE I discovered about koalas, the more I wanted to know. During the early 1980s, I helped veterinarian Peter Mitchell select French Island, 5km north of Phillip Island, as a study site for further research. From 1982 to 1985, Peter followed the lives of about 80 koalas living on a small isthmus called Redbill Creek, on the island's western side.

When Peter and I visited the study site years later to see how the koalas were faring, we were greeted by swarms of mosquitoes as we crossed the causeway over the tidal mudflats that bordered the site. As we pushed our way through dense waist-high bracken and grass, Peter scanned the manna gums. He pointed to a large male that would have weighed about 13kg. "He'll have a range of about 1.5ha that he shares with two or three females and other males," he said. Sure enough, about 30m away, we saw a 7–8kg female, and, 50m farther on, another female, with a young 10kg male in the next tree.

"The big male is dominant over the younger and smaller males, and he will defend the females if they are approached by other males," Peter explained. Females emit a high-pitched squeal to alert the dominant male that another male is approaching. On hearing this, he will race to the female's tree and, if the young male has not already fled, chase him away.

"Once, I saw a dominant male lunge at another male with a forepaw, bite his elbow and throw him out of the tree," Peter said, before emphasising that such exchanges are extremely rare. Indeed, out of

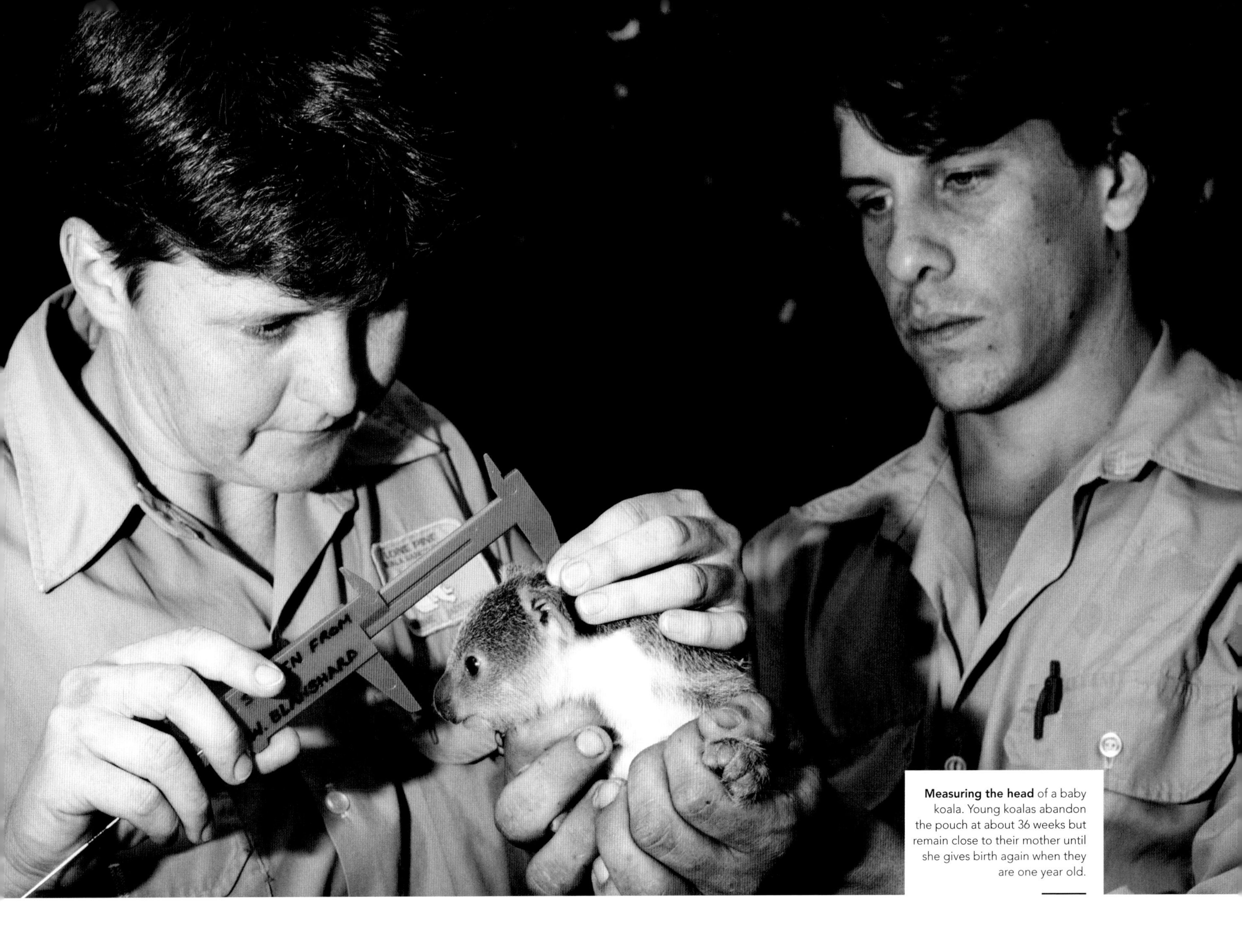

Measuring the head of a baby koala. Young koalas abandon the pouch at about 36 weeks but remain close to their mother until she gives birth again when they are one year old.

just over 10,000 sightings during his study, more than 90 per cent were of koalas alone in trees or mothers with a cub on their back. These sightings were made during fortnightly visits – lasting from two to 10 days – to the site. Peter monitored the koalas at least once during the day, and up to seven or eight times at night, when they are most active.

All the koalas were asleep during our visit. "I think their whole life is geared to using as little energy as possible," Peter said. "They sleep about 19 hours a day, change trees once or twice a night, avoid social conflict and, in the case of the dominant males, defend females only when necessary. Perhaps this is how they get by living on a diet as poor as eucalypt leaves."

NOT LONG AFTER visiting French Island, I flew to Brisbane to meet with zoologist Lester Pahl. I had lived in the city 30 years earlier while working as a zoology lecturer at the University of Queensland, and, as my plane descended, I was horrified to see that between Brisbane and Surfers Paradise most of the forests and woodlands that I had visited collecting frogs, spotting koalas and observing other wildlife were gone. Buildings had taken their place.

"It's only a matter of time before most of the remaining forests are cleared," Lester told me. He's working with councils and conservation groups to identify koala populations and try to protect them from the disastrous effects of development. "If councils don't act now it will be difficult to maintain koalas in the future," he warned.

Many koala experts agree that habitat loss and the rise in the number of cars and dogs that occur as urban areas expand pose the greatest threats to koalas. Koalas are not in danger of becoming extinct – in fact, in Victoria most populations are stable or increasing – but, if we don't look after their habitat, they could disappear from parts of northern NSW and south-eastern Queensland. Already they have disappeared from much of southern and western NSW.

The more we know about koalas, the more we'll be able to help them. And, as every koala expert I spoke to was at pains to point out, when you protect koala habitat you are also protecting that habitat for a diversity of other wildlife. ■

The platypus

Story by **Garry Hamilton**

Issue 12 Oct-Dec 1988

THE SOUND WAS very faint, just a gentle splashing in the distance. I sat motionless on the riverbank, listening intently. The splashing stopped. Then I heard movement through grass, a rustling in the darkness, followed by a soft plop in the pool in front of me. I held my breath; within the next few seconds I would, with luck, come face to face with one of Australia's greatest natural treasures: the platypus (*Ornithorhynchus anatinus*).

I was sitting by the Rocky River in Flinders Chase National Park, on Kangaroo Island. It was just on midnight and so dark I couldn't see the opposite bank only 2m away. Beside me was conservationist John Wamsley, who for 19 years has been re-creating a native environment at Warrawong Sanctuary, his 14ha property in the Adelaide Hills, where he has established populations of rare South Australian animals. He had come to this island some 13km off the SA coast to catch two platypuses for his reserve.

It was midsummer. Parts of the Rocky River had dried up and were just broken chains of pools along which platypuses moved every night in search of food. We had set up camp near a pool and strung a net across it. Twice in the past four hours we'd heard activity in the water in front of us but the net remained empty.

John sat up, alert – this platypus-trapping venture was the culmination of five years planning and, having twice missed his quarry already, he was determined to make it third time lucky. As the animal touched the net, John hurled his burly frame into the pool, grabbed the bottom of the net and scooped it out of the water. There, in the middle of it, sat a platypus, glistening in the beam of the spotlight. John whooped with pure joy. "Well," he called, "I'm wide awake now!"

WITH A BILL that looks superficially like a duck's, webbed feet, and thick, waterproof fur, the platypus has fascinated scientists and laypeople ever since one was caught beside a lake near the Hawkesbury River, north-west of Sydney, in 1797. It lays eggs but suckles its young, swims like no other creature on the planet, and males are armed with a venomous spur.

One of the features of the platypus that baffled early researchers was its single functioning ovary; the other ovary is poorly developed, as in birds. The implication was that the platypus laid eggs, but the idea of a furred mammal hatching from an egg flew in the face of prevailing scientific thought. →

The platypus is a carnivore, feeding mainly on shrimps, crayfish, insect larvae and worms. It hunts with its eyes closed, electroreceptors on the bill helping it to find its prey.

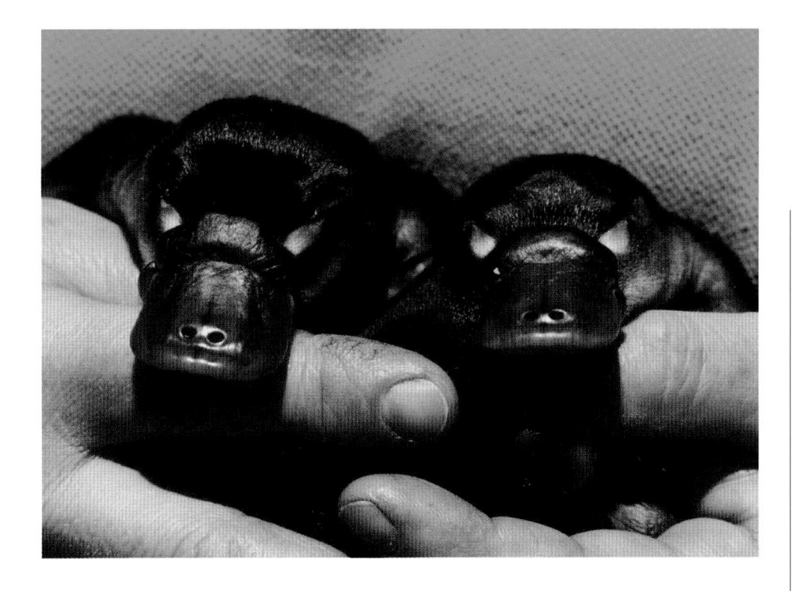

A female platypus typically produces two young, nursing them in her burrow for three or four months before they can swim independently. They grow quickly thanks to the energy-rich milk that she produces.

Another curiosity was the cloaca, the single opening for excretion and reproduction, a feature that gives this order of animals – the only other member of which is the echidna – the name Monotremata. In fact, monotremes share this feature with marsupials, but they remain unique as egg-laying mammals. The confusion was compounded by the fact that, although the platypus appeared mammal-like in most respects, it was found to have bones in its shoulder girdle similar to those in living reptiles and fossil mammal-like reptiles.

WHEN I MET TOM Grant, Scottish-born platypus expert, author and environmental consultant, he was working on a study for the Department of Main Roads, gauging the impact of a bridge-construction project on a platypus population on the Wingecarribee River, two hours south of Sydney. As we drove to the river he explained the challenges involved in studying platypuses: "Their secretiveness makes them difficult animals to study in the field," he said. "And in captivity they're hard to keep because they die and they don't breed. They're survivors in their own habitat, but once you take them out of it they die at the drop of a hat."

The platypus spends the day in its burrow and is usually seen only at dawn and dusk; even then the watcher needs patience. During the night, it dives for food, keeping its eyes, ears and nostrils closed as it hunts insect larvae and shrimps in the mud and rocks on the bottom. Staying under for about a minute, it stores its food in cheek pouches and then rises to the surface, where it grinds its meal on horny pads on its jaws. An adult can eat up to half its body weight in a night.

With few regular predators (carpet snakes, Murray cod, eels, foxes, eagles and crocodiles are thought to eat them occasionally), the species has a relatively long life in habitats that range from the icy river pools of the Snowy Mountains to warm Queensland rivers. Tom reckons they live for more than 12 years in the wild, although a captive specimen in Queensland is 22.

At the Wingecarribee River, Tom led me through a blackberry thicket to the bank, where he noted the soil and stones washed down from the construction area. Heavy sedimentation, he explained, blankets the bottom, probably affecting the quantity, variety and nature of small river creatures that the platypus eats. Little is known about the long-term effects on the platypus of this kind of disturbance.

Later, at a weir 7km from the bridge site, I was able to see how the platypus was coping with another kind of human presence. Treated sewage from nearby towns had turned the river into a paradise for green algae, which were growing on rocks and floating on the water. "It's been like this for years, yet platypuses are still here," Tom said. "But again, we have no clue how they'll cope in the long run."

The godfather of monotreme biology is Mervyn Griffiths, a tall, fit-looking 74-year-old who has been studying echidnas and platypuses for nearly 30 years. "The platypus's reproductive processes are different from those of most reptilians," Mervyn told me. Platypuses court and mate in the water, usually in September. After mating, the male plays no more role in reproduction. During gestation, the eggs (one to three; usually two) develop until they are grape-sized and ready for laying. About three weeks after conception, the female builds a nest at the end of her nesting burrow. Scientists aren't sure what happens next, but Mervyn believes that after the mother lays the soft, rubbery eggs she incubates them between her stomach and her curled-up tail.

"The echidna's incubation period is about 10 and a half days," Mervyn explained. "It's probably the same in the platypus because the egg is the same size and the temperature between the abdomen and the tail is about 31.5°C and in the echidna's pouch it's about 32°C."

The hatchlings are about 15mm long. Blind at first, they grow to two-thirds the size of their mother in the first 3–4 months, living only on her milk. The milk has to be exceptionally rich to produce such rapid growth. Mervyn has discovered it contains 60 times more iron than the milk of cows or humans and that 40 per cent of it consists of solids, compared with only 12 per cent in cow's milk.

The young leave the burrow about February. On average, adult males in New South Wales weigh 1.7kg and are 50cm long from bill to tail and the females 900g and 43cm.

STANDING WAIST-DEEP in the Rocky River on Kangaroo Island, John Wamsley untangled the platypus from the net and held it up gingerly by the tail, his thick, weathered hands trembling from the burst of adrenaline no less than the chill of his late-night dunking. As we searched for spurs it struck me suddenly how really bizarre this animal was. And then I realised why I had been so fascinated all along: despite its bizarreness, this wasn't some exotic inhabitant of a Brazilian rainforest or a weird creature dredged from the depths of the Pacific. This was a common resident of our own backyard rivers and creeks.

After a last fatherly inspection at camp, John lowered the animal carefully into a wooden box lined with gum leaves, closed the lid and fastened the clasps. With another young female, this platypus would travel by car, plane and helicopter and, 12 hours later, slide into a lake in John's sanctuary. If all goes well, they will form the core of a breeding colony that will populate other SA waterways.

We're lucky. If we have the time and patience to sit by a quiet stretch of waterway in eastern Australia we'll more than likely be rewarded with a sight of a platypus. But will future generations be so lucky? After my three-month association with these delightful and very special creatures, I'm convinced that, as their custodians, we have a responsibility to learn as much as we can about them and, through our learning, ensure that they don't just survive, but thrive. ■

Australian Platypus Conservancy biologist Geoff Williams with a two-year-old male platypus in Mullum Mullum Creek, East Templestowe, VIC.

Waterproof fur traps an insulating layer of air when the platypus dives, which helps it to maintain a constant body temperature of 32°C, even while foraging for long periods in cold water.

Secret world of the wombat

Far from being muddle-headed, as the children's stories suggest, the energetic burrower has a better-developed brain than any other marsupial. And its lumbering, bear-like exterior masks a remarkably agile frame.

Story and photography by **Mitch Reardon**

Issue 30 Apr–Jun 1993

THE COOL autumn sun dipped below the rim of the Rams Head Range in Kosciuszko National Park. In the golden aftermath, the mountains' thickly wooded slopes and the blue-grey clouds were perfectly mirrored in the Thredbo River's glassy surface. Sheryn Woon, my guide, squeezed my arm gently, directing my attention from that visual feast to a sudden movement near the base of a spreading manna gum.

"Wombat," she whispered, gesturing towards a strange-looking, shuffling creature that had appeared at the entrance of a large hole beneath one of the eucalypt's horizontally growing roots. I watched as it paused, one paw diffidently raised, its broad, blunt head drooping slightly as if the animal were still asleep. Only its widely dilating nostrils indicated that it was carefully testing the evening air before venturing out beyond the safety of its burrow. Reassured, it waddled into the darkening forest – a rotund, comical figure with inward-pointing hind toes and a broad rear end that swayed from side to side – on its regular nightly food run in search of a variety of native grasses and sedges.

Although telltale signs of wombat occupancy were everywhere – from an extensive system of burrows and well-used paths to droppings posted on tree stumps and in other prominent places – the animals themselves were frustratingly elusive. In two bone-chilling nights that crackled with frost, the only indication of wombats was a quick scuttling sound in the undergrowth as one fled at our approach. It wasn't until our third evening that we finally had our brief encounter. The perfection of the meeting left me exhilarated, although, like the common wombat (*Vombatus ursinus*) itself, it was without fuss or ceremony.

No-one knows better than Barbara Triggs that wombats are among the most difficult animals to study in the wild. Her quest to unlock the intricacies of their biology began when she was faced with raising a young orphaned wombat at her home in Croajingolong National Park in north-eastern Victoria. She had successfully reared orphaned kangaroos and possums, but knew almost nothing about wombats when her husband, Allan, brought home a nearly furless youngster whose mother had been killed on the road.

Barbara found that natural history books were no help in fostering the joey she named Bruno, because very little research had been done on wombats at the time. She would have to learn from the animals themselves if she was going to successfully return him to the wild.

Some of Barbara's research was done near her home, but much was carried out in the east Gippsland mountain forests, a three-hour drive away, where she used a caravan as a hide to observe wombats. "Their lives revolve around the burrow, and as they seldom leave before dusk my research began each evening at a burrow entrance, waiting for one to emerge." Her difficult task was made more so on discovering that a wombat uses up to 11 different burrows and that burrows may be used by several wombats, usually at different times.

Lacking the resources and expertise to fit radio-collars, she devised her own system of tracking them. She placed twigs across burrow entrances, and if they were dislodged she knew that a wombat was in residence. She also fastened sticky tape to the mouths of burrows to snag hairs from a passing wombat to help identify it. "A few hairs may not seem much to go on, but coat colours vary so widely – from glossy black to grey; brown, sandy and cream – that they can be as good as a signature."

Barbara's studies made her an authority on wombat behaviour, and she wrote two books about them. She believes that most people have a skewed perception of her favourite animal. "They are mainly nocturnal and shy of humans, so their true qualities remain hidden. People cling to childhood memories of Ruth Park's tales of the muddle-headed wombat, an endearing, lumbering fellow with 'stumpy paws and muddled-up whiskers', who, with the best intentions, always manages to get things wrong."

Professor Heinz Moeller, director of the Zoological Institute at Heidelberg University in Germany, discovered that far from being muddle-headed, wombats have the best-developed brain of any marsupial. A colleague, Dr Regine Hilbmann, investigated their play behaviour and learning ability and found them "very frolicsome" and relatively quick to learn – a sure indicator of a level of intelligence no-one had guessed at.

"WOMBATS are worthless!" Ron King, a sheep and cattle grazier in Victoria's eastern highlands, fumed when I questioned him about them. "I've slaved on the land all my life and I have a fair knowledge of the destruction wombats cause. In my opinion, they're worse than wild pigs." Ron is one of many farmers who detest wombats. "Fences are impossible to maintain. Kangaroos in their hundreds come through holes wombats make and it is no longer

Broad forepaws with strong, blunt claws help to make the wombat the earth-moving specialist of the marsupial world. The energetic burrower spends more than half its life underground, emerging mainly at dusk to feed.

economic to run sheep on a lot of my property because wild dogs get in the same way."

The first recorded encounter between wombats and Europeans was in 1797, when sailors from the *Sydney Cove*, shipwrecked on Preservation Island off Tasmania, dined on wombat flesh. They likened the creature to a badger and a bear, and described the meat as being "musky, with a not very agreeable flavour and very sinewy".

In fact, the wombat's closest relative is the koala. The two animals have similar rudimentary tails, paws and rear-opening pouches, as well as a common ancestor that lived about 25 million years ago. The gradual drying out of Australia that turned three-quarters of the continent from forest into semi-arid desert led to the extinction of several species of giant wombat between 25,000 and 15,000 years ago.

In the cooler, wetter highlands of south-eastern Australia – from Stanthorpe near the Queensland–New South Wales border south along the Great Dividing Range to the outskirts of Melbourne – the common wombat continues to thrive, despite the clearing of forest for settlement and agriculture that shrunk its range. But the much rarer hairy-nosed wombats, distinguished by their softer fur and longer ears, have fared less well since European colonisation. A southern species of hairy-nosed wombat that once extended as far east as the Murray River is now confined to parts of the Nullarbor Plain and a few isolated colonies in southern South Australia. Northern hairy-nosed wombats declined so quickly that they first became known to scientists as a skull found in the Wellington Caves, NSW, in 1869.

"WHEN Epping Forest National Park was proclaimed in 1971 to protect the last population of northern hairy-nosed wombats, it was estimated that there were just 35 animals left," Matt Widt, ranger-in-charge of the 3300ha sanctuary 100km north-west of Clermont in central Queensland, told me as we stood in the sandy bed of an ancient watercourse, staring at a cluster of five burrows.

The invasion of graziers and their livestock into the hairy-nosed wombat's austere habitat precipitated a crisis with which it was unable to cope. "Sheep, cattle and wombats eat the same grasses but the wombats have narrower preferences," Matt explained. Fossil records indicate they were once widespread in Victoria, NSW and Queensland but by the early 1900s only two populations were known to exist, one near Deniliquin in southern NSW and another in Moonie River, southern Queensland. When they both died out during a severe drought the species was presumed extinct. Then a tiny population was discovered in Epping Forest (see p120).

"A turning point came when cattle were finally excluded from the park," Matt told me. "But more research needs to be done to understand exactly what their requirements are." It's too early to say the species has been saved, but its chances are better than they have been in a long time.

A LIGHT DUSTING of snow covered Kosciuszko's distant peaks when Sheryn Woon and I arrived at Wild Bullock, her 440ha property near Jindabyne. This sheltered valley was where Sheryn intended to release wombats orphaned in road accidents and raised by human foster parents. We were there to introduce 18-month-old Oscar to his future home. He had still been suckling when his mother was killed by a logging truck.

"This is ideal wombat habitat," Sheryn said, as we took turns carrying Oscar, ensconced in a blanket-lined shoulder bag, into rugged eucalypt uplands interspersed with creeks and grassy meadows where she knew there was an abandoned wombat burrow. Tumbled from the security of his bag, Oscar tentatively explored the diggings. As his confidence grew, he disappeared down the tunnel for longer periods.

Finally he re-emerged to snuggle beneath Sheryn's sheepskin coat. She smiled fondly at him. "One day he won't come back. That day he'll become the founder of the Wild Bullock wombat colony." ■

A young female Lumholtz's tree kangaroo pauses while making her way down a tree trunk. The smallest of Australia's tree kangaroos, Lumholtz's average just 6–7kg.

STORY BY JOHN PICKRELL PHOTOGRAPHY BY BILL HATCHER

GHOSTS OF THE FOREST

Meet the mysterious monkey-like tree kangaroos of Australia and New Guinea – marsupials so counterintuitive that early naturalists couldn't believe they even existed.

Issue 113 ◆ Mar–Apr 2013

A FLYING KANGAROO has just launched itself from 20m up in the rainforest canopy and landed with a thud on the ground a little way away. We're in a relatively dry inland part of the Daintree Rainforest at Shiptons Flat, 35km south of Cooktown; the air is stifling even in the dry season and the ever-present hum of insects fills the air. Seemingly unperturbed, the kangaroo begins to hop away, but not before Aboriginal ranger Alwyn 'Peter' Henry throws himself after it, grabbing it. Panting from the effort and the heat, Peter holds the young male up and I get my first, thrilling close encounter with an animal that has fascinated me for many years.

Few people have ever seen a Bennett's tree kangaroo (*Dendrolagus bennettianus*); they are cryptic and elusive, skilled at blending in with the dense rainforest canopy. There are none in captivity and only rarely have they been photographed. We had just two days to trek through the bush looking for them, but there were no guarantees we'd find any, so this is an exciting moment. Peter is part of a team of Bana Yarralji Bubu Aboriginal Corporation rangers recently made custodians of the land here in Kuku Nyungkal country. Once, his people would have hunted these animals for food, but now they wear them as badges of pride, literally – there's one emblazoned on the ranger logo on his uniform.

It's clear that this is one eccentric kangaroo. It has a long tail with a tufted tip, similar to →

Bennett's tree kangaroos are found in montane and lowland rainforest over a small range from Cooktown to the Daintree River, QLD.

The feet of tree kangaroos are broader than those of their terrestrial cousins and feature padded soles to improve grip and sharp, curved claws for climbing.

the leaf monkeys of South-East Asia. It has muscly forearms that it can rotate out from and above its body. Its hind limbs, flicking with irritation, are significantly shorter than the norm for roos, as are its ears and snout. With its stocky build and thick brown fur, this feisty macropod has something distinctly bear-like about it.

"They show all of these secondary adaptations that you don't see in the standard kangaroo body plan," says Roger Martin, a research fellow at James Cook University (JCU), Cairns. "Huge development of the forearms to pull themselves up into trees; very long claws... [and] soft pads on the feet that enable them to grip; an extremely long tail that they use as a counter-balance."

You can see differences, too, in the way that these animals deftly move about in the trees. We occasionally see them hopping kangaroo-style between high branches – a distinctly unnerving sight because it's so unfamiliar.

In addition to the rangers and Roger, our expedition party includes photographer Bill Hatcher, and our expert trackers Charlie and Lewis Roberts. The brothers have lived all their lives on their property at Shiptons Flat, and are renowned as the most knowledgeable people on the flora and fauna of this part of Queensland.

Lewis, 62, says that as kids they never saw tree kangaroos. They were thought to dwell above 600m on peaks such as Mt Misery and Mt Finnegan. During the '70s, they began to see them in the foothills and then around the homestead. Now they see them regularly. "It's just a dramatic change," he says. Although they were heavily hunted, they proved too elusive to be completely wiped out on the mountaintops. There, they persisted, acting as seed populations that eventually recolonised the lowlands. Aboriginal lore often regarded mountain peaks as haunted or sacred places, and hunters avoided them, creating unintentional protected areas.

Roger believes that Bennett's tree kangaroos are now more abundant than they have been for perhaps 10,000 years. In this, the Bennett's is unique, for most of the 17 species and subspecies of tree roo across the Torres Strait are gravely threatened.

After a short while, Peter returns the roo to the ground. Before we even have time to think about it, it has hopped off into the scrub. Once it's a comfortable distance away, it will scramble back into the canopy, Roger says, perhaps to find the leafy crown of an umbrella tree to hunker down and snooze in, nothing more than its tail dangling down among the vines to betray it.

"TO ENTERTAIN THE idea that any kangaroo known to us, or approaching its formation, could climb a tree, would be ridiculous, the animal was not formed for such work," wrote William Hann, the first European to lead an expedition to Cape York, in 1872. Hann's party found many strange animals, says Professor Tim Flannery, but none struck him as more ridiculous than the tree kangaroo. It wasn't until 1884 that an Australian tree kangaroo was officially described, and that species, from the Atherton Tableland, was named after Dr Carl Lumholtz, the Norwegian who discovered it. The Bennett's wasn't found by naturalists until 1887.

These days, you're more likely to hear Tim talking about climate change, but his real passion is kangaroos, which is obvious by how animated he gets on the topic. He says it's surprising that tree kangaroos are almost as exotic to most Australians today as they →

Like the other tree kangaroos, Goodfellow's tree kangaroo has an extraordinary jumping ability and has been recorded jumping to the ground from heights of 10m without ill effect.

A young Lumholtz's tree kangaroo gets some exercise in a fig tree while being cared for at the Tree Kangaroo Rescue and Conservation Centre in Malanda, QLD.

were to Hann. A survey taken in Brisbane in 2003 revealed that only 36 per cent of respondents had even heard of them – and this in the capital of Queensland, home to Australia's two species.

It's difficult to say exactly why these fascinating animals are so little known, Tim says. "They're very cryptic and obscure and are all found in remote habitats… It's probably just that most of them are found outside Australia." Today, we know of 17 species and subspecies of tree kangaroo (15 in New Guinea), and they make up quite a chunk of the 70 known kangaroo species. They have remained so poorly known that Tim himself discovered four species during the 1990s.

AFTER SEVERAL DAYS of exhilarating success on the trail of Bennett's roos at Shiptons Flat, photographer Bill and I drive 270km south to the Atherton Tableland, home to Australia's only other species, Lumholtz's tree kangaroo (*D. lumholtzi*), which is smaller and greyer in colour than Bennett's. At Atherton we meet Margit Cianelli, who runs the Lumholtz Lodge, a bed and breakfast in 75ha of rainforest. Margit arrived in 1972 from Germany and when people heard she'd been a zookeeper, they started to bring her injured wildlife. It wasn't until 1990 that she was brought a tree kangaroo joey – thrown from the pouch when its mother was killed by a car.

He was very young – tiny, pink and hairless, Margit says. She contacted Woodland Park Zoo, which had experience in breeding tree kangaroos. They thought he was too small to survive, but she raised him successfully. When he died, he was a 3kg subadult spending most of his days out in the forest. "He died very suddenly…and I was very upset," she says. Baffled, Margit spoke to vets, zookeepers and pathologists, but none offered a convincing answer.

The following year, she took another joey in and it survived, and then a few years later another. "I always kept a record," she says. "After four or five I could actually see a pattern. The ones that died always died after they were old enough to be in the forests by themselves." They were all joeys that she had received at less than 500g, and they exhibited strange behaviour, trying to lick her face at night.

A Bennett's tree kangaroo leaps from a branch high in a tree in dry forest near Poverty Creek, 40km south of Cooktown, QLD.

"I gathered from these two observations that maybe they get something from mothers that they need to digest the foliage," she says.

Most kangaroos are grazers and have intestines full of worms that help digest grass, says Tim. "They'll step in and put their hands in areas where these worm cases are and then lick their hands to reinfect, so that worms get into their gut." Because tree roo droppings fall to the forest floor it was thought they couldn't be using the same trick, but Margit had another idea. She thought mothers might regurgitate stomach contents to 'inoculate' young against toxins in rainforest leaves. At around the time the idea came to her, Margit had a small joey named Timothy, after Flannery, and decided to try feeding him stomach contents from tree kangaroos killed on the roads.

Now, whenever she rears a joey, she feeds them small amounts of stomach contents and says the change is unbelievable. The animals become active, energetic and develop a shiny coat. "They become bright-eyed, bushy-tailed and gorgeous," says Margit, adding that she hasn't lost one in those same initial circumstances since.

Working with fellow carer Dr Karen Coombes, who runs the Tree Roo Rescue and Conservation Centre in Malanda, Margit radio-collars the young roos when they first go out into the forest, and watches over them until they are able to leave home for good and make their own territory.

Karen says the problems afflicting them stem from habitat fragmentation on the Atherton Tableland. What were once vast tracts of pristine rainforest have been cleared, forcing them to live in fragments. Tree kangaroos are highly territorial, so young animals eventually have to migrate out of patches to find new habitat. "They get hit by cars, or attacked by dogs," Karen says.

"THEY ARE ALMOST like the monkeys of the Australasian rainforest," says Dr Lisa Dabek, who runs the Tree Kangaroo Conservation Program in Seattle, USA. 'Ghosts of the forest' – the way New Guineans describe them – seems most fitting. They are just so elusive, Lisa says. Yet when you eventually discover them hidden in the dense canopy, they are so stunning and you can't believe you couldn't see them in the first place. ■

Numbat force

A group of numbat lovers has come to the rare marsupial's rescue in south-western WA.

Story by **Jane Hammond** Photography by **Robert Mclean**

Issue 130 Jan–Feb 2016

Members of the Numbat Task Force – (left to right): Robert McLean, John Lawson, Sean Van Alphen and Matthew Willett – ready their cameras in the Dryandra Woodland.

AT FIRST GLANCE, Robert McLean seems an unlikely conservationist. A meat-truck driver by day, he's a bloke who loves steak, beer and thongs. But most weekends you won't catch him putting his feet up watching the footy or imbibing the amber fluid at the pub. Instead you'll find him deep in the Dryandra Woodland on the frontline of a battle to save Western Australia's faunal emblem from extinction.

Robert's twin passions are photography and numbats (*Myrmecobius fasciatus*), and he has successfully combined the two into a constructive obsession. On weekends he heads inland, driving for several hours from his coastal home to the Dryandra conservation area 170km south-east of Perth, to find and photograph numbats. His unusual hobby has led him to form a strong bond with three other unlikely conservationists: airline worker Sean Van Alphen; power-company employee Matthew Willett; and John Lawson, caretaker of the Lions Dryandra Woodland Village and former stonemason. The group met while undertaking individual searches for the elusive marsupial, bumping into one another while following the network of old logging tracks that criss-cross Dryandra.

Together they formed the Numbat Task Force, initially to lobby for protection for the numbat from feral cat predation. But when plans were announced to site a major rubbish tip just 6km from Dryandra, McLean says that it was "all hands on deck" as they created a campaign to save the creatures. The four friends set up a Facebook page and now post every shot they can of the numbats they've captured on their cameras. Thanks to their efforts, and those of local WA Greens MP Lynn MacLaren, a decision by the state's Environmental Protection Authority not to assess the tip proposal was overturned. It was a significant victory for the team, and means that the potential impact of the waste facility on Dryandra will now be examined by the environmental watchdog.

It's hard work finding numbats and it takes a mixture of patience and perseverance. In the years that the four men have been photographing the small marsupials, they've seen the numbers in Dryandra plummet from more than 600 in the early 1990s to fewer than 50 today. "If the tip gets the go-ahead then the numbats won't stand a chance. The tip will attract feral cats and it won't take them long to move into this area," says Robert, who's worried that cats will wipe out the population.

Numbats are adventurous and at times seemingly ignore the presence of people as they dig up the forest floor in search of the 20,000 termites they need to eat every day. It's this apparent disregard for danger that puts them on a collision course with voracious feral cats. "Numbats are the clowns of the forest," Robert tells me as we drive at "numbat pace" through the woodland, keeping watch for the diurnal creatures. "They are like meerkats on steroids," he says.

THEIR LONG, BUSHY TAILS, striped backs, reddish coats and long snouts make them appealing to look at and their skittish behaviour is endearing. "Once you see a numbat in the wild, that's it – you're hooked," Robert says, and he's right. After two days of traversing the dusty tracks in the company of the four men I see my first numbat. It's just a glance but worth the many hours spent peering out from the back of a ute.

We look out for known numbats, including Picasso, named for his bushy, paintbrush-like tail; Sheriff, who lives in an area the task force members call Log City; Speedy Gonzales, named for his ability to run from the cameras; and Big Balls (I'll leave that one to your imagination). The group searches with two vehicles in convoy in the expectation that if the first vehicle misses a sighting the second will pick it up. They laugh and joke their way through the woodland, stopping to check on echidnas, snakes and other wild creatures.

Sean knows every bird species that inhabits the woodland and documents every sighting or call. Matthew is the quietest of the four and breaks into a huge infectious smile when a numbat is in his viewfinder. John lives at Dryandra and has a wealth of knowledge about numbat quirks and habits. He points out raised lines of earth on the forest floor, explaining that they're shallow termite galleries

Numbats were once widespread across southern and central Australia, but now there are only about 1000 left in the wild. Juveniles (pictured) are the most vulnerable to cats and foxes.

that the numbats use to reach the insects. The numbat's claws aren't strong enough to dig into the concrete-like termite mounds that dot the woodland. Instead they attack the termite colonies at their weakest points – the network of galleries the insects use to move between dead logs and other food sources.

DR TONY FRIEND, from the WA Department of Parks and Wildlife, has spent a lifetime monitoring and recording numbats, much of it at Dryandra. He says the Numbat Task Force has done a fantastic job of promoting the numbat and raising its status through lobbying, photography and social media. According to Tony, there are about 1000 numbats left in the wild, and he's optimistic that – if used carefully – a new feral cat bait called Eradicat will help to bring down cat numbers, giving numbats a better chance of survival. He has led a successful translocation program, reintroducing about 500 numbats, many bred at Perth Zoo, into cat-free fenced sanctuaries in New South Wales and South Australia, as well as other smaller reserves in WA. Dryandra has been the source of the genetic stock used in the zoo's captive-breeding program and the site of a number of releases.

Robert says he isn't so sure Eradicat will work in an area such as Dryandra, with its bounty of fresh food for cats, and he's worried that not enough is being done to tackle the scourge of the feral cat.

In July 2015 the numbat was named one of 20 priority species by Gregory Andrews, the federal government's threatened species commissioner. The numbat is "a remarkable Australian animal and a unique product of evolution", he tells me, adding that he's impressed by the passion of the Numbat Task Force. "We need people and groups like this to protect their local wildlife. Government alone can't tackle the crisis of species extinction," he says.

The numbat's new status means that it will have its own recovery plan and will be placed under the national spotlight. It's welcome news for the men of the task force, who've vowed to continue their grassroots campaign to promote and protect this adorable and engaging creature. ■

Leadbeater's possum

Considered extinct for nearly 50 years, this tiny marsupial is one of our most vulnerable mammals.

Story by **Ken Eastwood** Photography by **Jason Edwards**

Issue 75 Jul–Sep 2004

'CUTE'. 'ADORABLE'. Two words I usually hate because they're so overused. So I'm standing in a cold swamp in the dark, getting rained on, chest-deep in razor-sharp sword sedges, desperately trying to think of other words to describe the tiny furry face in front of me as it peers tentatively from a nest box 4m up a mountain swamp gum. A little pink nose, big dark eyes and alert triangular ears appear and disappear as Victoria's mammalian emblem checks whether it's safe to venture out.

Deciding to make a break for it, my 15cm furry friend springs agilely onto the nest-box roof and then launches off it, sugar glider-style, towards a leaning tea-tree sapling almost 2m away. Like a gymnast spectacularly missing her mark, the possum fails to catch on and plummets with a sickening crash to the ground. There's a moment's awful pause, then we hear it scurry away.

My companion, Dan Harley, laughs quietly. "You crazy thing," he says. "On a wet night, a big jump like that was never on."

For six years, this leech-ridden swamp called Yellingbo Nature Conservation Reserve has been Dan's main habitat, as he has carried out extensive research on the extraordinary population of Leadbeater's possums (*Gymnobelideus leadbeateri*) living here. Of the 4000 or so Leadbeater's left in the wild, nearly all live in mountain-ash and alpine-ash forests in Victoria's central highlands, at altitudes of 400–1100m. But this population of about 100, an hour and a half's drive east of Melbourne, has hung on in lowland mountain swamp gum forest just 110m above sea level. Their home – a gaunt 460ha reserve that's only 150m wide in places – is squeezed on all sides by cleared agricultural land.

Meagre as it is, Yellingbo is a very special swamp. It's the only wild place where you can see all of Victoria's plant and animal emblems – the pink, or common, heath, Leadbeater's possum and the endangered helmeted honeyeater. In fact, it's the only spot in which you're likely to see helmeted honeyeaters at all. In the gloom, common wombats lumber about, tiny insectivorous bats and owlet-nightjars zip through the trees, and the air fills with the calls of swamphens and southern brown tree frogs.

Dan seems so familiar with every sound and movement in the bush that I reckon he could personally introduce me to every creature. He's at ease sitting perfectly still for hours in the cold drizzle, waiting for possums to come out of hollows, while mozzies and leeches →

Alert and inquisitive, an adult Leadbeater's possum scampers down a tree trunk. Breeding Leadbeater's have an orange-brown stain at the tail's base, created by mutual licking around the scent gland and cloaca.

Cradled tenderly in a soft cotton bag, a 15cm Leadbeater's possum peers out at the world. Unlike most Leadbeater's, which live in tall upland forest, this possum's home is at Yellingbo, a lowland swamp 50km east of Melbourne.

suck on his exposed flesh. Once, a leech even took up temporary residence behind his eyeball. But he carries no grudges – this gentle 29-year-old happily rescues leeches struggling in puddles. He also drives slowly so as not to run over frogs and stoops to help a moth that has been stunned by our torch beams.

Dan has been undertaking his Monash University PhD on the Leadbeater's possums here – work sponsored by the Australian Geographic Society – but his research has extended way beyond that now, with ongoing surveys funded by Parks Victoria and the Threatened Species Network.

When Dan started his Leadbeater's study, he installed 150 nest boxes in Yellingbo. The possums generally prefer the small plastic or wooden boxes to the fairly scarce natural tree hollows, and the swing-top lid makes it easier for Dan to monitor the tiny animals. "Before the nest boxes, the possums were just getting by with crappy hollows," he says. "When the nest boxes went in, suddenly they had first-class accommodation." Nearly all the possums now use the nest boxes at least some of the time, giving Dan an opportunity to conduct long-term monitoring of the population.

FOR THE NEXT THREE YEARS, he checked the nest boxes every six weeks, discovering essential details about the possums' family life, dispersal and habitat requirements. He even learnt to speak their language.

"Tsss tsss tsss tss ts ts ts tsssss," Dan calls repeatedly into the darkness. Within minutes, two Leadbeater's have arrived to see who's in their territory. Curiosity getting the better of caution, they scurry silently up and down paperbark and tea-tree saplings around us, bouncing and jumping expertly from tree to tree. They don't stay still for more than a second, pausing only to lick at gum oozing from the trunks.

"In the mountain-ash forests, their main energy source is wattle gum," Dan murmurs. "But there's no wattle here. They are incising [chewing] some of the scented paperbark and the tea-tree trunks to get at the sap, but largely they're just licking the surface secretions off the eucalypt trunks."

After they've been feeding, Leadbeater's leave a viscous salivary goop, full of air bubbles, on the bark. "I've never heard of another mammal doing anything like that," Dan says. "We don't know what function it serves." One gorgeous possum scales a sapling 50cm away and peeks inquisitively around the trunk at me. Imitating Dan, I call to it: "Tssss tsss ts ts ts." Without hesitating, it launches straight at my mouth, landing spreadeagled on my face, its belly on my nose and its tiny front paws clinging to my glasses. Dan struggles to stifle his guffaws while it hangs there for what seems like eternity. Eventually it runs over my head and springs off my shoulder. "There aren't too many native marsupials that'll do that!" Dan says.

LIKE NEARLY ALL OTHER POSSUMS, Leadbeater's are nocturnal. For up to 16 hours a day they sleep in small colonies of 2–12 individuals, huddled together in warm, balled nests of finely shredded bark that look a bit like mulch you'd find at a plant nursery. There's generally one breeding pair per group.

"The basic community is not that dissimilar to humans – Mum and Dad with kids," Dan says. Non-related males are often tolerated in these groups and, very occasionally, non-related females. "They have a 'live-slow, die-old' strategy, with small litters of 1–2 and they live 6–8 years in the wild."

Peeping tentatively from its nest box, a Leadbeater's possum prepares for a night of foraging. With natural tree holes at a premium, nest boxes are popular with the possums.

At night, each colony generally stays within its 1–3ha territory, "but because they run up and down the trees, the total usable area of their range is huge". They occasionally change nest sites, possibly to foil predators.

Thankfully, foxes and feral cats don't seem to have been effective hunters of the tiny animals. In the wild, their main nocturnal predators are sooty and powerful owls. "But I reckon they're pretty hard for an owl to catch," Dan says. "They're so quick and quiet."

Habitat destruction and a lack of knowledge about Leadbeater's have been their major threats. The possums were for many years considered extinct. Until the 1960s, they were known scientifically only from five historical specimens, found from Mt Wills in north-eastern Victoria to the Bass River, south-east of Melbourne. Then, in 1961, after 50 years without being sighted, they were discovered living in the mountain-ash forests.

In 1986, to great surprise, they were found here at Yellingbo by researchers studying the helmeted honeyeater. Because they'd only been captured in high country, no-one had expected to find them in the lowlands – let alone a swamp. "For 30 years we'd been in this mountain-ash, high-country mindset, but people had forgotten the lowland records from more than 100 years ago. Originally they'd been called the Bass River opossum," Dan says.

Other researchers studying Leadbeater's have predicted that in the next 50 years populations of animals living in mountain-ash forests are likely to crash by up to 90 per cent: a result of too-frequent logging and major fires. "The possums there tend to use only natural hollows in trees that are 200–400 years old," Dan says. "But we're logging those forests on a 60–80-year rotation cycle." Dan says that this will make isolated populations such as the Yellingbo group even more important as a protected enclave of the species. Preservation and expansion of the small Yellingbo population is therefore essential.

Dan's discovered a couple of possums setting up camp more than 1km from the others, which encourages him. "We thought we'd lost this species once and now we've got a second chance," he says. ■

A Tasmanian devil defends a red-necked wallaby carcass in the Central Highlands of Tasmania. While they have acquired a reputation for ferocity, devils are actually relatively timid.

Dining with the devil

Story by **Derek Grzelewski**

Issue 70 Apr–Jun 2003

DUSK DESCENDS QUICKLY OVER the tall swamp-gum forest south of Smithton in north-western Tasmania. I grab my head-torch, spotlight, road map and a vacuum flask of coffee, and fire up the campervan's engine. As I head along a corrugated forestry road, my headlights probe the way ahead, revealing red and yellow eyes that stare warily out of the darkness. The night hums with the mystery of the unseen. In 1982, only a short drive from here, an experienced wildlife ranger reported seeing a thylacine, alive and so close he could count all 12 stripes arching across its back. I'm not looking for apparitions of the Tasmanian tiger. My quarry is its surviving relative, the Tasmanian devil (*Sarcophilus harrisii*).

I've always been fascinated by devils, yet although I've walked, climbed, camped and fly-fished through much of Tasmania's back country, I've not so much as caught a glimpse of one in the wild. Tonight, as I chug along, my heart races at the sight of every road-kill carcass. "Devils can't resist an easy meal, and they'll be less wary of a vehicle than a person on foot," Hobart zoologist Menna Jones told me earlier. "For them, roads are like free takeaway restaurants." Alas, this is my third consecutive night-long shift and the hours are passing by as if in slow motion. I see enough road kill to open a pet-food shop, but by 4am, finding a devil seems just as likely as coming across a thylacine.

Encyclopaedias and other popular sources sketch a vicious portrait of the devil, describing it as something between a bear cub and a pit bull terrier, with an impressive array of blunt chompers and the jaw gape of a hippo. Even long-time Tasmanian devil researcher, biologist Eric Guiler, called it ugly. Others have described the devil as "the smelliest, greediest, worst-tempered animal on Earth".

DAYS LATER, A GLIMMER of hope. On a guesthouse noticeboard I find a plea for volunteers to help in a study of the devils in Freycinet National Park, a peninsula of pink granite mountains forested with eucalypts, midway along Tasmania's east coast. →

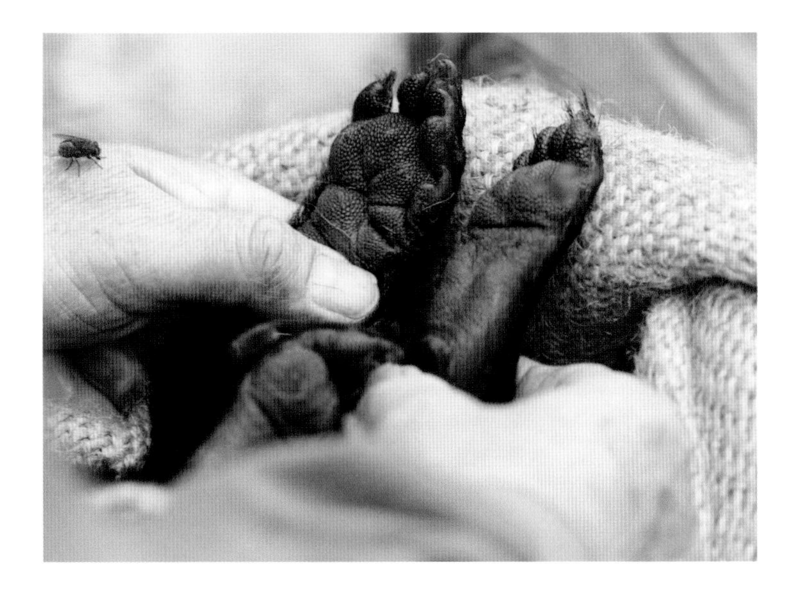

The soft pads of devil's front feet leave distinctive five-toed tracks. The digits have short, sharp non-retractable claws that are used for digging and grasping prey and food items.

Tasmanian devils are voracious predators, using their sharp teeth and powerful jaws to tear through skin and crush bones. When a group gathers to feed from a carcass they rarely leave anything behind.

I pack the camper and set out to meet Menna, a jovial woman who spends nine months of the year in the field studying dasyurids, the carnivorous marsupial family that includes Tasmanian devils, thylacines and quolls.

In 12 years of study, she has only ever seen half-a-dozen wild devils. Fortunately, the beasts are predictably easy to trap. In a 10,000ha area, Menna has captured 44 devils and fitted them with radio-collars spiced with cayenne pepper. The condiment is added to protect the electronic circuitry, because devils are equipped with an industrial strength digestive system and will gnaw away at anything.

Tasmanian devils have the biting power of a dog four times their weight, which gives a large, 12kg male the bite of a 50kg hound. Such a bite is a formidable weapon, and, to avoid seriously injuring each other, devils have developed a number of sophisticated rituals. They communicate and establish their hierarchy with nips and bites, and a new arrival at a roadside feast will often back into the carcass, soaking up all of the outrage of its fellow carnivores with its thick-skinned rump.

Only males fighting over a mate and females tired of a mate's attention really mean business. Head to head, they squabble, sometimes locking jaws on each other's cheek or neck and trying to pull their opponent's head off in a violent tug of war. The injuries from such duels can be horrific and leave the combatants' faces hideously scarred.

As we talk, Menna separates myth from fact. To begin with, devils only emit a scent when scared; a relaxed animal gives off a pleasant scent of lanolin. They are meticulously clean, grooming themselves like cats. Devils are, on the whole, shy and wary animals. But there's one particular trait that has been the devil's greatest undoing. When frightened, confronted, or made to feel uncertain, devils blush then yawn. Animal psychologists call this yawning displacement behaviour, and for the devils it has been a public-relations disaster. It gives them a ferocious look, which is ironic because, in reality, after showing off its fangs, the devil rarely attacks. It would much rather back off, creeping away slowly.

DEVILS ARE COMMONLY CONSIDERED the underdogs of the marsupial ecosystem, vermin in their own homeland. They have been blamed for raiding poultry yards and hunting sheep and lambs. In the past, it wasn't uncommon for farmers to bait or shoot them.

In 1986 Androo Kelly took over the Trowunna Wildlife Park at Mole Creek, in the Great Western Tiers. Androo is one of the devil's most ardent advocates, developing Trowunna into both a refuge for injured and orphaned animals and a centre for public awareness where, he says, people can see the devil for what it is.

At Trowunna, under tall eucalypts, Androo and I sit on the stone-wall fence of the devils' enclosure. It's just after feeding time and the residents still squabble over their daily rations of road kill, tearing off chunks and cantering away to eat them in peace, but always returning for more.

Once the feeding rush has finished, the devils make their way over to investigate us. Their faces bristle with whiskers, and in the dappled sunlight their jet-black fur has a henna-like sheen. I reach out with my hand and one of the animals approaches to sniff it. Its black wet nose bumps hard into my hand as if the animal has misjudged the distance.

Tasmanian devils, Androo tells me, live furiously hyperactive lives, running some 15km every night in pursuit of food or mates. Few live longer than five years and many, like the animal sniffing my hand, suffer from bad backs and arthritis, their once-impressive teeth worn down to stumps. It's tough going from the moment they're born. "The female gives birth to 20 young – each the size of a grain of rice – and they immediately set off on a long crawl to the mother's marsupial pouch," Androo says. It's an all-important race because the pouch only contains four nipples.

This running start sets the pace for the rest of their lives. And it perhaps also explains why, a week into my trip, I'm yet to see a devil in the wild. In order to do so, Androo tells me, I should book a seat at a devil restaurant. He recommends one in Marrawah, near the north-western tip of Tasmania.

By measuring tooth wear, scarring and the size of canines, scientists can estimate a devil's age. In the wild, devils can live to about six or seven years old, although most don't live past five.

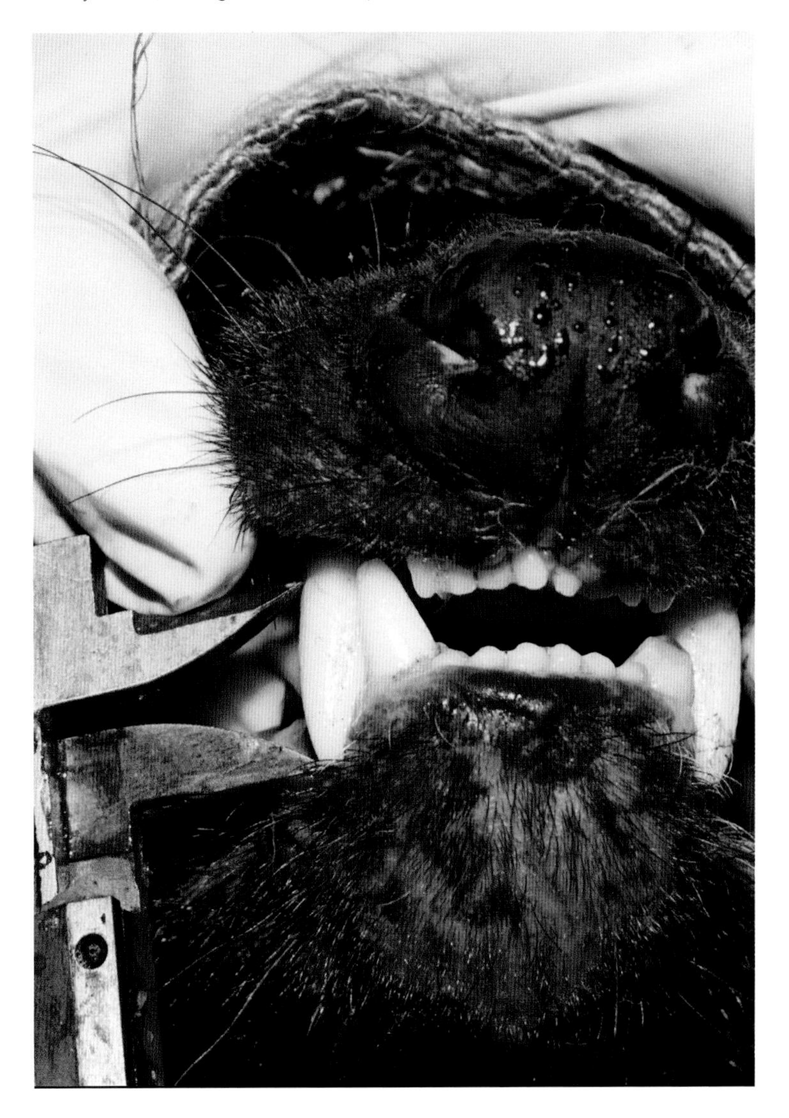

Devil facial tumour disease

AS THE 20TH CENTURY drew to a close, things looked good for the Tassie devil, its population having grown to what was said to be a historical high point of about 150,000 animals. Then, in 1996, Dutch photographer Christo Baars took a series of pictures of devils with grotesquely disfigured faces in the state's north-east. Those pictures were the harbingers of a scourge that would go on to send the species hurtling towards extinction.

The disfiguration was caused by what became known as Devil Facial Tumour Disease (DFTD), a deadly, transmissible cancer in which devils develop tumours on their mouths and faces that inhibit their ability to feed. They usually die of starvation within 3–8 months of the first symptoms.

The infectious cell line is passed through the devil's feeding and biting behaviour. Once introduced into a population, it spreads rapidly. Across Tasmania, average sightings on spotlighting surveys have declined by more than 80 per cent; in the north-east region, where signs of the disease were first reported, sightings have declined by 95 per cent.

The disease mostly affects sexually mature devils, and the species appears to be hanging on in the wild because a few individuals are managing to breed and wean their young before succumbing. Recovery efforts are focused on ways to immunise devils against the disease and the establishment of disease-free populations in areas cut off from the infected animals.

MARRAWAH IS A SMALL town perched on the edge of the ocean, 100km west of Burnie. Frothing breakers roll in under the leaden sky, exploding against the rocky shoreline, as a relentless salt-blasting wind blows. Geoff King, a farmer-turned-devil-restaurateur, welcomes me with a bone-jarring shoulder slap. Minutes later, we're bouncing along a rough track in his ute. We stop to pick up a dead wallaby Geoff pulled from his freezer earlier in the day. It has defrosted nicely; it smells ripe and when Geoff slashes open its belly, I find myself breathing through the collar of my fleece. Geoff ties a rope around the wallaby's feet and loops it around the towbar. "He's draggin' well," Geoff says, catching a glimpse in the rear-vision mirror of the wallaby fish-tailing around a corner as we drag it across the paddocks. "No devil will resist this beauty."

Geoff's land has always been marginal for farming but it's excellent for wildlife, so he turned it into a habitat reserve, setting up an experimental ecotourism business – the devil restaurant. But this is no ordinary restaurant. Here, it's the devils that eat, while the visitors watch on. Seating is limited because Geoff can only 'set the table' five times a fortnight, so as not to habituate the animals to food handouts. The restaurant is an old fisherman's cottage, painted white and cluttered with wicker craypots. Outside, Geoff fastens the battered wallaby to the ground with a wire pin and trains a soft light on the bait. He places a microphone near the carcass. We retire indoors and Geoff gives the viewing window a bit of a clean.

Suddenly, a speaker roars to life. The diners have arrived. One devil is crouched behind the bait, tugging at it and squinting into the light, another warily skulks in the half-shadow. The animals are tense, ready to dart off at the slightest disturbance, but slowly the irresistible aroma of rotting meat reduces their fear and they begin to feed in earnest.

A devil can consume the equivalent of 40 per cent of its body weight in half an hour, Geoff says. That's comparable to a human finishing off 25kg of steak in one sitting. Soon, one animal is so full it waddles off, almost dragging its stomach behind, but as if on cue, another arrives, then another. In the end, all that remains is some chewed-up fur and Geoff's wire fastener.

I can see Geoff is proud of the fact that with each visitor passing through his restaurant, the myths that paint the devil as an evil beast is dispelled a little, freeing these timid animals from their undeserved reputation. Before midnight, he switches off the spotlight. Darkness returns and we let the devils be. ■

Grey-headed flying-foxes drink in a unique way, skimming the water with their belly and then licking the wet fur as they fly and when perched nearby. They usually drink at dusk and night, but if the temperature rises above 35°C, they will do so during the day.

STORY BY DEREK GRZELEWSKI

FLYING-FOXES

Foresters on the wing.

Issue 62 ◆ Apr–Jun 2001

THE CITY WAS still asleep, but the commuters were heading back. In the pre-dawn darkness, rush hour hit Brisbane as thousands navigated the freeways, streets and rivers, and streamed in from the suburbs – all converging on a patch of mangroves behind the Indooroopilly golf course. The bats were coming home.

The cool morning air was thick with their black bodies, filled with the sound of leathery wings flapping like sails and an almighty row of squawking and screeching. Each bat descended like a bird of prey, its outstretched black talons reaching for a branch. Their furry forms fell into pendulum swings before finally coming to a rest. And there they hung, upside down in dark, grape-like bunches, grooming, yawning, stretching, examining wing membranes, cleaning their teeth with toothpick claws and chattering incessantly.

The sun came up and for a while the bats basked in its warm light, relaxing with wings drooping open. Then, as the background hum of human traffic rose to a dull roar, the bats gave themselves one last scratch and a final yawn. They spread and flapped their wings like someone shaking out a blanket and then wrapped themselves snugly within them – hugging their shoulders and burying their faces in the nooks made by their wrists as if they didn't want to know about the outside world. And inside their black cocoons they drifted off to sleep.

From where I sat, on a scaffold platform built beside the colony by zoologist Nicki Markus, it was easy to let my imagination run wild, to open the vein of creativity and sketch a storyline for a Gothic thriller. Where had they been all night? What stories had they been swapping, chuckling to themselves, their dark faces still stained with the remains of a midnight feast?

But forget vampire cliches. If these bats flew in through your bedroom window at night they'd head straight for the fruit bowl, not your jugular. These were puppy-faced, beady-eyed fruit-bats with a fondness for lychees and pawpaw. And you just can't keep them away from mangoes. Which, as you can imagine, often gets them into trouble.

FLYING-FOXES are such wonderfully bizarre creatures. Their fingers are as long as their arms, they look like dogs with wings, fly like birds, →

A grey-headed flying-fox is Australia's largest species, with an average wingspan of about 1m. It's a keystone pollinator and seed disperser for more than 100 species of native plant.

Unlike their mostly insectivorous microbat relatives, which use echolocation to find their way around, flying-foxes navigate by sight. In low light their eyesight is almost as sharp as that of a cat.

climb trees like primates and spend most of their lives upside down. They arrived in Australia via the Torres Strait some 2.6 million years ago and found a huge untapped ecological niche – the eucalypt forests. They fanned out along the north coast to Shark Bay in Western Australia and down the east coast to the shores of Victoria.

Although the vast woodland areas that once covered all of the east coast provided the bats with a continuous banquet of high-energy food, they had to remain extremely mobile. The flowering patterns of eucalypts often resemble fireworks displays – extravagant explosions of colour and scent that appear and disappear unpredictably – and flying-foxes must be able to move from place to place as one burst fades and another lights up.

Over millennia of mutual evolution, the two have become inseparably linked: the forest feeds the bats and the bats propagate the forest. When the bats feed, scooping out the flower nectars with their long, bristly tongues, pollen grains adhere to their fur, turning them into pale dustballs. And when they're gorging on fruit, they often swallow the seeds as well. Then, as they flutter from one tree to the next (flying up to 100km a night), they pollinate other flowers and disperse seeds in their droppings.

When Europeans arrived in Australia, the forests were cleared for pastures and fields of sugar cane, and stands of eucalypts were replaced by orchards. Although flying-foxes prefer their native food, changes in vegetation and the occasional drought, flood or fire mean they're sometimes forced to descend like a plague of locusts on orchards. Locusts with a 1m wingspan!

Such was the common dislike for flying-foxes, that during the 1920s the government hired Dr Francis Ratcliffe, a young, enthusiastic biologist, to spend two years studying the "problem", and to "discover some wholesale method of destruction which would once and for all relieve the growers of the onus of dealing with the pest".

The study of migratory animals required an equally mobile approach, and Ratcliffe virtually lived on his motorbike, visiting one flying-fox camp after another, travelling the red roads through woodland and rainforest, getting to know both the animals and the people of rural Australia. This adventure, he later confided, was the happiest time of his life, although his employers were probably less than thrilled with his findings.

"During this investigation one point of paramount importance has become evident," Ratcliffe wrote in his final report. "The assumption that the flying-fox is a menace to the commercial fruit industry of Australia is quite definitely false, and cannot be cited as a valid reason for the expenditure of public money on its control; the loss to the commercial fruit crop in Queensland is so inconsiderable as to be almost trifling."

I follow in Ratcliffe's footsteps, driving south, into New South Wales and the heart of stone-fruit country, where flying-foxes still flare tempers. When unusually heavy rains washed away eucalypt nectar along the coast of NSW and southern Queensland in 1998, the flying-foxes invaded the orchards en masse. Fruit growers in these areas reported crop losses of up to 95 per cent.

But the flying-foxes didn't get any of John Gough's fruit, although not for lack of trying. "You could see them buzzing around like mozzies behind a flyscreen," he told me. The Goughs watched the invasion of their peach and nectarine orchard outside Lismore, northern NSW, from behind the safety of full-exclusion netting – developed by John – which covers all 5ha of their trees like a giant mesh tent.

"We started off with droopy nets, but both bats and birds got caught in them like fish, and we had a hell of a job untangling them," he said. "And by the way, the birds do just as much damage, but it's the flying-foxes that cop all the blame. Must be something to do with their looks."

He eventually worked out a wire-tension system, and finetuned the size of the mesh. To his delighted surprise, the net also helped to produce better fruit, calming the air, protecting the trees from hail and windburn and creating a microclimate similar to that of a glasshouse.

Until 1998, such nets were considered a luxury, but the near-total annihilation of the crops that year forced many growers to rethink their methods of deterrence and the netting company couldn't keep up with the orders. "It's the best insurance you can get against flying-foxes," John told me, "and you also buy yourself many nights of stress-free sleep, which is priceless."

A mixed flock of black flying-foxes and little red flying-foxes heads back to its camp in the Keep River NP, NT. The widest ranging of Australia's flying foxes, the little red often joins the camps of other species.

I WAS BACK IN BRISBANE, hoping to meet with Les Hall, a biologist who'd spent a lifetime researching bats and was now Australia's foremost flying-fox expert. Les was still unpacking after surveying bat populations in Borneo, but I tracked him down in the grounds of the University of Queensland. Nearby stood a row of queen palms, and underneath them, a drift of half-chewed fruit – a sure sign that flying-foxes were about.

Yes, they're around, Les told me, but despite the fact that they're protected in all of Australia's states, their numbers are declining rapidly throughout their range. During the 1930s, Ratcliffe cited accounts of camps "...half a mile [800m] wide, and about four miles [6.4km] long", containing "millions" of flying-foxes. He also recalled seeing up to 200,000 animals in one place. Today, Les said, half of the entire population of grey-headed flying-foxes would fit into one such camp.

"Their ability to adapt to the huge changes that humans have wrought on their environment is truly astounding," Les said. "Very few native animals have been able to do that so well, but their adaptations can only go so far. There is a simple reason why they are moving into our cities: we have deforested so much of Australia that they have nowhere else to go.

"I see their trouble as our wake-up call," Les continued, "and by being so close to us – almost too close for comfort – they make sure that we get the message loud and clear."

That night I stood with Nicki Markus under the tall gums that host the Ipswich flying-fox camp, watching the bats flying out at dusk: falling down like ripe fruit, unfolding their wings into a glide and flapping away, out into the suburbs.

"Look at them," Nicki said in amazement. "All this traffic and not one collision." Partly sponsored by the Australian Geographic Society, Nicki's three-year study has painted a surprising picture: despite all of the apparent chaos and hubbub, a flying-fox colony is an orderly arboreal suburb, with each animal knowing its own piece of branch. Through many hours of observation she has glimpsed moments both of jest and of heart-stirring tenderness, of flying-foxes hanging together, cuddled up in each other's wings, of mother-infant interplay that seems so familiar that it's difficult not to bestow the animals with human attributes.

"If people only cared to look at flying-foxes more closely, the animals wouldn't be in such trouble," Nicki said. "Our forests are now an archipelago, patchy and scattered, and the flying-foxes are one of the only links between the islands. They are the foresters keeping the ecosystem together. If we are to keep the remnants of our forests healthy, we need the flying-foxes. The two are inseparable." ■

Quoll on the run

Australia's four quoll species were well known to early colonisers, but a long history of persecution has them on the run. Now researchers are working to reverse the fortunes of these fascinating marsupial carnivores.

Story and photography by **Mitch Reardon**

Issue 54 Apr–Jun 1999

A FLASH OF RED-GLOWING eyes and spotted fawn fur flickered on the road verge before disappearing into the cold night, leaving me with a fleeting impression of lithe grace and beauty. Three hours had passed since I had set out from Cradle Mountain Lodge, 110km west of Launceston in Cradle Mountain–Lake St Clair National Park, with activity officers Sonia van de Wolfshaar and Laurie Wootton, to spotlight for quolls, Australia's largest marsupial carnivores after the Tasmanian devil.

In pre-European times the combined distribution of Australia's four quoll species – another two species occur in New Guinea – covered the whole country, but now each is restricted to a greatly reduced area, although thankfully none have become extinct.

Tasmania's two species, the eastern and spotted-tailed quoll, have fared best, particularly the former, which can be relatively common in suitable habitat. But tonight's experience was enough to convince me that if I was going to observe and photograph shy and elusive wild quolls, I would have to appeal to their carnivorous nature. It was time to find some bait.

DARKNESS WAS FALLING, spicing the air with the scent of stringybark and black peppermint blossoms. Sitting quietly in a bush shack turned rudimentary photographic hide, I became aware of a ghostly presence flitting among the eucalypts. Then a sinuous form, its rich reddish-brown coat dappled with bold white spots that continued almost to the tip of its tail, materialised at the edge of the circle of dim light cast by an overhead lamp. Stalking purposefully – at one point standing bolt upright on its hind legs to sniff the air and survey the surroundings – a spotted-tailed quoll, the mysterious 'tiger cat' of Australian bushlore, followed its moist pink nose straight towards a road-killed rabbit pegged out as bait.

When it reached the rabbit it pounced with lightning speed, just as it would with live prey. Clamping powerful jaws around the →

A wary spotted-tailed quoll pauses outside its hollow-log den. Although they usually spend the daylight hours asleep, these quolls sometimes bask in the sun and will even hunt during the day.

Like a starry night come to life, about 15 per cent of eastern quolls are cloaked in a coat of glossy black fur that contrasts dramatically with their white spots, the result of a recessive gene.

base of the rabbit's head, it delivered the quoll's trademark killing bite, a brisk shake of the head helping to drive its sharp canine teeth home, severing the rabbit's spinal cord with an audible crunch.

The closed, wet forests of Tasmania's south and west coasts and central highlands are home to the birds, reptiles and medium-sized mammals that the spotted-tailed quoll prefers to eat. As befits a forest dweller, it's an agile climber, equipped with a thumb-like projection called a hallux on each hind foot and ridged footpads for grip. It's been known to traverse the tree canopy while hunting and even been seen leaping from a limb to knock down a sleeping bird then catching it in mid-air before landing on the ground.

The quoll I was watching was a female, recognisable by her smaller size (males are larger in all quoll species). She was making the most of a welcome alternative food source – carrion. Holding the meal down with her forepaws, she chewed busily. Suddenly she froze, every sense alert. Rigid with aggression, she rose to her feet and gave a deep hiss that switched to a growl as a big male quoll loped confidently into the lamplight. As he approached, the female let loose a staccato shriek like a burst from a circular saw. With a mighty effort she jerked the rabbit free of its tether and began awkwardly dragging it away. The male responded by bounding straight for the food and grabbing hold, whereupon the female leapt into the air and landed in front of him, shrieking into his face.

The tension was palpable. At about 3.5kg the interloper was almost twice the female's size but she wasn't going to be bullied. A short tug of war ensued, culminating in an armed truce as, more-or-less amicably, they fed from opposite ends of the carcass.

Just as the male began licking his forepaws clean, the rabbit meat almost finished, both animals propped to attention then slunk off into the shadows. A moment later the black bulk of a Tasmanian devil loomed into sight. With a warning snort that brooks no argument, Tasmania's top terrestrial carnivore advanced with a curious rocking-horse gait and snatched up the rabbit's paltry remains before it too disappeared into the night.

MY VISIT to Tasmania wouldn't have been complete without a better sighting of an eastern quoll. That opportunity came when quoll researcher Diane Moyle, a PhD student at the University of Tasmania, invited me to visit her study site at the Vale of Belvoir, a tussock grass and sedge landscape 8km north-west of Cradle Mountain Lodge.

Curtains of slanting rain drenched the high plains as I hiked with Di and her companion, Allen Lyngkuist, on an inspection tour of their quoll traps. Diane has an almost proprietary connection to this place, although she conceded that winters could be brutal. Exactly how eastern quolls survive in this uncompromising environment formed the basis of her research.

We visited 35 traps that day, most of them sprung and occupied. At the first, I peered beneath the plastic sheeting taped to one end of the small cage to provide the captive with shelter from the elements. The quoll lay quietly, its chin resting on its forepaws. Placing a bag over her hand, Di reached in and gently slipped it over the animal's head. Covering its eyes has a calming effect and Di lifted it from the cage without a struggle.

With practised assurance, she quickly weighed it, measured the length of its tail, body and feet, the thickness of the base of its tail (where quolls store fat), its head width at the cheekbones, and checked its teeth for wear, all indicators of age and condition.

Di had previously established that although eastern quolls often remain active during heavy snowfalls, they sometimes enter a shallow form of hibernation called torpor for a few hours in order to cope with harsh conditions. Their body temperature drops by up to 10°C and their metabolism slows, helping them to conserve energy. She believes "this happens when quolls have been hunting in bad weather and haven't found enough prey to replace the energy used".

THE BEST NEWS regarding Tasmania's quolls is their healthy abundance. Unfortunately, the situation in mainland Australia is very different. From historical accounts we know that eastern quolls were once abundant over much of eastern New South Wales, Victoria and south-eastern South Australia. However, persecution, fox predation, habitat loss and an epidemic – perhaps toxoplasmosis, a disease caused by an intestinal parasite found in domestic cats – was thought to have led to mainland extinction during the 1960s. Then, in 1989, a road-killed eastern quoll was found in Barrington Tops in NSW. Recently a team of ANU researchers released a group of wild eastern quolls from Tasmania into the Mulligan's Flat Woodland Sanctuary in Canberra, where they hadn't been seen for almost 80 years.

The western quoll, or chuditch, once found across 70 per cent of the continent, is now confined to the south-western corner of Western Australia. Classified as endangered, it fell victim to land clearing, pesticide use by farmers as well as direct poisoning, inappropriate fire regimes, barbed wire fences, illegal shooting and, in particular, predation by feral cats and foxes.

But the news isn't all bad – ongoing attempts to re-establish western quolls in parts of their former range led to a trial reintroduction to SA's Flinders Ranges in 2014. About a third of the first-release population was lost, probably to feral cats, but most of the surviving females bred and there's now a population of 150, about half of them locally born.

SMALLEST OF THE four Australian species, the northern quoll is also classified as endangered. There are now big gaps in its historical range, which once extended uninterrupted from south-eastern Queensland to the Kimberley in WA. Land clearing, foxes and cats all contributed to its decline but the most insidious recent threat is the spread of the cane toad. The toad's potent poison kills quolls that try to eat it. Following the toad's invasion of Kakudu, quolls became extinct at one study site and almost extinct at another. The danger toads pose is so profound that some northern quolls were relocated to the toad-free English Company Islands, off the Arnhem Land coast, where they're thriving.

The best hope for the northern quoll's long-term survival lies in photos retrieved from remote-cameras that show that quolls in the Queensland population, where cane toads have been present for decades, have become toad-averse. On a trip to Kakadu, I came across one of those toad-avoiding northern quolls while spotlighting along a quiet back road. As she disappeared into the woollybutt woodlands I wished her and her kind all the luck in the world – I felt sure they were going to need it. ■

Meri Oakwood gazes affectionately at a 35g, three-month-old northern quoll orphan that will be hand-raised by staff at the Territory Wildlife Park until it is ready to fend for itself in a few months time.

CHAPTER TWO

BIRDS

While Australia's distinctive mammals tend to grab the headlines, our birds are equally striking. Almost 900 bird species have been recorded from Australia and its offshore islands and territories – roughly 10 per cent of the global total.

Of these, 165 are considered to be vagrant or accidental visitors, 13 are believed to be extinct in the wild and 27 are introduced species; roughly 45 per cent of the total are Australian endemics.

Australia's oldest endemic birds are the emus, cassowaries and parrots, whose origins date all the way back to Gondwanan times. The first two of these are, of course, remarkable in that over the course of that long evolution they've dispensed with that most bird-like of attributes, the ability to fly. Emus have made up for the loss by learning to run particularly quickly – they can sprint at speeds of up to 50 km/h. They can also use their wings to make rapid turns. Raising one while pointing the other towards the ground, like a kid playing airplanes, an emu can swivel through almost 180° without losing speed.

The songbirds, a ubiquitous group found the world over that includes more than a third of all bird species, also evolved here. In the Northern Hemisphere, songbirds tend to fit the 'classic' bird mould – sparrows, starlings, thrushes and the like. In Australia, they've taken on some more outlandish forms, such as the pheasant-sized lyrebirds, arguably the world's greatest singers. Impressive mimics, lyrebirds are capable of incredible vocal variety and can even produce more than one sound at the same time.

Australia's songbirds gave the world the familiar cup-shaped nest; evidence suggests that the archetypal nest shape evolved several times in Australia as long as 40 million years ago. However, it's also thought to be where another, more unusual nest was invented. The megapodes, a group that includes the endangered malleefowl and the brush turkey, build enormous mound nests – in the latter's case, they're typically about 4m in diameter and 1.5m in height – and then let the decomposing vegetation within do the work of keeping their eggs warm. The megapodes are also unique in that the adults make no effort to look after their chicks, which can run and feed themselves pretty much from the moment they emerge from the nest, and can fly within a day.

Given the length of time that birds have been in Australia, it's little surprise that they've played a major role in the evolution of the continent's ecosystems. Australia is the only place in the world where bird-pollinated trees form vast forests and where forests are dominated by nectar-feeding birds. Indeed, many of our best-known plants, including banksias, bottlebrushes and eucalypts, are bird-pollinated. Among the more important pollinators are the wattlebirds and lorikeets, but one of the most prolific is the brown honeyeater, which is known to visit more than 300 different types of flower from more than 25 families.

It's believed that this penchant for the sweet stuff has had some unusual side effects. As the horrified early settlers reported, Australian birds are, on the whole, noisier than their cousins. They're also more aggressive. Both of these traits have been linked to their fondness for sugary nectar. Because nectar is a renewable resource, it pays to defend the flowers that provide it, hence the tendency towards high-volume argy-bargy among our birds.

Our birds are also considered to be more intelligent than those found elsewhere. Palm cockatoos, which have very large brains in relation to body size, are among the few bird species known to make and use tools. Males have been observed using their powerful beaks to fashion a drum-tool from a live tree branch and then using it to beat on the edge of a tree hollow, making a distinctive sound that can be heard more than 100m away. And Australian magpies are capable of solving relatively complex problems and can play hide and seek at a level comparable that of a three- to five-year-old child. They also use their beaks to point towards danger – and other magpies use the information provided to spot the danger themselves. ■

Previous page: One of the world's largest songbirds, the superb lyrebird is known for its spectacular mimicry. About 80 per cent of its call is copied from a mixture of natural and mechanical sounds.

A male palm cockatoo feeds on nonda plum seeds near the Lockhart River on Cape York in far north QLD.

STORY AND PHOTOGRAPHY BY **MITCH REARDON**

RAINBOWS IN FLIGHT

Issue 63 ◆ Jul–Sep 2001

FLYING IN on wings of iridescent green, red and amber, small flocks of rainbow lorikeets shot like a fusillade of exquisitely hued arrows through stands of tall eucalypts in Tinchi Tamba Wetlands Reserve on Brisbane's northern outskirts. Propelled by a high-energy intake of pollen and nectar, their wild shrieks ricocheting from tree to tree, the colourful parrots hurried from their feeding grounds to a communal roost.

Soon after sunset, their reunion neared its riotous crescendo. Massing in their hundreds, lorikeets were landing in roost trees, stridently squabbling over choice perches, gossiping with their neighbours and preening their mates, then taking off for flitting sorties, only to return and continue socialising for another half-hour before settling for the night.

I'd joined ornithologist Roy Sonnenburg on one of his regular visits to the 370ha reserve. "Mature eucalypt forests provide just about everything a lorikeet could wish for," Roy told me, "including high-rise living. Although," he cautioned, "not just any roost site will do. Choosing the right place is a matter of survival."

Branches near the top of forest red gums offer lorikeets safety from predators and shelter from wind, rain and cold. At dawn they would once again hurtle forth, screeching high-pitched contact calls, their glorious plumage reflecting the early light as they renew their search for flowering plants. ⟶

The aptly named rainbow lorikeet brings a bright palette of plumage to our cities and towns, announcing its presence both with its brilliant colours and its raucous calls.

A fussy female lorikeet takes in the view from a tree hollow, where she may eventually lay her clutch of 2–3 eggs. Lorikeet pairs often return to the same nesting hollow year after year.

Sprouting their first set of adult feathers, these three-week-old chicks will leave the nest in 4–5 weeks. When the chicks fledge they'll be as big as their parents: about 30cm long and weighing 105g.

RAUCOUS, GAUDY BIRDS such as rainbow lorikeets (*Trichoglossus moluccanus*) aren't easily overlooked. In 1774 a rainbow lorikeet became the first Australian parrot to be portrayed in colour when Peter Brown's publication *New Illustrations of Zoology* invited Europeans to admire their beauty. Since then, most of us have become so accustomed to seeing them, even in city centres, that we take little notice. It's only when newcomers express wonder and delight that we relive the sheer joy many of us felt on first seeing these elegant creatures.

True to their name, rainbow lorikeets' plumage draws from a vibrant palette that includes a violet-blue head, dappled blue, orange and yellow belly, a coral-red beak and eyes, and green wings and tail. Northern rainbows – also known as red-collared lorikeets because of the red collar at the nape of their neck as opposed to the green collar displayed by eastern-seaboard birds – were once considered a separate species, but are now recognised as a subspecies, one of four found in Australia.

Believed to be relatively recent emigrants from New Guinea, rainbows are the most widespread of Australia's six lorikeet species, occurring in much of the continent's east and north. Although all six species are still common in the wild, a looming housing shortage may put their future at risk. Lorikeets nest in hollow limbs or cavities in trees, preferably eucalypts standing near water. It's a neighbourhood also popular with humans. Urbanisation, land clearing and the removal of old-growth forests are responsible for a decline in the availability of housing for lorikeets and other animals.

EARLY ONE morning I came upon a typical lorikeet banquet in Jervis Bay National Park on the New South Wales south coast. Noisy chatter led me to a multitude of rainbows harvesting a paperbark's golden flowers. Lorikeets are highly mobile, chasing unpredictable floral feasts from forest to forest. Each morning at daybreak they disperse widely in small flocks, sometimes travelling more than 100km on daily round trips.

The birds' passionate clamour was both a celebration of their new-found prosperity and an expression of their fiercely competitive nature. Constant squabbling over the tastiest fare is a feature of lorikeet life. These are parrots with attitude that seem to relish face-to-face confrontations.

Despite the sound and fury, brash encounters between lorikeets are usually over in a flurry of threats and body language, with the bigger bird inevitably forcing smaller ones aside. When the contestants are more evenly matched, sharp bites are exchanged until one of the combatants loses its nerve and retreats.

I was able to get close enough to observe the lorikeets' most fascinating adaptation, an evolutionary innovation alluded to in their generic name, *Trichoglossus*, which means "hairy tongue". The tongues of other parrots have a dry, hemispherical end to them, totally unsuitable for gathering pollen. Lorikeet tongues, on the other hand, are tipped with numerous tiny, fleshy bristles known as papillae, which extend during feeding and act like a mop to remove pollen and nectar. When not in use, the retractile bristles are folded away.

Pollen supplies lorikeets with protein, while nectar gives them energy in the form of carbohydrates. If plentiful, nectar enables them to accumulate body fat. Although these two staples make up the bulk of a rainbow's diet, fruit, seeds and the occasional insect are also consumed. So energy-rich is this diet, that the birds can usually satisfy their nutritional requirements in 2–3 hours.

Thoroughly gorged by late morning, the rainbows retired to the treetops' deep shade and sat out the midday heat conversing in a quiet

Flocks of wild lorikeets that have lost their fear of humans clamber over delighted visitors for a twice-daily handout at Currumbin Wildlife Sanctuary in south-eastern QLD.

twitter, idly stripping leaves and occasionally feeding or preening. Then a sudden piercing alarm scream catapulted them into flight.

There had been several other alarms that day, all of them false, and the lorikeets had quickly looped back in a smooth, sweeping arc. This time it was different: the lorikeets fled and didn't return. Intrigued, I scanned the surrounds with my binoculars and eventually spotted the culprit – a brown goshawk melding perfectly with the scrubby bush it was using as cover.

This time the goshawk had failed, thanks to the lorikeets' social behaviour. Flocking means many eyes on the look-out for danger, ensuring a very effective early-warning system. When I returned the following day I discovered a small explosion of grey feathers where the goshawk had caught, plucked and consumed a lone dove.

ONE OF THE BEST PLACES to get a close look at free-ranging lorikeets is Currumbin Wildlife Sanctuary, 25ha of gardens and native-animal displays in the heart of Queensland's Gold Coast.

"On a good day, 700–800 lorikeets arrive at 8am and 4pm for a feed of special nectar mix, vitamins and minerals," wildlife presenter Kate Munro told me as rowdy colour bursts of self-confident lorikeets mobbed me and other visitors holding trays of the sticky liquid.

Kate was quick to assure me that the lorikeets don't depend on human handouts. "We only supplement, not replace, naturally available tucker." Flowering native trees have been planted in the grounds to provide additional food. During peak flowering seasons very few lorikeets bother to visit the trays. "Of course, tourists are disappointed when there's a no-show," Kate said, "but they seem to understand when we explain why."

LORIKEETS PERSONIFY THE WILD SPIRIT of the natural world they inhabit, but when they turn up outside that world they can be very unpopular. Some orchardists complain that lorikeets have acquired a taste for cultivated fruit, particularly pears, apples and grapes. In Queensland, particularly during drought, sorghum and maize crops are raided.

During the late 1960s, nine rainbow lorikeets were released →

The flowers of a swamp bloodwood provide a rainbow lorikeet with an energy-rich meal of pollen and nectar. Moving on to another bloom on another tree, the lorikeet unknowingly transfers grains of pollen that have stuck to its feathers, and so helps to cross-fertilise these trees.

in Perth by a homesick east-coast man. "They adapted very successfully," Peter Mawson, senior zoologist with the Western Australian Department of Conservation and Land Management, told me. Before long there were reports of competition for nesting hollows between the introduced rainbows and WA's slightly larger ringnecks, known locally as Port Lincoln and 'twenty-eight' parrots.

"Rainbows have been seen entering nests and ejecting the chicks," Peter said. "Our rainbows are classified as 'acclimatised fauna' but if I could get rid of them I would consider it."

Rainbow lorikeets are even less welcome in Auckland, New Zealand, where, in 1992, a bird breeder illegally released some captive-bred rainbows. Conservation officers such as Art Polkanov are concerned that they may compete with native birds and bats for nest cavities and with honeyeaters for food. As manager of the NZ Department of Conservation's Rainbow Lorikeet Project, Art is hoping to capture all of the wild lorikeets and sell them to local commercial aviculturists. "But free-ranging lorikeets are declared an 'unwanted organism'!"

ONE SPRING MORNING, while relaxing on my sundeck, I watched a pair of rainbow lorikeets begin their courtship ritual. The male, his body flushed with hormones, pumped up and down on his squat legs as if some internal spring had suddenly been released. His animated display would eventually trigger an alteration in the female's internal chemistry, making her ready to ovulate and, crucially, willing to mate.

That time hadn't yet arrived and with a dismissive squawk, she flew away. The male next turned his attention to me and hopped closer. He looked up at me and I guessed what he was thinking and sat very still. It took two false starts but finally trust won out and he flew up and alighted on my shoulder.

It was a magical moment but I baulked when I felt a gentle little nibble on my earlobe. Suspecting that the lorikeet's insatiable curiosity might eventually demand a more probing bite, I gently pulled my head to one side. The movement broke the spell and the lorikeet took off, flying hard, perhaps as pleased by the novelty of our meeting as I was. ■

Attracting lorikeets to your garden

Although rainbow lorikeets can be abundant in urban areas, they'll often bypass gardens if conditions aren't quite right. Here are a few tips for enticing these colourful larrikins into your urban oasis

A WELCOMING HABITAT for lorikeets requires a mix of food, shelter and water. You can create the right environment by planting a selection of pollen- and nectar-rich trees and shrubs, in particular eucalypts, paperbarks, bottlebrushes, grevilleas and banksias. In the process, you'll be making your garden a refuge for a diversity of other species, including honeyeaters.

1 Find out which native plants occur in your area by contacting your council or the Society for Growing Australian Plants/Australian Plant Society. By carefully choosing your plants, you can ensure that some species flower in winter when other blossoms are scarce.

2 If you're planning to feed wild lorikeets, it's vital that you choose the correct ingredients, in order to avoid dietary deficiencies. Fresh fruit such as apples, pears and grapes, a seed mix suitable for small parrots, mixed greens and sprouted seeds are all lorikeet-friendly. A prepared "Wet Lori Mix" is available from pet shops. Honey, bread and water are NOT suitable, nor should refined sugar, in any form, be used.

3 Any and all leftovers must be disposed of promptly to prevent spoilage and all feeding dishes should be cleaned regularly. Remember that this type of feeding should only ever supplement the birds' natural diet, not replace it.

4 You can emulate natural nesting hollows by placing a section of hollow log or a nesting box about 5m up a shady tree. The nesting box should be about 23cm long by 25 wide by 35 high, with a 7–15cm diameter entrance hole located near the top of the front of the box.

5 Nesting boxes should have a perch placed just below the entrance hole and a small wire ladder inside. It's a good idea to have a removable lid so that the box can be cleaned out annually.

6 A regular source of fresh water, which the birds will use for both drinking and bathing, is essential. A shallow dish or birdbath will do.

Beating around the bush

A long-term research project on Cape York Peninsula is returning unusual insights and incredible photographs of the little-known palm cockatoo.

Story and photography by **Christina N. Zdenek**

Issue 126 May–Jun 2015

SCREECH, SQUAWK, SMACK! I couldn't believe my eyes. I'd just witnessed two male palm cockatoos (*Probosciger aterrimus*) clash in mid-air above a large, hollow tree and viciously wrestle, using their enormous beaks, before finally tumbling to the ground. During several years of researching 'palmies', I had never seen such intense conflict.

And the tussle didn't end there – although the tall, tropical grass concealed the rival males from view, for what seemed like an eternity I could hear a horrible, loud growling coming from the now-grounded, brutal battle. This extreme aggression could only mean one thing – whatever they were fighting over was worth dying for.

We're near to the Lockhart River in a remote part of Cape York Peninsula in far north Queensland. Despite the fact that the nearest city, Cairns, is some 700km away, birders flock here from all over the world and brave rudimentary dirt roads and perilous river crossings to see the iconic palm cockatoo in the wild. It's no wonder, because this is a truly spectacular species. Cockatoos are distributed across New Guinea, Indonesia, the Philippines, the Solomon Islands and Australia – and of the 21 known species, the palmy is the heaviest and one of the largest.

On occasion, when their mood is right, their bald red cheeks can flush with blood, turning from pale red to deep scarlet. If that's not intriguing enough, perhaps more curious is their drumming behaviour. Like no other creature in the world, palmies fashion thick sticks from branches, grip them with their feet and bang them on trunks and tree hollows.

This is clearly an example of sticks being used as tools, but unlike Jane Goodall's famous chimpanzees, which use tools to forage, palm cockatoos don't obtain treats in return for drumming. So why do it? Since the discovery of the behaviour in 1984, drumming by palmies has been a mystery to scientists, who've puzzled over what the behaviour entails and in what context it occurs.

These questions and more have been a source of fascination for Professor Robert Heinsohn of the Australian National University in Canberra. Thanks to a grant from the Hermon Slade Foundation, Rob was able to employ me to do the groundwork and find the answers. Between us, PhD student Miles Keighley and I currently work across more than 10 Cape York sites, recording vocal and display behaviours in an effort to better understand this bird, and determine the extent to which its populations are genetically related.

PALMIES ARE INFAMOUS for being skittish and elusive. Most people are lucky if they just get a fleeting glimpse of this unique and majestic creature flying overhead. Many birders have to come back to the region around the Iron Range National Park several times before finally getting a decent view and photo of a palmy. For the past seven years, however, I've been very fortunate to encounter them at close quarters on many occasions – sometimes even having three birds fly into a tree directly above my head.

I'm often asked how I manage to get so close to palmies without spooking them. I would like to think that it's down to ninja-style stealth, but the answer is more likely to do with the birds themselves. They are a highly intelligent species with a large forebrain, and what's probably an excellent memory; I believe that they're almost certainly capable of recognising different human faces. There's certainly precedents for such an ability. Several other bird species – pigeons, crows and North America's northern mockingbird, for example – have been shown to discriminate reliably between familiar and unfamiliar humans based on facial features, sometimes up to years after just a single encounter.

I've been spending up to six months at a time in the field, returning to the same study sites for seven years now, and it's quite possible that the birds recognise me personally and understand that I present no threat to them. Indeed, it may be this that has allowed me to record their rare drumming behaviour on a remarkable 38 occasions over the past two years.

Staring into the glaring sun, my tiring arms struggle to keep a 10m-long extendible pole vertical against the gusting wind. Between morning and afternoon sessions spent watching the behaviour of birds, my volunteers and I spend the hottest part of the day doing numerous tree-hollow inspections. If I'm having a bad day, as the mounted camera reaches a tree hollow for a coveted view of the nest

Palm cockatoos share nesting duties. This male, right, incubates during the day, while the female, left, will do so at night.

inside, hostile green ants might crawl up my legs from the ground and begin to bite my sweaty skin, spraying copious amounts of stinging formic acid into the tiny bites. Clenching my teeth against the pain, I try to focus on the task at hand. It's an important job because tree hollows are essential nesting sites for these birds – I had seen firsthand that they were ready to fight to the death over them – and without ready access to suitable hollows in large, old-growth trees, they aren't going to survive.

The creation of a palmy nest is a very slow process, starting with a century-old tree. First, this tree needs to be ripped apart by a cyclone, leaving it as a trunk without a canopy. Then, a small fire needs to create a scar at the base, allowing termites, fungi and bacteria to enter. Eventually, a fully hollowed-out trunk is formed in which a pair of palm cockatoos might nest – if it has the right dimensions and shape, and is strong enough to withstand fires and cyclones.

Despite hundreds of hours checking dozens and dozens of hollows in 2014, I only found five active nests. Needless to say, palmies are very particular in their nesting requirements and their chosen trees are a precious commodity.

Palm cockatoos have a very low rate of reproduction and reproductive success. My predecessor on the research program, Dr Steve Murphy, found that these long-lived birds breed, on average, just once every two years, and invariably lay just a single egg per clutch. This egg has a relatively low chance of hatching (61 per cent) and an even lower chance of reaching adulthood (39 per cent). In fact, palmies have one of the lowest overall breeding success rates of any parrot (second only to Australia's eclectus parrot), and computer modelling by Robert Heinsohn has shown that the Iron Range population is more than likely in severe decline.

Worryingly, the research suggests the population could be extinct within 100 years. The problem continues to be exacerbated by extensive land clearing for bauxite mines on the western side of Cape York, excavation of quarries throughout the peninsula, and inappropriate fire regimes that can burn down the 200-year-old hollowed-out trees that are vital for nesting.

In recognition of these facts, a few years ago, the federal government nominated palmies for a review of their conservation status. They were listed as 'near threatened' but in May 2017, they were moved into the more severe category of 'vulnerable', which will offer them increased protection.

If palm cockatoos are willing to fight to the death for ideal nesting hollows, perhaps then, for the survival of this striking species, it's worth us fighting to keep these old hollowed-out trees in the wild landscape of Cape York. ■

STORY BY **NICK DRAYSON** PHOTOGRAPHY BY **BILL BACHMAN**

THE MAGPIE, AUSTRALIA'S ICONIC BIRD

Issue 68 ◆ Oct–Dec 2002

THE KOALA SEEMED TO appear from nowhere. It ambled out of the long grass, gave a cursory glance towards our vehicle, and walked straight up the ironbark as if the tree were horizontal. "Nick," said Corinna Lange, "please try to keep your eyes on the magpies." Chastised, I put my eye back to the spotting 'scope.

"Blue-pink-blue, red master, adult female." Corinna began looking through the data sheets to match the colours I'd called off – each magpie is identified by a different coloured leg band – while I let my attention wander. The koala had reached a high branch and was silhouetted against the cloudless sky. A restless flycatcher zipped around it, and down by the creek, four rainbow bee-eaters perched along a fence like emeralds on a necklace.

That's the problem with the Strathbogie Ranges of central Victoria in November – there's always so much to see. But I wasn't here for koalas or bee-eaters. I was meant to be watching *Cracticus tibicen*, the Australian magpie. Magpie researcher Corinna, and Jane Hughes, a professor in the Faculty of Environmental Sciences at Griffith University in Brisbane, have been observing magpies around the Victorian town of Seymour for 10 years. Jane is particularly interested in interactions between two of the different races within the species: black- and white-backed magpies.

Generally, white-backs are found in southern Australia while black-backs are found in the north. Another race, which lives on the western side of the continent, has white-backed males and ⟶

Dawn outside Melbourne's Shrine of Remembrance and a male Australian magpie tries to persuade a guard to move on. Males often aggressively defend the nesting area during the breeding season. Research has shown that most Australians have been swooped at least once.

Hanging baskets make ideal artificial nests for magpie fledglings being cared for by Melbourne animal-rescue specialist Nigel Williamson. These birds will soon be reintroduced to the wild.

In Rushworth in north-eastern VIC, Daryl Britten feeds Maggs, a female magpie who comes down regularly to collect grubs whenever he's chopping firewood.

black-backed females. Seymour sits on the confluence of the southern and northern races. Here, they mingle and interbreed.

According to Jane, magpies are highly territorial. "Each territory is occupied by 2-20 birds and all adults in a group defend the boundaries," she said. "Much of this defence is passive – the sight and sound of magpies is usually enough to keep others away." But the birds aren't averse to a little physical contact. Any transgression of their boundaries can signal them to swoop en masse on an intruder.

"OK, TIME'S UP," CORINNA said. "No surprises today." We'd been watching and recording the birds for 20 minutes. In that time, we'd identified six birds, all of which had been seen here before. The group appeared to be stable. It was time for morning tea.

"We thought we had magpie genetics pretty much worked out," Jane told me over a cup of tea as we sat in a nearby shearing shed. "But we began to notice some strange exceptions that we couldn't explain," she continued. Jane and her team have been working on DNA fingerprinting of magpies for some time. "We're getting a really clear picture of exactly which magpie is related to another," Jane said. "To say we've had some surprises is putting it mildly."

It has long been assumed that among magpies the dominant male in a particular territory fathers almost all of the chicks. Jane's recent DNA analysis challenges this. Her research shows that extraterritorial matings are common: up to 50 per cent of fledglings are fathered by males outside the group. But there's more. According to Jane, the female magpie sitting on an egg and raising a chick isn't necessarily its mother. "No-one has ever seen precisely what happens," Jane said, "but it's probable that some female magpies lay their eggs in other magpies' nests."

A NUMBER OF METHODS are used by ornithologists to catch birds, from climbing up to nests and taking fledglings before they can fly to using various kinds of net. Jane has devised a simple and humane method of trapping magpies in specially made wire cages. The cage has a wire funnel leading into it, through which the birds crawl to reach the grated-cheese bait. A trap is put in place within a known territory, left open and baited for a few days beforehand to let the magpies get used to it. Once the trap is set, it takes just half an hour for magpies to enter. After they do, a researcher takes them out and bands them.

"During the 10 years I've been researching magpies," Jane said as we drove down the tree-lined country road, "the groups and territories have changed slowly as old birds disappear and new ones enter or form new territories." We were heading towards a new territory that had been recently formed by birds from adjoining territories. "We're still trying to band this year's brood," Jane said.

Inside the trap, three birds were feeding. "I think we've got a new one," Jane said. Before I'd switched off the engine she was out of the car and stealthily heading for the trap. Within half a minute, she had opened the back of the trap and was passing me out a young magpie. As I held it, wings folded, close against my body, Jane released the remaining banded birds. They immediately flew up into a nearby tree.

I held out the left leg while Jane gently but efficiently closed the first band – a piece of metal with an ID number and a toll-free phone number to call if the bird is found dead – with a pair of pliers. Then she added a red band that denotes the bird was banded in 2001.

"You choose the colours for the other leg," she said. I consulted the list of available combinations and chose a patriotic red, white and blue band, which Jane carefully closed over the bird's right leg. Then, taking out some nail clippers, Jane clipped off a few millimetres from one of the magpie's claws. A minute drop of blood appeared from its tip, which Jane coaxed into a small plastic vial.

"That's all we need for DNA analysis," she said. The data – time, date, bird ID, age and sex – were carefully noted in an exercise book. Later, it would be transcribed onto a computer database, the basic ore from which results and conclusions are later refined.

It was time to release the magpie. "Just open your hands," Jane said. I did, and with a squawk of what sounded to me like pure indignation the young magpie flew up into the tree, where it was greeted with carols of concern.

Magpies are accustomed to being part of a family, which may explain why orphaned magpies often respond well to human company. The Lund-Gunter family from Sunday Creek in central VIC give their one-year-old orphan the run of the house.

THE MAGPIE'S LIQUID, WARBLING SONG is one of the quintessential sounds of Australia. The plethora of alternative names for the Australian magpie, including flute bird, organ bird, piper, piping crow-shrike and singing crow, attest to this. Magpies and their songs feature in a number of Aboriginal legends as well as the descriptions of early European visitors and colonisers. The magpie's song has also inspired musicians and poets. "For each is born with such a throat, as thanks his God with every note," wrote Australian poet Judith Wright. It has also comforted our World War II troops, who sang Alfred Hill's *I thought I heard a magpie call* – "I thought I heard a magpie call across the Tasman seas, and close my eyes to visualise a row of tall gum trees."

However, perhaps magpies are best known for their less endearing behaviour – swooping. To find out more about this infamous habit, I talked to Jane's colleague at Griffith University, Dr Darryl Jones. Darryl has been investigating magpie attacks for close to 20 years.

In Brisbane, Darryl has discovered that about one in five male magpies within a territory will swoop on humans during the nesting season. Of those, some only swoop pedestrians, others only people on pushbikes and others again, only posties. "It not unusual for a postie to be swooped by magpies a few hundred times a day during the peak season," Darryl said.

Various theories explain why magpies dive-bomb humans and other animals. The most obvious is that swooping scares away any threat to their nests and nestlings. But this doesn't explain why only some magpies swoop and why they're so selective. It's possible that they swoop only those animals that they've learnt to associate with a threat.

Another theory is that males are simply showing off to females: that by engaging in such acts of derring-do they demonstrate their strength and fitness to father chicks.

Whatever the cause, Darryl says the best solution is to learn to live with magpies, as most Australians have come to do. However, if a male is really aggressive, particularly towards children – the occasional serious eye injury has been reported from magpie attacks – you'll need to remove the stroppy male. "Trapping and moving the male at least 40km away will ensure it doesn't return to its old territory," Darryl said. "But keep in mind that once that male is removed, another usually takes its place, feeding and caring for any nestlings or fledglings as if they were his own."

In the bush, however, they're much shyer. As Jane explained, swooping is more of a problem for humans in towns and suburbs, where magpies have grown used to human presence. "You're lucky to get within a hundred metres of the magpies round here." ■

Albatross Island

A tiny fleck of land in the Bass Strait is home to a colony of shy albatrosses numbering more than 5000 nesting pairs.

Story by **Peter Meredith** Photography by **Matthew Newton**

Issue 127 Jul–Aug 2015

ALBATROSS ISLAND is a windswept speck in the Bass Strait. Named for its best-known (but by no means most numerous) inhabitant, the shy albatross (*Thalassarche cauta*), it covers just 18ha and lies some 35km off north-western Tasmania. Some of its rock substrate is exposed to the elements; the rest is carpeted in a vibrant mass of ground-hugging vegetation, including several varieties of succulent.

Although it's a paradise for birds and visually stunning, Albatross Island can be less than comfortable for human visitors. For a start, the locals are prone to making a racket day and night, especially when they're breeding. And the accumulated bird guano gives off a pungent smell that can be detected some way off the island. It has no human-made structures, and because it's a state nature reserve, you need a permit to land there.

The reason for the island's protected status is the vast numbers of birds that call it home. Some 5200 pairs of shy albatrosses breed here every year, together with an estimated 20,000 pairs of fairy prions, 2000 pairs of short-tailed shearwaters and 350 pairs of little penguins, among other avian visitors. A few fur seals also visit.

As impressive as these statistics are, both bird and seal numbers were higher in the past. George Bass and Matthew Flinders reported seeing the island "almost covered with birds" when they landed there in 1798. It's estimated there were about 20,000 breeding pairs of shy albatrosses on the island then, but in the 1800s sealers put an end to that. After almost wiping out the island's seals, they turned to albatrosses and sold their feathers as hat adornments and for stuffing pillows and quilts. By 1909 the number of albatrosses had plummeted to 250–300 breeding pairs. That turned out to be a low point from which the population recovered steadily, until recently.

From the early 1980s, the island's albatrosses have been the focus of a long-term scientific study that aims to track their numbers and find out where they go and what they do on their travels. Dr Rachael Alderman, a senior wildlife biologist at Tasmania's Department of Primary Industries, Parks, Water and Environment, began coordinating the program in 2003. She has been visiting the island at least twice a year, sometimes four times, ever since. Her visits coincide with critical events in the albatross calendar – such as egg-laying in September and chick-fledging in March.

A female shy albatross lays a single egg in September and then she and her mate will take turns to incubate it, spending about five days on the nest and then five days foraging at sea.

The shy albatross, with a wingspan of about 2.5m, is smaller than its better-known cousin, the wandering albatross, which has a wingspan of 3.5m. The global population breeds only on three islands off Tasmania: Albatross Island, Mewstone (10,000 breeding pairs) and Pedra Branca (200 breeding pairs).

The shy albatross doesn't range as far as the wandering albatross, which may circumnavigate the globe for several years after it has fledged and left the nest before returning to its birthplace to breed. Non-breeding juvenile and immature shy albatrosses tend to remain in the waters of southern Australia, occasionally crossing the Indian Ocean to South Africa.

An adult shy albatross has a wingspan of up to about 2.5m. Dr Rachael Alderman, at left, Julie McInnes and Kris Carlyon check a bird for moulting feathers.

When they're breeding, wandering albatrosses may cover thousands of kilometres in search of food. In contrast, breeding shy albatrosses don't stray much more than 200km on their foraging trips and stay away for no longer than about 10 days.

"They keep to the Bass Strait region and return to the colony all year," Rachael says. "One reason for that may be that the Bass Strait environment is productive and predictable enough year-round to allow the birds to stay."

Shy albatrosses are long-lived and slow to reproduce. They live for about 35 years, are in their prime between 10 and 25, and generally form lifelong, monogamous pairs. A female lays a single egg in September and she and her mate take turns to incubate it over 10 weeks, one sitting on the nest while the other is away foraging. The chick hatches in December, fledges in March and departs in April.

"Of the eggs laid in a given year, fewer than half become a chick that makes it to the end of the breeding season," Rachael says. "And we know from our research that fewer than half the chicks that survive to leave the island make it back again."

How Rachael establishes these facts is down to the strategies that she uses in her research program. One is to count breeding pairs and chicks every year, which yields a measure of breeding success. Another, known as 'capture, mark, recapture', involves fitting leg bands to chicks before they leave the nest and reading the bands of returning birds. Rachael and her coworkers also fit GPS trackers to birds in order to trace their journeys.

All the data from the program are pieces of a gigantic jigsaw puzzle that will one day yield a coherent picture. Some trends are already emerging; breeding success, for instance – the survival rates of juvenile birds and the number of breeding birds have both begun to decline in the past 10 years. Why this is happening is still a mystery. It may be linked to the numbers of albatrosses killed as fishing bycatch or to climate change and associated changes in the ocean and the weather.

"With this project we're trying to understand the cumulative impacts of all of the threats that the birds face as much as follow single lines of inquiry," Rachael says. "The cumulative impacts can be quite massive." ■

STORY BY KEN EASTWOOD PHOTOGRAPHY BY JIRI LOCHMAN

SUPER BIRD

Faster than a speeding ute, tougher than the roughest ruck-rover and able to leap three metres at a single bound, the world's second-largest living bird is Australia's own. The emu.

Issue 58 ◆ Apr–Jun 2000

I'LL NEVER TIRE of seeing emus in the wild. They're gangly, awkward-looking characters, but an emu (*Dromaius novaehollandiae*) is such an Australian ambassador it became an obvious choice for the national coat of arms.

It's an adaptable battler, surviving above the snowline and out in the desert. It's athletic, with an explosive sprint of up to 70km/h, a cruising speed of 45km/h – still considerably faster than the quickest Olympic runner – and an ability to swim powerfully across rivers such as the Murray. It's as tough as the country it lives in: stories abound of emus going under moving cars or even road trains, then running off to live another day. It's a bit of a larrikin too, as shown by its crazy, dancing courtship antics and an insatiable curiosity that leads it to investigate – and often swallow – keys, camera lenses and mobile-phone batteries.

On Mileura, a 2500sq.km sheep station near Meekatharra, Western Australia, Stephen Davies was up to his elbows in the guts of an emu. It wasn't a pretty sight. As he fished around inside the opened belly, one of his students from Perth's Murdoch University asked: "Do you want a hand Stephen?" "No," he gently replied, "I want the gizzard."

For 40 years, Stephen has rolled up his sleeves and his swag and headed 800km north of Perth to the wind grass, mulga and open spaces of Mileura to study emus and other animals and plants of the region. With infinite patience, he would sit for days on hilltops watching emus walk past, learning that they moved towards clouds. Through banding, he discovered that emus can travel more than 900km in nine months. And during one 11-year observation period, when he used planes, motorbikes, cars and his feet, Stephen determined that although emus can be found in large mobs of more than 15, most move in singles and pairs, about 26km →

Clawing and bashing its way out of its speckled 700g egg, a striped emu chick gains its first glimpse of daylight. On emu farms, chicks occasionally need help from a human hand to break out of the 1mm-thick eggshell, but once hatched can usually run around within 24 hours.

Although most emus roam in singles or pairs, families stay together until the young strike out on their own, at 6–18 months of age. Larger mobs may also be seen, particularly if food resources are scarce.

As well as a binocular field of view of about 140°, which is similar to human vision, emus have extraordinarily good long-distance sight, clearly detecting movement more than 1km away.

apart. "They really don't like each other," he told me as we huddled by a campfire on the station. "Even a pair of emus will tend to walk 100–300m apart. It's generally only where there's a food resource, or young birds, that they'll group."

In 1959 Stephen was commissioned by the CSIRO to help figure out what caused emus, in some years, to descend on WA's wheat paddocks. It takes only a few 40–50kg emus to trample and destroy a crop. That's why they're still officially classed as pests in WA and 1100km of barrier fences protect the bulk of the state's grain.

According to Stephen, if there's an abundance of food, emus will naturally disperse in all directions. This makes them nomadic, not migratory. However, if there's a food shortage, they'll head towards rain. In this part of WA this usually means north in summer, where cyclone rains bring on fresh grasses, and south – towards the wheat – in winter.

"There are three theories about how they know to move towards rain: they see the clouds, and head towards them; they hear the thunder; or they smell the humus in the leaf-litter after rain," Stephen said. "I think they see the clouds. They have excellent vision – much better than ours – and you can see cyclone clouds from hundreds of kilometres away."

In 1976 some 100,000 emus – about half the WA emu population, and perhaps 10 per cent of Australia's emus – lined up on the northern side of one of the barrier fences, literally dying to get to the other side. Smaller build-ups have occurred more recently. But Stephen isn't worried about the effect the fences may have on emu numbers. "There are many times more emus now than when Europeans first colonised the country, because we've increased the number of watering points," he said. "Emus need to drink every day, and we've made it so much easier for them to survive."

THE DEAD EMU SPRAWLED at Stephen's feet, in an incongruously pretty patch of mauve and white everlastings, had been shot for scientific research. Gemma Graham, one of the University of WA researchers who had accompanied us, needed a section of its brain for work on the hormones that slash the emu's appetite during the breeding season. Another researcher, Emma Taylor, needed some of its blood to study genetic differences between emus in different parts of the country. Someone else needed the liver. And Stephen wanted the gizzard for ongoing work on emu diet. The bird's death also gave Stephen a chance to deliver an impromptu anatomy lesson to his protégés.

With now-bloodied fingers, he stretched a skin membrane low on the bird's neck, explaining that it was the air sac that mature birds – particularly females – inflate and resonate to make a loud, low booming or drumming sound to call for mates and claim territory.

Then Stephen pulled back the insulating twin-shafted feathers to expose one of the bird's 20cm-long wings. Like some other flightless birds, the emu's breastbone lacks the keel that flying muscles would attach to, so the wings are virtually useless. Pushing more feathers aside, Stephen showed us a 1.5cm claw on the end of the wing. "There's a lot of variation between emus – and even on the same bird – in the size of the claws, which is an indication of how unnecessary the claws have become," Stephen said.

Afterwards, he sliced open the gizzard to show me its partially digested contents. It was full of calyx lobes – plant parts that support the fruit – from poverty bushes. "As you can see, they get very fixated on one food source," he said, poking through hundreds of the once bright-pink lobes. Emus will eat many things: young shoots and stems, fruits, flowers, seeds and insects. But they tend to binge on one item at a time until there's none of it left.

Stephen stood to wipe his hands, the anatomy lesson over. Nearly 2m tall, with a longish neck and tufts of hair sprouting out of his head at crazy angles, he looked uncannily like a particular bird...

As in many other flightless birds, it's the male that incubates the eggs. In an astounding feat of endurance and dedication, a male emu will squat on a pile of 5–20 eggs for 56 days without eating, drinking or defecating. Some males lose up to a third of their body weight at

Standing only to turn the eggs, a male emu will sit on a clutch for eight long weeks. Although laid three days apart, the eggs hatch within a day or so of each other.

this time, living solely off extensive fat reserves and dew on the grass around them.

On an emu breeding farm at Mount Gibson, 270km north-east of Perth, I picked up a fluffy emu chick for a cuddle, its strong legs kicking and scratching me. One of the farm's owners, 62-year-old Morna Bennett Wheeldon, laughed. "A chicken chick is so fragile, so tiny, but when you've got an emu chick in your hand you really feel like you've got something."

The chicks lose their attractive camouflage stripes after 3–5 months. In the wild they follow Dad around – Mum usually departs after laying the eggs – for 6–18 months, reaching full height around their first birthday.

"They're the easiest things in the world to farm – until you go to shift 'em," Morna said. "Then they act as though they're feral. You can't catch 'em, you run around after 'em, you get worn out, you fall over, they kick the insides out of you, and they're a pain in the arse. But generally, you've just got to watch that you don't get in the way of their feet when they're attacking another bird."

During the early 1990s, the emu industry had taken off like rabbits. Investors paid thousands of dollars for each breeding emu as pyramid schemes encouraged more and more people to farm the productive bird. By 1994 there were about 180,000 emus being farmed on more than 1300 Australian properties.

However, no-one was focusing on marketing the products – the meat, oil, leather and eggs. This meant that the market, flooded with emus that were costing farmers a packet to feed, collapsed. Many birds were uselessly slaughtered and buried; others were set free in the wild, where they probably died, having no bush-survival skills. Today, very few emu farms survive.

Morna said she certainly didn't regret taking on the farm, which keeps about 5000 emus. "They're such peaceful birds to have," she said, resting on a log by a docile nesting male, a rainbow decorating the sky behind her. "You're out in the outback collecting eggs, and you've got the sounds of other birds, the smells of the bush and the sight of fresh rain on the trees. It's just glorious."

Mt Gibson emu farm has subsequently closed and the property is now part of the Mount Gibson Sanctuary, overseen by the Australian Wildlife Conservancy. ■

The march of the brush turkey

This tenacious bird has been defiantly spreading across the east coast to reclaim much of its pre-European range.

Story by **Alasdair McGregor** Photography by **Esther Beaton**

Issue 132 May–June 2016

AT FIRST I THOUGHT I was seeing things. There had definitely been no over-indulgence the previous evening, but I nevertheless awoke bleary-eyed to the sight of a very large, blackish bird perched awkwardly on the wall of my upper storey balcony. Because I live on Military Road, one of Sydney's busiest thoroughfares, it seemed a strange place for an Australian brush turkey (*Alectura lathami*) to roost.

The natural range of the bird – also known as the bush or scrub turkey – stretches along the east coast from far north Queensland to the Illawarra, south of Sydney. It has never been endangered, but after several centuries of habitat loss and predation by cats and foxes, it did become scarce across large areas.

So what was this prehistoric-looking creature doing in the concrete jungle of Neutral Bay, 4km from the city's CBD, rather than in the deep shadows of the forest? Until the past 20 years or so, turkeys were virtually unknown south of the Hawkesbury River, but, as I soon discovered, they've been on the march in recent decades, determinedly reclaiming their likely historic range. Some Sydneysiders greeted their arrival as a wildlife good-news story, but for others, it meant the outbreak of war in the suburbs.

The brush turkey is one of about 22 species of megapode, which means 'big feet'. These birds don't sit on their eggs to incubate them, but rather lay them in large mounds of decaying vegetation, relying on the heat generated within. Megapodes are only found in the Indo-Pacific region, with three species in Australia – the malleefowl, orange-footed scrubfowl and the brush turkey. Unique among all birds, megapode parents are the ultimate delinquents, and play absolutely no part in the rearing of their young.

But back to where things begin: the male, with an almost obsessive purposefulness, constructs his mound, which can take on gargantuan proportions as sand, soil, leaf-litter, sticks and twigs are raked into a carefully shaped compost heap with the aid of those big feet. A typical brush turkey mound can measure up to 4m in diameter and stand 1.5m high. The male will then mate with a number of females, and his mound might eventually contain up to 50 eggs. A female may produce between 20 and 30 eggs in every six-month-long breeding season.

ONCE THE FEMALE lays her egg 40–150cm down, however, that's it – her progeny is entirely on its own, effectively orphaned before its shell has cracked. She plays no part in tending the mound, with the burden of maintenance falling entirely to the male. Climate control is his obsession, and rotting compost his tool in sustaining an even incubation temperature.

To achieve this, he first uses his beak as a probe, inserting it into the mound as far down as the level of the eggs. His palate acts as a thermometer, and, depending on the temperature he senses, he removes or adds leaf-litter as needed.

But exactly why have these tenacious builders and fussy housekeepers successfully reclaimed significant parts of their range in an environment as substantially altered as Sydney's? Slow moving and not particularly agile flyers, brush turkeys might easily be caught. They are said to be a good food source, just like their commercially reared namesake, and would certainly have been part of many an Aboriginal meal in pre-European times. Brush turkeys were also on the colonial menu and featured in cookbooks. During the Great Depression in the 1930s they became welcome fare on meagre dinner tables, but legislative protection of fauna and flora after World War II effectively saw hunting cease.

As with so much wildlife, predation of chicks by foxes and cats remains a silent scourge. Sustained fox baiting in recent years has helped, yet, according to Dr Ann Goeth, a Sydney-based wildlife behaviourist, brush turkey expert and educational consultant, the easing of predation is only part of the answer.

A number of changes in the urban environment have helped the turkey resurgence gain momentum, she says, such as the spread of introduced lantana in bush gullies. Newly hatched chicks without any

At Kincumber, on the NSW Central Coast, Sophie Warman and her dog Jasper watch as a brush turkey steals food from the dog's bowl. Uneaten pet food provides a ready source of sustenance for these undiscriminating foragers.

parental protection are vulnerable to predation, so dense thickets provide a perfect haven. This is perhaps a factor in the survival of brush turkeys in my suburb, with a steep, remnant bush gully and patches of lantana several streets away.

"People often feed brush turkeys, directly or unwittingly, by leaving their pet's bowl sitting about outside," she says. "They are total omnivores and will eat anything." Uncovered compost heaps are an additional source of profitable pickings, with scraps, and the worms and insect larvae they encourage, eagerly devoured.

On a broader scale, the fashioning of leafy gardens in the more affluent suburbs has unwittingly mimicked the brush turkey's preferred habitat. As wide lawns have given way to dense plantings and bush gardens, and as garden gurus have exhorted gardeners to mulch well in the crusade to conserve water, the male turkey has decided it's Christmas every day. And this time he's definitely not on the menu.

Loose, moist mulch with which to construct a magnificent edifice is every male brush turkey's fantasy. The more plentiful his raw materials, the more palatial his mound, and the more females he's likely to attract. The more females he attracts, the more eggs will be produced. With ample supplies of home-delivered mulch, and an abundance of food and suitable trees and shrubs in which to roost, safe from predators, brush turkeys moved right into the suburbs and made themselves right at home.

OF COURSE, MOST GARDENERS don't share a turkey's view of landscape heaven. Male brush turkeys have been known to demolish a freshly planted and mulched garden in a day, stripping young plants from the ground with seemingly malicious intent. Shocked gardeners, despairing of their ruined investment, have contemplated murder, but instead resort to what they mistakenly consider a more sensitive and less drastic remedy – relocation. "You might as well kill them straight away," says Ann. Brush turkeys are territorial, and moving them only leads to conflict with other turkeys. Not-so-lucky ones either starve, or end up as road kill.

Whatever the future population dynamics of the species, it seems they're here to stay in urban environments up and down the east coast. Strategies such as using pebbles or gravel as mulch, and protecting young seedlings, might sooth the nerves of anxious gardeners, but I for one can only admire the tenacious bird that came one night to roost on my inner city balcony. A wildlife success story indeed. ■

CHAPTER THREE

OCEANS

From the violent maelstrom of the Southern Ocean, which batters the continent's southern reaches, to the warm, placid waters of the north, Australia's marine environment covers an area of almost 14 million square kilometres.

Every state and territory (with the exception of the Australian Capital Territory) has a coastline and it's on this coastal fringe that most of us live – 85 per cent of Australians live within 100km of the ocean – so it's unsurprising that so much of our national identity is tied up in marine treasures, from our stunning beaches to icons such as the Great Barrier Reef, the Bass Strait, the Great Australian Bight and Ningaloo Reef.

The Australian marine environment is home to a spectacular array of species: 33,000 different organisms have been described from Australian waters, 17,000 remain to be catalogued, and perhaps as much as ten times as many are yet to be discovered. The described species are dominated by molluscs (8525 species), crustaceans (6365) and fish (5184). They're joined by an impressive collection of marine mammals – including 45 species of whale, dolphin and porpoise, 10 species of seal and sea lion, and the endangered dugong – and marine reptiles, including more than 30 species of sea snake and six of the world's seven species of sea turtle.

Many of these species are permanent residents, while others are temporary visitors, migrating long distances between feeding and breeding grounds. Among the latter are humpback whales that make tandem annual migrations up and down the east and west coasts. In the west, they follow what's known as the humpback highway, making their way up to their breeding and birthing grounds off the Kimberley coast. Before returning south, they rest up for a while in the waters around Ningaloo Reef, the world's largest fringing reef, which plays host to the highest density of humpback whales in the Southern Hemisphere; as many as 40,000 individuals stop off in the reef's sparkling waters.

Ningaloo is also one of the few places on the planet where manta rays can be reliably located year-round. One of the other places is located off the east coast, in the waters surrounding Lady Elliot Island, the southernmost coral cay on the Great Barrier Reef. Both sites host resident populations of the smaller, coastal manta, which can reach a wingtip-to-wingtip width of 5.5m, and can swim at speeds of up to 24km/h, driven along by majestic sweeps of those big pointed wings, like enormous underwater birds of prey.

But of course Ningaloo is best known for its whale sharks; nowhere else do these marine behemoths reliably congregate in such large numbers and so close to land. The largest fish in the ocean, growing to a length of more than 12m and weighing as much as 21 tonnes, whale sharks are the archetypal gentle giants, slow-moving filter feeders that gather together to gorge on plankton at about a dozen locations worldwide and then disappear for months at a time.

Not all of Australia's marine creatures are as benign as these three, and arguably none is as feared as the great white shark. In Australia, great whites have been recorded from north-west Western Australia around the south coast to Mackay in central eastern Queensland, from right up against the coast out to depths of about 100m; however, they can dive to depths of 1000m and are capable of crossing ocean basins. Growing to at least 6m in length and weighing up to 3t, these fast-swimming torpedo-shaped apex predators are often found in the waters in and around fur seal and sea lion colonies. They are remarkable animals, equipped with a circulatory system that features counter-current heat-exchangers that allow them to keep their body temperature up to 14°C above that of the surrounding sea water, enabling them to inhabit a wide range of water temperatures. ■

Previous page: A collection of remoras clings to the tail of a whale shark. The world's largest fish, whale sharks are ocean-traversing behemoths that have been known to dive to depths of up to 700m.

A blue whale mother and calf swim through the open ocean. The calf is 'blowing' as it exhales, creating a powerful column of spray that can reach 15m in height.

With a majestic sweep of its broad, wing-like pectoral fins, a manta ray powers out of the blue of the open ocean. At top speed, these enormous filter feeders can travel at about 24km/h.

STORY BY **ELIZABETH GINIS**

MANTA RAYS

Demystifying these enigmatic creatures of the deep.

Issue 66 ◆ Apr–Jun 2002

STAINED COBALT BLUE, the back of a manta ray is difficult to distinguish from the ocean in which it lives. Its underbelly, however, is a stark white canvas splashed with grey – a dash here, a dot there – and I'm staring up at one, just an arm's length away.

Together we hang, as though suspended on a puppeteer's strings, before glassy bubbles from my regulator float upwards, tickling the animal's belly, making it squirm and then slowly move away on silent, beating wings.

Manta rays are often encountered around the coral bommies, or outcrops, of Lady Elliot Island, a compact coral cay at the southern extent of the Great Barrier Reef Marine Park. They congregate here to be preened by cleaner wrasse – small fish that feed on skin parasites and pieces of loose flesh.

And my aquatic mate hadn't finished with the service. In two wing-beats it moves to the opposite side of the bommie, and suspended once again, is now eyeball to eyeball with me. The experience is pure, unadulterated magic.

Among the largest, yet least-known, of fishes, there are two described species of manta ray: *Manta birostris*, a large ocean-going species found throughout tropical, subtropical and warm temperate oceans, and *M. alfredi*, a smaller species found in coastal waters in the Indo-Pacific and tropical east Atlantic. In Australia, they're typically encountered along reef edges in Queensland and Western Australia, where tidal action pumps rivers of eggs, larvae and tiny crustaceans – the manta's preferred diet – into the open sea; but they've also been spotted as far south as Montague Island in southern New South Wales.

Like other members of the shark and ray family, the manta's internal structure is based on tough but flexible cartilage, not bone. And it's cartilage that helps this graceful animal 'fly' through the water.

Sharks are a manta's distant cousins, but eagle and cownose rays, which are closely related, look so similar to them that people often mistake them for young mantas. But once you've identified a manta's distinctive features, there's little confusion. A manta has cephalic lobes – large, fleshy protrusions that sprout forwards like horns from its snout; a very broad, rectangular mouth at the front of the →

In several spots around the world's oceans, manta rays form regular feeding aggregations, coming to together to feed on concentrations of plankton, which they filter from the sea water with their gills.

head; and, a short, barbless tail. Mantas also grow larger than other rays – wingspans stretch to 9m and they can weigh 1500kg. They move swiftly in open water, at up to 24km/h, but are more often seen by humans being preened by wrasse at 'cleaning stations', or while feeding. Primarily solitary, they congregate in shallow water to breed, resembling squadrons of stealth bombers when they do.

Despite the growing fascination with manta rays, little is known of these enigmatic creatures' biology, behaviour or movements. What we do know is that the markings on the belly of a manta are akin to a human fingerprint, so by recording and creating a database of images of different mantas, we learn more about the resident populations, such as the one at Lady Elliot Island.

WE HAVE NO IDEA WHAT the standing Australian or manta ray global population is, nor what impact humans have on these amazing animals. But given they're unprotected species, and humanity's track record in driving wildlife to the brink, it's time we knew more.

While research can be carried out on dead manta rays, it's far more difficult to study them while they're living. They usually die in captivity, refusing to eat and apparently experiencing huge stress when confined. Mature mantas living in an aquarium in Okinawa, Japan, have survived for a length of time in a tank, but the tank is huge – 200 tonnes of sea water kept at 24.7°C – and they've been there since just after birth.

Georgia Aquarium remains the only aquarium in the USA to exhibit manta rays, and conducts fieldwork to further manta knowledge. Aerial and boat surveys and satellite tagging are used to understand how and where the animals use the waters of northern Florida, while in Mexico, manta rays have begun to appear in increasing numbers in the same location where the large aggregation of whale sharks show up every summer to feed.

Lady Elliot Island is an important aggregation site for *M. alfredi* and is integral to the work undertaken by Project Manta, a multidisciplinary research program based at the University of Queensland. Founded in 2007 to investigate the population biology and ecology of manta rays in eastern Australia, it uses 'citizen science' to collect photo-ID data. Professional and recreational divers provide photographs and sighting information of manta rays along the entire east Australian coast.

The Project Manta team visits Lady Elliot Island several times a year. On these expeditions the team conducts research including photographing, observing and recording manta ray behaviour. It also collects samples of water and plankton, and takes oceanographic measurements of water currents, conductivity, temperature and depth.

MOUTH AGAPE AND FLAPPING SLOWLY in swirling loops towards the sun-dappled surface, a manta feeds. As I watch, motionless, nearby, the gigantic filter feeder unfurls its cephalic lobes and uses them like slender, artistic hands, sweeping water into its cavernous mouth.

On scuba at 10m near Lady Elliot's Lighthouse Bommie, I'm a guest at the manta's dining table, and it's fair to say that I'm mesmerised. Nearing the surface, and having finished the first course, the manta points its lobes to the sea floor and plunges down, stopping a metre from me. Then, it begins its spiralling ascent – believed to concentrate or herd the plankton – once again.

Manta rays, like whale sharks, feed on plankton by filtering water through their gills, which are composed of pinkish-brown spongy tissue arranged in flattened, horizontal plates. But mantas haven't always been filter feeders. Nine to 12 rows of grinding teeth are remnants of an evolutionary era when mantas hunted larger prey.

Today, however, the only biting a manta does is during mating. Believed to be sexually active from about five years of age, manta rays mate in the summer in depths of 1–10m when water temperatures are 26°C to 29°C. Playing a game of cat and mouse just before copulation, several males court a female, swimming closely behind her at faster-than-usual speeds (9–12km/h).

This courtship lasts for 20–30 minutes before the female decreases her speed, allowing a male to nip the tip of one of her pectoral fins (wings), severely hampering her swimming ability. The male then positions himself on the underside of the female, abdomen to abdomen, and inserts one of his claspers (paired sex organs developed along the inner margins of the pelvic fin) into her cloaca (vent). This usually lasts 90–120 seconds.

After the sperm has been released, the male continues to bite the female's fin for a minute or so before swimming off. Another male, which will have been circling the couple during mating, then moves in and repeats the process. After the second encounter, the female swims away, leaving other courting males behind – reinforcing the belief that the most dominant males mate, ensuring the continuity of the strongest gene pool.

Gestation takes about 13 months, during which time the one or

A manta ray rests near the sea floor in Coral Bay on Ningaloo Reef in WA. Ningaloo is one of the few places where mantas can be seen year-round.

two developing pups are wrapped in a thin-shelled 'egg' that hatches inside the mother. Soon after, the female gives birth in relatively shallow water, where the pups remain for several years before expanding their range further off shore. When born, they're 1–1.5m in width and weigh up to 11kg. Their fins are wrapped in an S-shape – one above and one below the body. They double their size in the first year of life.

RESEARCH INTO MANTA RAY ANATOMY has concluded that the brains of these intriguing animals are among the largest of all cartilaginous fishes, and that the portion of it that deals with reasoning is highly developed.

I pondered this fact when I met Superman – a 4m-wide manta named for the white, diamond-shaped blaze on his otherwise blue-black belly – while snorkelling off Lady Elliot. He had circled me a few times, an inquisitive eye following my movements, before moving in close enough for me to touch. And then we were swimming together – wing-beat and fin-kick – on the surface of the ocean; just Superman and me.

Had he sized me up and reasoned that, given his size and stature, I posed no threat? Or was he coming in closer to inspect an oceanic curiosity? I'll never know the answer – but like any good comic-book heroine, I fell for my superhero that day: hook, line and sinker. ■

Manta rays

Scientific name: *Manta birostris, M. alfredi*

Distribution: Throughout the world in tropical seas between 35°N and 35°S, mainly over continental shelves

Size: <9m across

Weight: <1500kg

Speed: <24km/h

Colour: Blue-black to greenish grey-brown above, frequently with irregular paler shoulder patches; predominantly white underneath with pale-grey markings but sometimes same as above with white markings

Food: Plankton sieved through gills

Reproduction: Give birth to 1–2 live young

Lonesome leviathans

The world's largest animal is also one of its rarest. John Pickrell joins a research team trying to piece together a picture of the lives of the mysterious blue whales that pass through Australian waters.

Story by **John Pickrell**

Issue 133 Jul–Aug 2016

WE'VE BEEN PLAYING a waiting game. Today is our 11th day sailing across the Great Australian Bight and around the south-western tip of Western Austalia on the research vessel *Whale Song*, and we're yet to encounter a single blue whale.

Over the course of the voyage with the Centre for Whale Research (CWR), I've learnt that the study of blue whales is characterised by long periods of hopeful observation. Seemingly endless hours and days are spent scanning the horizon with binoculars and listening below the waves with hydrophones for infrasonic rumblings.

Finally – 1100 nautical miles (2037km) from our starting point at Port Lincoln in South Australia, and just a few hours from our destination of Fremantle – we detect the distinctive calls of several pygmy blue whales. CWR marine biologists Curt and Micheline Jenner, and Curtin University acoustician Associate Professor Robert McCauley, triangulate the source of the sound, and we motor towards it.

We're above the Perth Canyon, a several-kilometre-deep trench in the sea floor that's a favoured blue whale feeding ground – what Mich describes as a "cafe", or a pit stop along migration routes. Deep below us, whales use the sides of the canyon to corral swarms of krill.

Whale Song wends ever closer to the blues, which are cruising at 4 knots. Finally, a whale surfaces 20m off starboard, and we get to hear the surprisingly loud puff and see the lingering vapour of the blow, and then the huge back of the animal arcing through the surface of the water.

The whales surface briefly to empty and fill their lungs, before diving again for anywhere between eight and 12 minutes. They may complete this cycle up to 13 times before making a more powerful dive that finally pushes their tiny dorsal fins – and rarely, their tail fluke – above the surface. All this time Mich and CWR research associate Carrie Skorcz use stopwatches and clipboards to record the length of dives and number of blows. They also take hundreds of pictures of the dorsal fins, which, using thousands of images in a database, will later be matched to individual animals.

What we see above the surface is brief, but through the waves you get a sense of the scale of these up to 25m-long animals – about the same length as our fishing-trawler-style vessel. Above the water they appear grey, but just before and after breaking the surface they glow a brilliant turquoise, the reason that mariners dubbed them 'blue' in the first place.

"Blue whales are very serene and totally together," Mich tells me. "Humpbacks are the clowns of the ocean and the jesters of the sea, they play and frolic and bash and crash. Blue whales, on the other hand, are like public statesmen, they are composed and dignified... Mostly they just go about their business and ignore you."

THE FACT THAT blue whales are difficult to find isn't terribly surprising, because there are so few of them. Two centuries ago they were abundant, estimated at about 300,000 worldwide – and that's just blues; great whales of all kinds must have numbered in the many millions.

Whaling all but decimated populations and by the time the last blue whale was hunted in 1973, there may have been just a few thousand left. "They were totally exploited to within a whisker of extinction," Mich says. Today, there are thought to be 10,000–25,000 blue whales globally, 1500 of them being the pygmy blues around Australia. Populations are increasing, but the recovery is slower than for many other whales, such as humpbacks. Understanding why this is so is one of the key questions the CWR has sought to answer.

Blue whales (*Balaenoptera musculus*) are found in all of the world's oceans except the high Arctic. The subspecies most commonly found around Australia is the pygmy blue whale (*B. m. brevicauda*). Reaching as much as 25m in length, they aren't pygmies by any standard, except when judged against Antarctic blue whales, which can reach lengths of up to 32m.

Blue whales are very probably the largest animals that have ever lived, bigger even than the largest dinosaurs. A large blue weighs up to 180 tonnes, as much as 30 African bull elephants. Somewhat poetically, the largest of all animals feeds on one of the smallest – tiny marine crustaceans called krill, which are often less than 1cm in length. Using 300–400 baleen plates in the roof of its mouth, a blue whale may filter out of the water as much as 4t of krill a day, equivalent to about 21,000 meat pies.

The Centre for Whale Research acquired *Whale Song* (far left) in 2010. This 28m purpose-built marine mammal research vessel has been sound-silenced to military specifications, making it perfect for conducting acoustic surveys.

Above the waves blue whales tend to look grey, but just below the surface they seem to glow with a brilliant turquoise hue. Dwarfing a human diver, a 180t blue whale is twice the size of a long-necked sauropod dinosaur.

CWR research suggests that the prey patches may never be in the same precise location twice. Curt believes that when whales discover abundant krill they call to signal to others what they've found. It's the only plausible answer he has to explain how many whales seem to suddenly appear at spots rich with krill. It's also possible they employ powerful sounds – their song is the loudest noise made by any animal; at more than 150 decibels, it's louder than an airliner taking off – to corral krill, says Rob. "They chase krill, which aren't necessarily in tight clusters. If they are dispersed, they're not going to get much to eat, but if the krill are all balled up then it makes feeding easier."

IN AUSTRALIA, THE development of oil and gas resources in important habitats is a pressing threat to the blue whale. Mich says they realised whales were feeding at Scott Reef, 270km north-west of Cape Leveque, when the ship's engineer pulled handfuls of krill out of the water filtration system. Here they discovered that the whales regularly swim through a 500m-deep channel. "They know where they are going," she says. "Those whales are coming from the Banda Sea on their return journey… They feed on krill in the narrow channel between the circular north reef and the horseshoe-shaped south reef."

There has been a development proposal here that would involve drilling for oil in the channel, which could deter feeding behaviour. Rob has shown that seismic surveying alone produces enough noise to disperse krill. "If there are no krill then whales are missing out on a feeding opportunity. They have to wait another five days until they get to the next feeding ground at Ningaloo, and another five before they get to the Abrolhos… What are the consequences if they can't feed at Scott Reef? Who knows, but it won't be good. Of course, if there's an oil spill, there are absolutely dire consequences."

Scott Reef is one feeding ground that the CWR hopes will one day be set aside as a reserve, and, thankfully, the current low global price of oil means that it isn't worthwhile to develop it, at least for the moment. "Our hope is that it continues to remain uneconomically viable," Mich says. "Scott Reef is a jewel in Australia's crown, but it needs protection."

Elsewhere in the world there are other threats that are even more pressing. Off the coast of California, blue whale numbers have rebounded, partly because they were less heavily exploited than Southern Hemisphere populations. Nevertheless, strikes with ships both there and around Sri Lanka are a major new threat. In 2007 four blue whales killed in collisions washed up on southern California beaches – more than likely a fraction of the total killed, because most sink out at sea.

When blue whales hear a boat, they perform a slow-sink response, but it's often not fast enough to escape large container ships, which can be 300m in length and moving at 35 knots. Although whales are magnificently adapted to their underwater realm, this is a novel threat. Using sonar to detect whales is one solution, but putting even more noise into the seas may just lead to further problems. Curt says the simplest answer is for boats to travel at less than 15 knots, giving whales time to move out of the way and decreasing the chance that a collision will kill them.

BEYOND UNDERSTANDING blue whales themselves, Curt believes they are a great barometer for measuring the health of our planet. "They are a global animal. They feed on krill, the most abundant source of energy and protein on the planet, and a resource touched by just about everything else," he says. Getting accurate counts of krill abundance is nigh on impossible, but you can count blue whales, he adds, and this is what the CWR and their coworkers have set out to do.

Blue whales are the great survivors, despite the enormous pressure we've put them under, says Mich. "Whales have been around for 30 million years. To have been around for so long, they must have done something right to survive all that time navigating across oceans…socialising, calving, feeding. We have to do as much as we can to reduce our impact on their home."

For those very few blue whales today that are 80 or 90 years of age – survivors of the whaling era, when the oceans would have thrummed with an infrasonic chorus of hundreds of thousands of their kind – the world must seem a very lonely place indeed. ■

The mermaids of Moreton Bay

Flirtations with mariners of bygone eras made dugongs the stuff of romantic legends. Today, Australian scientists are uncovering the truth about these mysterious creatures.

Story by **Karen McGhee** Photography By **Darren Jew**

Issue 118 Jan–Feb 2014

IT'S AN IDYLLIC spring morning on southern Queensland's Moreton Bay and conditions are perfect for finding mermaids. Flocks of shearwaters bob on a glassy sea. Green turtles regularly break the surface for noisy breaths between dives to graze on seagrass meadows. Pied cormorants pop up periodically, their long necks like submarine periscopes. And pods of sleek-swimming bottlenose dolphins steer inquisitively towards our boat.

Photographer Darren Jew and I are not, of course, looking for mermaids, but the creatures believed to have sparked the legend. Soon enough a perfect ocean-going tail – shaped like a dolphin's but at least 1m wide at its trailing edge – breaks the water and waves briefly, Brisbane's distant skyline glistening behind in the early light.

It's easy to see how lonely sailors might at one time have thought this signalled a creature of submerged beauty. But minutes later we see a face that's more Dr Seuss than Nereid. Clearly, those old mariners liked spinning tales, or were influenced by rum and isolation.

The exquisite tail and contrastingly comical face belong to one of Moreton Bay's 800–1000 dugongs (*Dugong dugon*), which live adjacent to one of Australia's most rapidly developing regions. The creature's odd-looking head emerges just long enough to retract the valves that keep water from its nostrils while submerged and, with a snort, it sucks in fresh air before quickly disappearing.

LIMITED SURFACE TIME is a dugong trademark. Along with their preference for turbid water, it's a major reason they're so elusive and why few Australians have ever seen one. Yet they're the most common marine mammals in northern Australia's coastal waters, outnumbering seals, whales and dolphins. They're also big, with adults reaching lengths of about 3m and weights of 400–600kg.

Dugongs occur near seagrass meadows in the tropical and subtropical waters of about 40 Indo-Pacific countries. Australia is the species' stronghold: perhaps 70,000 cruise the shallows of at least 10 different locations along the 25,000km of our northern coastline from Shark Bay, Western Australia, to Moreton Bay. The Torres Strait has the biggest population, with surveys suggesting at least 15,000 are there.

Their diet consists mostly of seagrass, and adults can consume more than 25kg a day. This habit, along with their cumbersome, barrel-like bodies, has seen dugongs commonly called sea cows. But Dave Holley, Shark Bay Marine Park coordinator, who's worked with WA's dugong populations since 2000, suggests they're better described as sea pigs because they prefer digging up seagrass rhizomes and roots rather than grazing leaves. This feeding behaviour creates tell-tale feeding trails of disturbed marine sediment.

University of Queensland researchers carefully raise a dugong from the water in a specially built sling in Moreton Bay, where the local dugong population has been studied for several decades.

Like many herbivores, dugongs deal with difficult-to-digest plant matter using a very long, bacteria-filled intestine. Their odd face is also an adaptation to a seagrass-chomping lifestyle; the distended, trunk-like upper lip angles sharply downwards and is covered in sensitive bristles that help to locate and manipulate seagrass in murky habitats.

Dugongs aren't, however, strict vegetarians. Professor Helene Marsh – a dugong doyenne who has studied the species for decades – says recent research has documented these mammals at the southern extreme of their distribution eating ocean floor invertebrates, including worms and crustaceans. "It looks like it's important during winter in places such as Shark Bay and Moreton Bay," explains Helene, who's based at James Cook University, Townsville. These dietary supplements could be a vital protein source in waters where temperatures dip to about 18°C – the species' lower limit. →

Researchers restrain an adult dugong near the water's surface so that it can be measured and tagged. Because dugongs are easily stressed, handling is kept to a minimum.

After noticing that captured dugongs sometimes suffered from stress-induced muscle wasting, the researchers developed a rodeo-style method for catching them.

MORETON BAY'S MERMAIDS are at the south-easterly limit of dugong distribution. During the past two decades, this population has, under the direction of University of Queensland marine zoologist Dr Janet Lanyon, become the best studied in the world.

When Janet began the work in the early '90s, aerial survey evidence suggested dugong populations along Queensland's most urbanised coastline were declining significantly. Seagrass-habitat destruction, boat strikes, net entanglements and pollution were taking their toll in the increasingly busy waterways of Moreton Bay and Hervey Bay, 300km to the north. At that stage, much of the information on the species had come from aerial surveys and autopsies of animals drowned in fishing nets or struck by boats. "No-one had done much hands-on work with dugongs and we had little understanding of population biology and life history parameters from wild populations," Janet explains. "We also had a limited understanding of their behaviour and social interactions."

Moreton Bay's wild dugong population was accessible enough to be closely monitored and Janet's idea was to study it by capturing, marking and recapturing. But handling dugongs could be perilous. Work by Janet's mentor, Helene Marsh, and others indicated dugongs could experience stress-prompted 'capture myopathy' – muscle wasting that can lead to death. Janet and her colleagues eventually overcame the problem by modifying a rodeo-style capture developed for sea turtles. It meant the animals didn't need to be pulled from the water, no nets were involved and tagging proceeded in a rapid sequence at the water's surface.

For the past 14 summers, Janet's team has conducted a mark-and-recapture program with huge success. "We've now tagged close to 800 different animals, including some we've recaptured seven or eight times over the years," she says, "and we're getting some really good information about how these animals grow and mature, and their social dynamics."

Recently, they began investigating dugong communication. Above water, you won't detect much noise. But submerge your head near a dugong herd and you're likely to hear chirping. "They sound like little tweeting birds and we've found that the animals here [in Moreton Bay] sound different from the animals in Hervey Bay: they vocalise at different frequencies," Janet says, adding that research also suggests social behaviour going on in the herds.

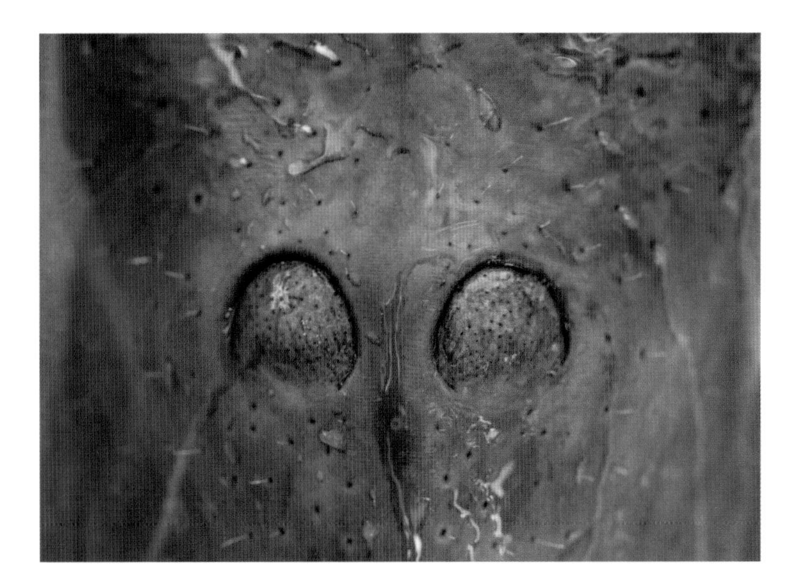

The valves that keep a dugong's nostrils clear of water while they're submerged retract fully when the animal surfaces to breathe. During short feeding dives, the valves form a tight seal across the airways.

Despite being air-breathers, dugongs spend as little time at the surface as possible, preferring instead to remain in the obscurity of the often murky waters in which they live.

Anecdotal evidence suggests animals released at a distance from their herd will find their way straight back, and that a frightened herd will move together. It's not clear, however, whether group movements involve 'chatter', or some sort of tactile pressure-sensitive sense, such as the 'lateral line' system that provides fish with information about their surroundings. Dugong skin isn't smooth like a dolphin's – it's sparsely covered in hairs 1–2cm apart. There's a theory – as yet unproved – that these may function as pressure sensors detecting vibrations and movements in the surrounding water.

Janet's team has also been conducting annual health assessments of Moreton Bay and Hervey Bay populations for the past seven years and there are indications that what happens on land can affect dugong health. After the 2011 Brisbane floods, significant rises in heavy metals were detected in the blood of Moreton Bay dugongs, probably due to an influx of coastal run-off. About nine months later, researchers documented a drop in the animals' body condition, and suspect a link.

ALTHOUGH MOST AUSTRALIANS living on the temperate east coast would rarely see a dugong, the animals are intrinsic to the culture of northern coastal communities. Many Aboriginal and Torres Strait Islander languages have multiple names for dugongs according to their stage of development.

"Indigenous people have always had a very close relationship with dugongs, historically and traditionally treating them as kin," explains Joe Morrison, CEO of the Darwin-based North Australian Indigenous Land and Sea Management Alliance. This cultural connection is linked to their long history as food for many northern communities. There is evidence from the Torres Strait, for example, that dugongs have been harvested there for at least 4000 years. Dugong meat remains an important protein source for many remote indigenous northern Australian water-based communities that legally – under state and federal native title legislation – hunt these animals for non-commercial purposes using traditional methods.

Concerns that many ocean-going species now need careful management to ensure their long-term survival has been spurring many of these communities to step up monitoring and management of dugongs and other marine resources in their jurisdictions. "We've always taken the view that it's indigenous people that have the most to lose if species that are culturally significant for people go extinct," Joe says.

It's becoming clear that modern conservation science can learn much from indigenous ways when it comes to dugongs. In late 2012, rangers from the Bardi Jawa community – one of 14 groups within the Kimberley Land Council – travelled to Abu Dhabi, where the biggest dugong population outside Australia survives. There they shared their skills at catching and tagging dugongs in an exercise that saw satellite tags successfully fitted to three adults so their movements in the Persian Gulf could be tracked by conservation scientists.

More recently, the Torres Strait Regional Authority's Land and Sea Management Unit took out the 2013 Banksia Gold Award for sustainable environmental programs, largely based on its dugong management, which embraces a traditional indigenous harvest.

These days there's growing evidence dugongs are most at risk from threats associated with living near busy urban coastal areas and that, as is true for vulnerable species, habitat loss is the most enduring threat to these seagrass specialists.

There's new evidence, however, of an even larger looming threat. It has long been thought that the dugong population in WA's Shark Bay World Heritage Area, the world's second-largest at about 10,000 individuals, was secure. But alarm bells began sounding after the 2010–11 summer, when heatwave conditions saw unprecedented west coast water temperature rises.

"It hit some of the seagrass pretty hard," Dave Holley says. "We're now keeping a watching brief [for the consequences]." If such events recur, as predicted due to climate change, the long-term impacts could be devastating for dugongs. ■

Explosion of life

A mass spawning of marine life creates an unforgettable spectacle for scientists and filmmakers aboard an AGS-assisted expedition to the Great Barrier Reef.

Story by **Howard Whelan** Photography by **Kevin Deacon**

Issue 32 Oct–Dec 1993

A sea cucumber or trepang rises into its spawning stance. The forehead of the female in front begins to bulge and she then releases her eggs, perhaps in response to sperm in the water.

HOVERING ABOVE THE LAGOON'S sandy bottom, I could just make out the dim outlines of my companions, and beyond them the dark amphitheatre of coral that surrounded us. Nearly 15m above, *Gemma*'s hull was a black silhouette against the silver surface of the Coral Sea. The November full moon was clearly visible beyond as a shimmering white orb.

Images of trepang, also known as sea cucumbers, filled my mind. Until this evening, my interest in them had amounted to no more than curiosity about their supposed aphrodisiac qualities – the main reason for the South Pacific's trepang fishery. But the past half-hour had changed all that. Urged on by the moon and the tide, a smattering of sea cucumbers had crawled to open areas of sand or climbed to high points on the reef.

Then, about an hour after dark, they began rising and swaying, dancing a lithe lambada in the gentle current. David Hannan, our underwater cinematographer, illuminated the scene with his powerful camera lights. One of his star performers was green with ochre-tipped spikes. Rising from a fantastic bed of pink coral, it moved from side to side and began ejecting a thin stream of sperm from a tiny hole in its head. The male, casting his sperm into the vast waters of the Coral Sea, relied on chance and the current to bring it into contact with the eggs of a female of the same species.

When David switched off his lights and my eyes adjusted to the darkness, I could just make out the tubular shapes of several creatures rising to nearly 2m nearby. Synaptids are also sea cucumbers, but they bear little resemblance to the trepangs. The night before, I saw a synaptid making its way across the sand. It looked like a latex tube with bubble-pack bumps on the outside. I could see its internal organs through its translucent skin, and when I picked it up, it was so sticky I had to peel it off my wetsuit.

Feathery arms filtered nutrients from the sand and carried them to its mouth. Nothing was known about how these amazing creatures reproduce, so when David turned his lights on again and revealed a synaptid standing fully erect, releasing sperm into the water, I was elated.

OUR AUSTRALIAN GEOGRAPHIC EXPEDITION had come to Myrmidon Reef, a coral-crowned sliver of continental shelf two days sailing from Townsville, in Queensland, to study and film one of the world's great natural spectacles – the mass spawning of coral and other reef animals. In the week after the November full moon, the 2900 reefs that make up the Great Barrier Reef (GBR) would become a 2000km-long maternity ward.

Two boats had carried our 13-strong team to the study site – a luxurious 22m game-fishing motor cruiser and the 12m yacht *Gemma*. It was 14 November. We had arrived on 10 November, on the afternoon before the full moon. Since then, our activities, like those of many of the marine creatures beneath us, had been governed by the moon. Using data collected since mass spawning on the GBR was confirmed in 1981, we had spent our days searching out and marking specific coral colonies, taking specimens back to the boats and breaking them open to see if the egg and sperm cells inside were 'ripe'. At night we were in the water for up to six hours at a time, watching for anything that would increase our knowledge of mass spawning.

So far, the only animals we'd seen spawn had been trepangs and synaptids. I asked marine scientist Russell Kelley why there had been so little activity. "The information we're working with is scant," he replied. "Remember, from the observations we have so far we can make fairly reliable predictions, but there are holes in it."

He explained that of the nearly 400 species of hard coral on the

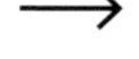

Like delicate pink flowers, tentacles surround the polyp mouths of a *Montipora* coral. Members of the genus *Montipora* typically form thin, leafy plate-like colonies, usually on shallow-water reefs.

Tiny egg and sperm bundles emerge from a *Goniastrea retiformis* colony. In the hours before their release, the bundles could just be seen appearing in the mouths of the polyps.

GBR, only about 160 have been observed spawning. "And a coral reef is home to hundreds of species that aren't corals," he added. "They're diverse, wonderful places to study, and they're largely unknown."

AFTER DUSK ON 15 November, five nights after the full moon, I drove the inflatable dinghy with David, his brother Peter, my wife, Rosy, and an alarming amount of underwater camera gear, lights, diving gear and spare tanks to the mooring buoy we'd placed between two huge coral outcrops about 500m from our anchorage. By the time I returned to *Gemma* to pick up Russell, motored back and descended into the darkness below, it was after 8pm. Signals from the other divers expressed frustration – still nothing happening.

I followed Russell on a 15-minute lap around the bommie, as the coral outcrop is called, descending to 20m to check coral colonies. Back at the bottom of our mooring line, Russell stopped to inspect a coral and suddenly began gesticulating wildly with his torch. I reached him just in time to see a colony of *Montipora* coral releasing hundreds of light-brown egg bundles into the water. The bundles, about as big as poppy seeds, bounced among the coral polyps before being swept out into the current. We continued swimming up a gully and watched about a dozen colonies of five different species spawn.

We weren't seeing an avalanche of eggs pouring off coral slopes. From a distance I could see an occasional puff, rising above a clump of coral and spreading into a misty cloud. Up close, I could see individual egg bundles rising in the water to form a radiant coral halo. Something was happening that, in the vast scale of the surrounding ocean, could easily pass unnoticed.

"I was convinced the Montys were doing something because their polyps were standing up proud," Russell said later, as we lay on *Gemma*'s deck munching cold lasagne under the stars. "We saw the first little raft of egg bundles coming off. They were just starting to flit away like they do," he said. "Up the gully, there was this big plate coral with four big brittle stars sitting on top just stuffing themselves with eggs. It was beautiful."

THE NEXT EVENING, AS I finned my way across the reef flats, I contemplated what I had learnt so far. Until this trip I had never been night diving, and, as most polyps only emerge after dusk to feed, I had never experienced coral as a living, eating, mating creature. I had always thought of it as little more than an assortment of pretty rocks, ranging from bulletproof boulders to brittle staghorns, from the expansive plate corals to the hard tracery of the related gorgonian sea fans. It had been difficult enough coming to grips with the shapes and colours of the things that I had seen, let alone the fact that the bizarre flowers, the tubes, the boulders and the hair-like strands of matter were, in fact, animals.

As I neared the edge of the reef flats I knew that something special was happening tonight. Fish that normally would have been in their night-time hiding places were still out. There were egg and sperm bundles rising to form a slick on the surface. Nearly everywhere I looked I could see starfish, featherstars and hermit crabs moving over the reef eating eggs and sperm. Schools of squirrel fish swept by. There was life everywhere, as if the boundary between day and night had been forgotten to allow everything to participate in this orgy of birth and predation.

When I held my torch upright, the lens was quickly covered by tiny, flesh-coloured worms, millions of them. Attracted by the light, they piled up and spilled over the side and down into a forest of coral branches with their polyps out, tentacles grasping at the passing worms and stuffing them into their mouths.

Nearby, colourful little *Spirobranchus*, known as Christmas tree worms, emerged from a boulder-like coral and began emitting sperm. Looking closer, I could see that a minuscule reef prawn with iridescent pink eyes had positioned itself down current to feed on the *Spirobranchus*'s release.

Some distance away I could see David's long, pencil shaft of light sweeping back and forth across the corals. Suddenly it zeroed in on something and then bang! Massively powerful lights were switched on and the whole chasm was lit up, colours exploding from the candlepower of David's filming lights. Night no longer hid the momentous event taking place around us. Pink, orange and yellow bundles of eggs and sperm seemed to be erupting everywhere and a haze of new life clouded the water.

The following night most of us were back in the water, but we experienced only strong currents and saw nothing spawn.

On 18 November, I made my last dive on Myrmidon. As we reached the drop-off, I looked down and was greeted by a black and empty scene, like a theatre after the performance was over. ■

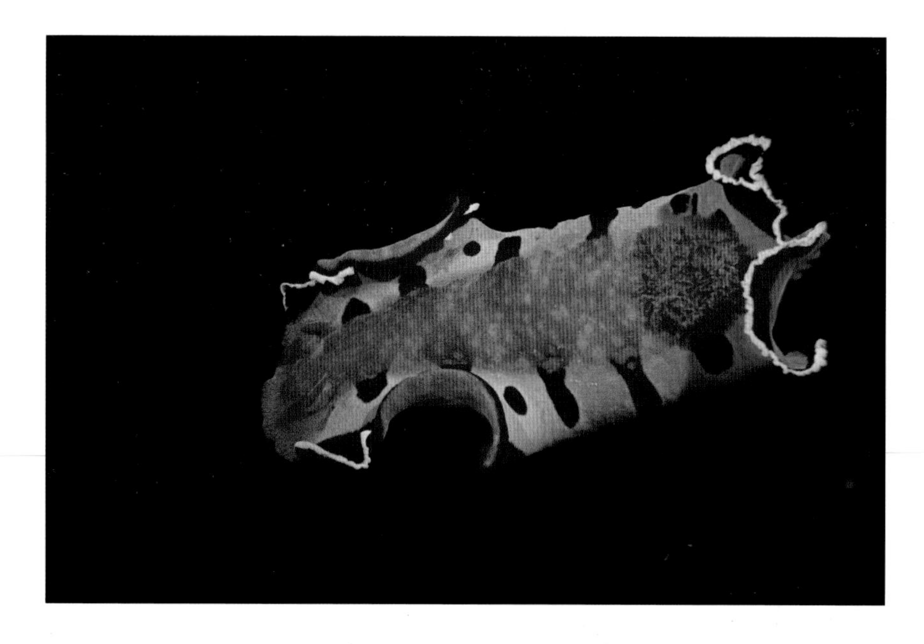

The Spanish dancer is a large and colourful nudibranch (sea slug) that can move through the water by rippling the wide, frilly edges of its mantle, or parapodia, giving the impression of the whirling skirt movements of a flamenco dancer – hence its common name.

As the polyps in a *Platygyra daedalea* colony release their pink egg and sperm bundles (opposite), they are simultaneously catching small, orange polychaete worms that have been attracted by the camera's lights.

Encrusted in corals, sponges and myriad other invertebrates, the wreck of the *SS Yongala* hosts an extraordinary abundance of marine life, including schools of Moses perch, at bottom, and mangrove jack, at top right.

STORY BY **KAREN MCGHEE** PHOTOGRAPHY BY **DARREN JEW**

OASIS IN THE DEEP

From a tragic maritime disaster south-east of Townsville, a vibrant reef was born. Dive down with us and explore the wreck of the *SS Yongala*.

Issue 114 ◆ May–Jun 2013

MOMENTS BEFORE THE *SS Yongala* left the northern Queensland port of Mackay, on 23 March 1911, captain William Knight received warning of a possible cyclone brewing in the vicinity of its destination. But 62-year-old Knight had weathered many cyclones before, and the large, iron-hulled steamship was well built and well equipped.

The *Yongala* was in prime condition, serviced and maintained with pride by its owner, the Adelaide Steamship Company. It could handle big seas and had a schedule to keep. At this time in Australia, the movements of such ships were anticipated and relied upon by tens of thousands of people.

Its next stop was Townsville – then an isolated frontier town of 18,953 with few connections to the outside world. But in a tragedy as momentous and unfathomable as if a passenger jet vanished today without trace, neither the *Yongala* nor the 122 people aboard ever reached harbour.

THE *YONGALA* WAS one of several coastal traders that serviced Australia's major ports around the turn of the 20th century. But this fast and luxurious vessel was in a league of its own as it plied the populous eastern seaboard, from Melbourne to Cairns. Even today, submerged and slowly corroding 15–30m down, it remains something special. Since becoming a gravesite more than 100 years ago, the *Yongala* has evolved into a unique artificial reef, now regarded as one of the world's great scuba diving experiences.

"You get this amazing abundance of wildlife… It really is mind-blowing," says marine biologist Dr David Wachenfeld. It's one of the main reasons the site, due east of Cape Bowling Green and in the Great Barrier Reef (GBR) Marine Park, is now enjoyed by more than 7000 divers a year.

The 110m-long wreck lies 20km inshore from the nearest ribbons of natural hard coral reef. It rests on a predominately flat and featureless underwater 'plain' of sand that stretches away in all directions like a marine desert. The *Yongala*, in contrast, is an oasis. The surrounding waters ripple with huge numbers of large fish and being in a designated marine park green zone means no fishing or collecting is allowed, which has undoubtedly helped to maintain the site's biological richness. →

Sea turtles are frequent visitors to the wreck of the *Yongala*. Both green and hawksbill turtles are often observed feeding or sleeping on and around the wreck.

Built in Newcastle upon Tyne in England and launched on 29 April 1903, the *Yongala* was a steel passenger and freight steamer. It sank during a cyclone on 23 March 1911. All 122 passengers and crew died.

David is a recreational diver and amateur underwater photographer as well as a scientist. He visits the *Yongala* several times a year for the sheer pleasure of it, and has done so for 20 years. "There are incredible schools of giant trevally and other trevally, barracuda, small- and large-mouth nannygai and other snappers, and lots of emperors," he says, "[as well as] schools of cardinal fish in numbers you couldn't even estimate." The fish aggregations are sometimes so dense they obscure the wreck.

The site is also known for its resident giant groupers, which lurk, mostly solo, watching territories near cave-like entrances to the disintegrating hull. Filter-feeding whale sharks sometimes take advantage of the area's plankton-rich waters. Occasionally, humpback whales also swim close as they migrate to or from northern calving grounds. And then there are sea snakes, marine turtles, bull sharks, eagle rays and occasionally large manta rays, adding to a marine menagerie unlike anything seen elsewhere within the GBR Marine Park.

"And, before [Cyclone] Yasi in 2011, if you looked at the wreck from 20m away...it seemed as though it was covered with fur," David says. "But when you moved closer, and looked more carefully, you'd see it was absolutely chock-a-block with filter-feeding invertebrates." These small, sedentary creatures live permanently attached to the *Yongala*, and are a clue as to why there's so much life. Yasi removed some of this covering but it's recovering rapidly.

THE DYNAMIC biological community thriving at the *Yongala* wreck site is an ecological anomaly that's resulted from a serendipitous combination of events and circumstance. And it began, of course, with the sinking of the *Yongala* into the underwater realm.

That tragic event is thought to have occurred just before midnight on 23 March 1911, when the *Yongala* was three-quarters of the way through its 99th voyage in Australian waters. It was en route from Melbourne to Cairns and had left the port of Mackay early in the afternoon, just before 2pm. On board were 73 crew, 29 first-class passengers, 20 second-class passengers and more than 600 tonnes of cargo and livestock, including two bulls and a racehorse named Moonshine.

The Dent Island lighthouse keeper sighted the *Yongala* just after 6pm, steaming northwards past the Whitsunday islands at up to 17 knots (about 32km/h) into the path of a cyclone. The *Yongala* never made it to her next port, Townsville, and was listed as missing on 26 March. A huge search was mounted, but hope was eventually abandoned for the crew and passengers and a Marine Board of Queensland inquiry later that year concluded the *Yongala*'s disappearance was one of "the mysteries of the sea".

FROM A BIOLOGICAL PERSPECTIVE, the most significant feature about the *Yongala* is that it became a hard substrate on an otherwise sandy sea floor. The waters in which it lies are relatively nutrient-rich due to coastal run-off from the Cape Bowling Green estuary just 12 nautical miles (22km) to the west.

The wreck is exposed to strong currents that operate like planktonic highways, carrying an endless supply of minuscule plant and animal life. Plankton includes the larval dispersal stages of invertebrate animals that have sedentary adult lives, such as sponges and soft and hard corals. While suspended in the water column, these tiny creatures are primed to detect locations suitable for settling, which is exactly what the *Yongala* is – an attachment site bathed in nutrients and shallow enough to receive traces of sunlight. The nutrients come from coastal run-off but the wreck also fertilises the surrounding water as its metal corrodes and releases iron. When iron is added to sea water it initiates blooms of planktonic algae. And wherever there's lush plant life, no matter how small, animal life quickly follows.

Once a few animals settle on a location, reefs can build exponentially. Research has shown that their noises and smells can, like the neon lights of a city, be detected from afar and draw more and more passing travellers looking for a home.

There's an equilibrium of sorts – even a kind of symbiotic relationship – that develops between the wreck and the community it supports, explains Paddy Waterson, marine archaeologist with the Queensland Department of Environment and Heritage Protection. Growth of the *Yongala*'s invertebrate life is catalysed by the iron

The wreck attracts large schools of pelagic fish, including barracuda, trevally, kingfish and mackerel. It's also home to some resident giant Queensland groupers, which can grow to more than 2m in length.

released by corrosion, but the dense covering of life also slows that process, partially sealing the ship's metal from direct contact with sea water. And so, as more and more life has settled on the *Yongala*, it seems to have helped to preserve, rather than hasten, its demise.

"Basically, the *Yongala* has already held together longer than a lot of iron shipwrecks and it's the artificial reef that's formed over it that's protected it," Paddy says. "It's helped to hold the ship together." Just how well the relationship has worked was revealed in early 2011 after Cyclone Yasi sandblasted the soft corals and other invertebrates from the wreck's upper level, revealing fine details such as rivets.

The role of plankton in underpinning the biological diversity of the *Yongala* was highlighted in a fish survey conducted during the 1990s by researchers at the Australian Institute of Marine Science (AIMS) and Queensland Department of Environment and Heritage. It identified 122 fish species in 27 families, but Alistair Cheal, an AIMS ecologist and one of the survey's researchers, believes the number of fish was underestimated. The survey focused on large, obvious species. But, Alistair says, if smaller, more cryptic species – such as gobies and blennies – were included, the count would rise by as many as 30.

Whatever the number, it's the fish types thriving at the *Yongala* that help to create a unique biological community. There's a profusion of fish at two particular stages in the food chain: at lower trophic levels, there are large numbers of plankton eaters, including fusiliers and damselfish; and at the top levels, there are huge numbers of predators, with fewer species filling the gaps between.

MYSTERY SURROUNDED the *Yongala*'s fate for decades and stories emerged of a ghost ship in the area where it disappeared. During World War II, a minesweeper reported a possible sandbank in the area. In 1947 reports from a naval hydrographic vessel fuelled further speculation. Divers finally located the wreck in 1958, after a fisherman hoping to make a salvage claim dragged a grappling hook across the area. There are, says Paddy, many theories about what happened. There are no rocks nearby but the effect of local tidal flows, combined with the impact of huge seas created by the cyclone, meant the ship would have been riding enormous waves. Wave heights of more than 9m were recorded there during 2011's Cyclone Yasi.

"One of the most popular theories is [the *Yongala*] kept taking water, the pumps couldn't cope and eventually it just couldn't breach out of the waves and the bow went down – straight down," Paddy says. No life rafts were launched and people were still in their cabins, many undoubtedly suffering from seasickness. The *Yongala*, it appears, was swallowed by the sea. ■

Great white, troubled waters

Australian scientists lead the way in demystifying this mighty shark.

Story by **Karen McGhee**

Issue 73 Jan–Mar 2004

WE CRUISED out of Esperance on the commercial fishing boat *Quadrant* with more than 30L of tuna oil, several huge blocks of frozen salmon mince, thousands of dollars' worth of purpose-built satellite-tracking gear and high hopes for a history-making voyage.

Drawing on the knowledge of local fishers and expertise of CSIRO biologists Barry Bruce and John Stevens, we steered a course for the Eastern Group of the Recherche Archipelago, 112 nautical miles (207km) away, in search of great white sharks (*Carcharodon carcharias*).

In 2000 Barry and John became the first researchers to successfully satellite-track a juvenile white shark. Now they were going after bigger fish and another world first. With support from the Australian Geographic Society and Aquarium of Western Australia, they were planning to attach a satellite tag to an adult and follow its oceanic wanderings.

"It will be an incredible challenge," said Barry, checking gear and contemplating the logistics of securing a $5000 satellite tag to a 5m, 1.5-tonne carnivorous fish. "But then if it were easy, someone would've already done it."

We steamed all night through the poorly charted, scenically spectacular, meandering chain of Recherche Archipelago islands and finally dropped anchor, on the sheltered northern side of Daw Island, the largest of the Eastern Group; notorious for its death-adder population and home to colonies of fairy penguins and New Zealand fur seals. The ocean was 15°C and the air on deck only a little colder, but a bitter wind that felt as if it had blown across Antarctic pack-ice chilled us to the bone.

John slipped on rubber gloves to mix the berley – a heady brew of tuna oil and minced salmon. Barry marked two thin ropes into metre-long segments, attached floats and whole salmon and tossed it all off the stern to help gauge the size of any sharks we attracted. As John ladled berley into the ocean, the air filled with squabbling seabirds and the water teemed with herring. "Now," he said, "we watch and wait."

FEW OTHER creatures, real or imagined, are surrounded by as much myth, mystery and speculation as the great white shark. Its massive size, multiple rows of razor-sharp teeth and powerful jaws have made it the stuff of legend.

Some of the biggest misconceptions involve great whites' hunting capabilities and motivations. They're routinely portrayed, for example, as mindless killing machines and perfect predators. But like tigers, lions or other top-of-the-food-chain carnivores, their hunting is not always flawless. Seal colonies patrolled by these fish have their share of scarred and injured animals that have successfully hauled themselves ashore after close calls.

It's also clear that white sharks aren't driven to kill for killing's sake. Barry prefers using the word "motivated" rather than hungry for these fish: they have large meals infrequently, don't feed every day and won't hunt unless motivated. This is why people have managed to swim with white sharks in open water without being attacked, although this practice is widely condemned as foolhardy. It also explains accounts of large whites swimming with seals in apparent harmony.

Being visual predators, white sharks hunt by day, are thought to have exceptional eyesight and, judging from the structure of their retinas, see in colour. When it comes to other senses, however, recent research concludes their equipment is standard shark issue.

Much of the mythology surrounding white sharks involves their interactions with, and more specifically consumption of, humans. Death in the jaws of a huge shark appears to be a widely shared primal fear for our species and white sharks have probably been responsible for more human deaths than any other marine predator. But, as tragic as they are, attacks are rare. Bee stings really do kill more people. According to Taronga Zoo's Australian Shark Attack File, sharks have on average killed fewer than one person a year in Australian waters during the past 200 years. Allergic reactions to bee stings annually claim between two and three Australians.

THE PRESS CLIPPINGS on white sharks give the impression they must be among the planet's best-researched creatures. The reality is, despite its celebrity, the great white remains more poorly studied than many other sharks. It's partly because white sharks are hard to find: being top predators they have a naturally low abundance. These huge fish also make unwieldy and expensive research subjects.

A major dilemma for researchers has been how to study these fish away from the influence of berley. Tossing a pungent mix of fish flesh and oil into the water is the best way to encourage large ocean-going sharks to the surface and around boats where they can be observed. But this can stimulate a narrow range of extreme reactions, a kind of berley 'high' in which they sometimes thrash around and gnash away at anything they can.

That, unfortunately, is the state in which most people see white sharks. And it's one reason why there's so much excitement about

Great white sharks are dark on top and white beneath. Known as countershading, this pattern helps to camouflage them from prospective prey – when viewed from above, they blend into the ocean's dark depths, while from below their white belly disappears into the sunlit surface waters.

the potential for CSIRO's satellite-tracking project. During the early 1990s, Barry began to realise that the best way to learn about the many unknown facets of white shark lives was by tagging and tracking them. Back then he and his colleagues would attach acoustic tags to adults around Dangerous Reef, east of Port Lincoln, South Australia, and then follow the pings emitted by the tags for up to 26 hours at a time, often in an aluminium dinghy considerably smaller than the fish they pursued.

The work provided the first insights into the extraordinarily complex movements of white sharks, identifying elaborate, sophisticated and seemingly purposeful patterns. "It was like opening a window into the secret lives of these sharks," Barry recalls. "Acoustic tagging was the first time we had an opportunity to get a feel for what these animals were doing when berley wasn't there."

Since then Barry, John and their Australian colleagues have tagged more than 200 white sharks using both acoustic and simple ID tags. The technology that makes satellite-tracking of ocean-going animals possible has been developing since the mid-1990s and already promises to provide enormous, otherwise unattainable, insights into the marine environment. Using equipment designed and built specifically for white sharks by engineers and electronics experts at CSIRO Marine Research in Hobart, Barry and John satellite-tagged a 1.8m juvenile female, nicknamed Heather, in Victorian waters in 2000 and tracked her for 49 days before losing her signal. In 2001 they tagged Neale, a 2.4m juvenile male, and tracked him for 123 days and 3000km between Tasmania and New South Wales.

From Kalgoorlie miners to Brisbane schoolkids, Neale and his travels evoked a large and overwhelmingly positive public response. CSIRO was swamped with emails of support, while Barry and John were interviewed on multiple television programs. Impelled by listener interest, John Laws' nationally syndicated morning radio show provided regular updates on the young shark's movements. In one of the strongest signs that the fear, loathing and ignorance the public has traditionally had for these fish is being replaced by genuine interest and even warmth, Neale became a minor celebrity.

One of the most valuable features of the tags attached to Neale and Heather, and those since developed by CSIRO for great white adults, is that they can provide almost real-time data on a shark's movements. To date, information suggests white sharks can cruise hundreds of kilometres between feeding spots and sometimes to considerable depths – more than 1000m is the record. Barry and John are developing a theory that they refer to as the "cafe-highway hypothesis" to help explain these long-distance travels. "The data we're seeing suggest that these fish move, perhaps even migrate, along certain predictable routes – underwater highways – often stopping at and returning to the same 'cafes' along the way to feed," Barry explains.

Why these fish seem to repeatedly swim past what would appear to be perfectly good feeding locations in favour of other sites is yet to be explained. But if the 'highways' and 'cafes' can be identified then scientists should be able to advise people how best to avoid unwanted encounters with white sharks.

BY LATE on our fourth day of berleying it became clear we'd not achieved what we'd set out to do – not this time, anyway. Why did we fail to find any white sharks? Was it a sign of the species' decline? Or was it simply bad luck?

Dave Riggs, a cinematographer with us to record any tagging activity for CSIRO animal ethics committee records, speculated that sharks in the area may have been distracted by a whale carcass reportedly wrapped in fishing line and floating somewhere close. He'd also heard southern right whales were calving nearby and reasoned that whale placenta might have proved a stronger lure than our berley trail.

For Barry and John, however, the white shark no-show was not unusual. This was the nature of great white research: they were disappointed but far from dejected and were soon discussing how, when and where it would be best to mount their next attempt.

We weighed anchor, set course for Esperance and prepared for another night of steep rolls on the rhythmic swells of the open ocean. "We'll do it, and we'll do it soon," Barry said with a confident grin.

And when they do, they'll undoubtedly open the biggest window yet into the secret lives of white sharks. ■

STORY BY **KARA MURPHY** PHOTOGRAPHY BY **DARREN JEW**

WHALES AT WAR

In a violent humpback whale mating strategy, lusty males fight for access to females, sometimes even to the death.

Issue 120 ◆ May–Jun 2014

A SPEEDING HUMPBACK slices through the swell. The vapour from her blow rises and dissipates into the tropical air as she heads towards the open ocean from Hunga, the westernmost island in the Kingdom of Tonga's Vava'u group. Her pace is understandable: three huge, 13m males are in pursuit, trying to displace her current escort from his enviable position beside her.

Her escort isn't about to swim away gracefully. Lunging through the water, he inflates the ventral pleats extending from his chin to his belly button to make himself look bigger than his sizeable 40-tonne bulk. Occasionally, he dives down deep to blow bubble curtains. He may even try to strike his challengers with his pectoral fins and tail flukes, or ram them with his head.

I'm watching the action from the stern of the 7m yacht *Dream Catcher*. Skipper Ali Takau is aiming to be about 40m in front of the female or beside her – the best place to drop off swimmers, he says.

Humpback whales migrate each year from high-latitude summer feeding grounds in the Arctic and Antarctic to winter mating and calving areas in the tropics, such as around Tonga. For tourists, the region is unlike other humpback wintering areas. Here, as long as you're with a licensed operator, you're not restricted to boat-based vantage points. You can join them in the water and observe from a distance determined safe by guides.

Whale swimmers tend to have a wish list of observations: a calf and mother; a singing whale (always male, often alone, hanging upside down and sending out his complex songs to attract a female); and, finally, the frenetic, multi-whale mating battle.

In Tonga, this battle is often called a 'heat run', but this is misleading because there's little hard evidence that females are in oestrus, says Associate Professor Michael Noad,of the University of Queensland's Cetacean Ecology and Acoustics Laboratory. Some experts believe, however, that lone females are in heat and are attracting males, or that they have already mated and their escorts are guarding them to prevent further matings, explains Dr Adam Pack, an expert on marine mammal behaviour at the University of Hawai'i at Hilo.

⟶

In the waters near the Kingdom of Tonga, a group of competitive male humpback whales chases a female. The function of this behaviour, which can involve dives to a depth of up to 200m, is unknown, but is believed to be related to reproduction.

Researchers have found that the female's principal escort tends to be the largest or second-largest male.

Despite all the effort put into the underwater battling, it's unknown whether any of these feisty males even mate with the female during these clashes. However, she is the centre of attention: she tends to stay near the front of the group and isn't aggressive, but she may produce trumpeting sounds and slap her 5m-long pectoral fins on the water's surface, Adam says.

'Secondary escorts' are often seen trailing the principal and may jostle with each other. Sometimes an escort becomes a challenger and attempts to displace the principal escort. The size of these groups can range from three to more than 20 whales. On the east coast of Australia they often include three or four whales, Michael says, but the Hawaiian breeding ground groups tend to be larger.

Although group size varies, the whales' behaviour doesn't, says Professor Scott Baker of the Marine Mammal Institute at Oregon State University. A founding member of the South Pacific Whale Research Consortium, Scott has studied humpbacks for more than 30 years, and has helped to chart typical aggressive behaviours of males in competitive groups – some of which can result in serious injury or death.

HUMPBACKS SPEND ABOUT 90 per cent of their time under water. To better understand them, Adam and his team attached small cameras to the backs of male escorts in Hawaii. They found the whales would dive to depths of up to 200m, even down to the sea floor, where they would battle with one another. And, rather than behaving passively, the female in these cases appeared to "solicit male attention by stroking her pectoral fin very close to the principal escort and riding in the male's slipstream", Adam says.

Research by Adam's team has shown that size matters. "Mature-sized females [12m or larger] prefer being escorted by the largest mature-sized males [11.5m or larger], and large females attract greater numbers of escorts than do smaller ones," he says.

If he maintains his position, the principal escort typically doesn't remain with a female longer than a day. During this time, the competitive group often whittles down to just the female and principal. Exactly when they part is unknown, but researchers believe that, once impregnated, the female departs the breeding grounds, where she has been fasting, to return to the feeding grounds. The male remains behind to seek opportunities to mate as long as his fat reserves allow.

Despite this research, much about humpback mating behaviour remains a mystery. As for swimmers entering the water when male humpbacks are competing, neither Scott nor Adam is convinced it's safe. However, I'm willing risk to it, and several days into my trip I get the chance.

I slide into the water and kick towards the only whales I can see. Whether it's a female and her principal escort, or challengers, I don't know, but they don't appear aggressive. They are diving in concert through rays of sunlight and my imagination follows them long after our swim is over. ■

Many aspects of whale behaviour are still poorly understood. Humpbacks are known for frequently breaching – when the whale jumps clear of the water – but the function of this behaviour is unclear.

Gentle giants of the deep

Every autumn, large numbers of whale sharks, among the most elusive creatures on Earth, gather on WA's Ningaloo Reef to take advantage of a protein bonanza.

Story by **Geoff Taylor**

Issue 34 Apr–Jun 1994

SUDDENLY, THERE IT WAS, a vast shape right under the bow of our cruiser. My heart was racing as I looked down at one of the largest creatures I had ever seen. With a head that seemed wider than our hull, it dwarfed our 5m vessel. I guessed it must have been 7m long. It swam just below the surface, and as we followed it I hurried to don mask and snorkel so I could dive over the side for my first encounter with the biggest fish in the world.

Clutching my camera, I swam next to it, awed by its massive bulk. I was only 2m away, yet it seemed unperturbed by my presence as it slowly powered forward with rhythmic sweeps of its huge tail. The spots and stripes on its head sparkled in the sunlight. The huge ridges along its body reminded me of the dinosaurs; here indeed was a living fossil, a giant survivor of a bygone age.

On that afternoon, in March 1983, we were diving on Ningaloo Reef, off the coast of Western Australia. During the previous year, we had searched unsuccessfully for this elusive creature on the reef, but on that afternoon we dived with not just one, but a second and then a third. And then on the way home we encountered two more. After five sightings in one day I knew I was onto something extraordinary.

MY INVOLVEMENT WITH WHALE sharks (*Rhincodon typus*) started in 1980 when my wife, Joanna, and I were diving on a wreck at Ningaloo with a team from the WA Museum. When a team member reported seeing a whale shark outside the reef, I was determined to return and search for more.

Two years later, I started working in Exmouth, gateway to the northern end of the 260km-long reef. Early that year, while game fishing outside the reef, we saw two whale sharks. I was keen to dive with them but Joanna quickly reminded me that the deep water outside the reef was also home to less friendly sharks.

That winter, I searched the reef in vain for whale sharks. It wasn't until nearly a year later, in March 1983, that I finally succeeded in diving with them. Incredibly, the weekend after my first encounter, I dived with another seven.

It was becoming obvious that whale sharks could only be found at Ningaloo at a certain time of the year. We occasionally saw them at other times, but the greatest numbers always appeared in autumn, particularly in April. →

Swimming with their mouths agape, whale sharks are able to take in large amounts of water (more than 600 cubic metres of water per hour) and filter out the plankton on which they feed using 20 special filtering pads.

On several autumn days in 1985, they seemed to be everywhere along the reef front, and we spent hours diving with them. Here we were, seeing one of the rarest creatures in the world in exceptional numbers. Why? I had several theories. Most of the sharks appeared to be swimming north. Perhaps they were migrating. Or maybe they'd been brought here by the warm waters of the south-moving Leeuwin Current, which flows strongly at this time of year. It was also possible that they were congregating to mate.

In July 1985, when Joanna and I were making plans to leave Exmouth, I got a phone call from the ABC asking if I'd be interested in filming whale sharks for a TV documentary. It was the sort of thing I'd long dreamt of doing. I bought an old Bolex 16mm movie camera, organised an underwater housing and arranged five weeks leave for the following autumn. Would the sharks be there?

During our first 10 days on the water, we encountered only one or two a day. Then in April, the weather improved, and so did the numbers. Over two days, we dived with more than 26. Many were inquisitive and sought us out. Twice they hung behind the boat for several minutes, and we were able to reach out and stroke their heads.

BY THE EARLY 1980s, scientists had unravelled one of the wonders of the natural world: coral spawning on the Great Barrier Reef. In March 1984, biologist Chris Simpson found that corals found on Australia's west coast usually spawn 7–9 nights after the March and April full moons. When I heard about this, it struck me that here was a natural phenomenon big enough to explain the whale sharks' presence. We'd seen the greatest quantity two or three weeks after the spawning. This suggested that they were feeding higher up the food chain – not on the spawn itself but on other creatures that had fed on it.

I continued searching for whale sharks from 1987 to 1990, noting their appearance in relation to coral spawning. In 1989, having spotted very few from boats, I made my first aerial search. That April, two weeks after the coral spawning, I flew down the reef in a single-engined Cessna and found them much further south than in previous years, off Yardie Creek and Ningaloo. On the way back, I counted 28 in 30 minutes. Nowhere else in the world had anyone seen so many of these creatures in such a short time.

The success of the aerial survey made me realise the scientific limitations of our boat searches. With the help of a research grant from the Australian National Parks and Wildlife Service, I made regular aerial surveys along the northern part of the reef during the early 1990s. These confirmed that the whale sharks' periodic arrival coincided with the huge explosion of life in autumn. I found no evidence of migration along the reef; instead the sharks seemed to be moving in from deeper water offshore. I found them consistently in the north-flowing current just outside the reef rather than in the clear, warmer water of the south-flowing Leeuwin Current further out.

In 1991 the missing link in my theory – that whale sharks feed on creatures higher up the food chain after the coral spawning – finally fell into place. Tropical krill, tiny shrimp-like crustaceans, gathered in huge swarms along the reef front two weeks after the spawning, themselves laden with eggs and spawning.

They may be the world's largest fish, photographed here by David Doubilet, but whale sharks are relatively leisurely swimmers, cruising along at about 5km/h. They can cover huge distances, however, migrating for thousands of kilometres at a time.

Normally krill stay in deep water during the day, migrating to the surface at night. When spawning, however, they may swarm on the surface in daytime. During our searches we spotted individual whale sharks lunging through the slicks of krill and their spawn. Impressive though this was, it paled beside an incident that took place at dusk one day later that year.

The sea was almost calm as we motored along in local fisherman Danny Cassidy's boat towards a spot where we'd seen a good number of whale sharks earlier in the day. Just as the sun was about to touch the horizon, a whale shark broke the surface. And then it was gone. A moment later another appeared, followed by a third, the glow of the setting sun catching their dorsal fins.

Soon they were all around us, charging through the water, creating large bow waves. Tiny creatures leapt out in front of them trying to escape. One group of about seven sharks twisted and turned in pursuit

of their prey, their tails thrashing well clear of the water. This had to be one of the most exciting sights of the natural world – whale sharks in a feeding frenzy.

The following year, a surprise lay in store for us when we tried trawling for the whale sharks' prey during another feeding frenzy. Instead of krill, as expected, our net was full of the larvae of crabs and mantis shrimps.

THE PHOTOGRAPHS I'VE TAKEN over the years confirm that the intricate pattern of markings on each whale shark is as distinctive as a human fingerprint. Many of these leviathans also carry scars, inflicted by propellers and predatory sharks, that make them instantly recognisable.

In 1992 I began compiling a photographic database to help identify individual sharks. I also tagged 25. At last I could prove that I wasn't seeing the same sharks over and over. I estimated the population of the northern reef area at more than 200.

Since my first paper on whale sharks in 1989, news spread rapidly, reaching photographers and shark enthusiasts around the world. Among the first to come to Ningaloo were photographer David Doubilet and shark experts Rodney Fox and Eugenie Clark.

Since then, film crews, wildlife photographers and divers from all over the world have come to Ningaloo in search of whale sharks. Like me, many hope to fill gaps in our knowledge of one of the last surviving giants on this planet. But this has created a huge dilemma for government bodies responsible for protecting this rare species. How much disturbance can whale sharks stand and what legislation is appropriate to protect them? They are a phenomenal tourist resource, but one that must be managed properly if future generations are to enjoy these truly gentle giants. ■

Live fast...die young

The story of the giant Australian cuttlefish.

Story by **Pip Moran** Photography by **Tony Karacsonyi**

Issue 51 Jul–Sep 1998

IT WAS LOVE AT first sight. We met during a dive in the 15°C water off Ulladulla, on the New South Wales south coast, among a tumble of algae-encrusted boulders. I slowly swam towards the object of my fascination, one hand tentatively outstretched. Hovering midwater, stabilised by the undulating motion of its skirt-like fins and pulsing with vivid colours, the giant Australian cuttlefish (*Sepia apama*) regarded me with brightly intelligent eyes before tilting the tips of several of its eight swaying arms in my direction.

As I trailed my fingers through the creature's tangle of sucker-lined arms, which emerge from its face like an elephant's trunk, bursts of blue, purple and green rippled over its mottled-brown skin. I ventured to stroke its back. Beneath my fingers, the delicate skin slid over its oval-shaped mantle, the elongated sheath of muscle cloaking its internal cuttlebone. It was difficult to equate this living, pulsing being with the dry white cuttlebones that are washed up on beaches and end up in birdcages. Yet it's this 'bone', with its many layers of porous, calcified shell sandwiching tiny test-tube-like gas-filled cells, that gives the animal its neutral buoyancy. And in giant cuttlefish, which can grow to more than 1m in length – the largest of the world's 100-odd cuttlefish species – the bone is big.

The wild cuttlefish I was patting like some family dog belongs to the same class of mollusc as squids and octopuses – the cephalopods. My encounter was interrupted by a dark form emerging from a narrow passage between two nearby rocks. It was Tony Karacsonyi, dive buddy and guide for the duration of my four-day underwater exploration. Tony is a former fisheries inspector who nurtures a passion for the underwater world in general, and giant Australian cuttlefish in particular.

For the past few years, from June to August, he has dived intensively around the reefs off Ulladulla, photographing and observing these captivating creatures, which each winter gather in droves to mate and spawn off our eastern and southern coasts. Privy to some of their favourite haunts, Tony had led me to this popular cuttlefish trysting place just 600m from the shore where, 12m underwater, I was experiencing firsthand the seductive effect these animals have on humans.

"Cuttlefish are good company," Tony had told me earlier. "Spending time with them is never boring because they're such highly intelligent creatures."

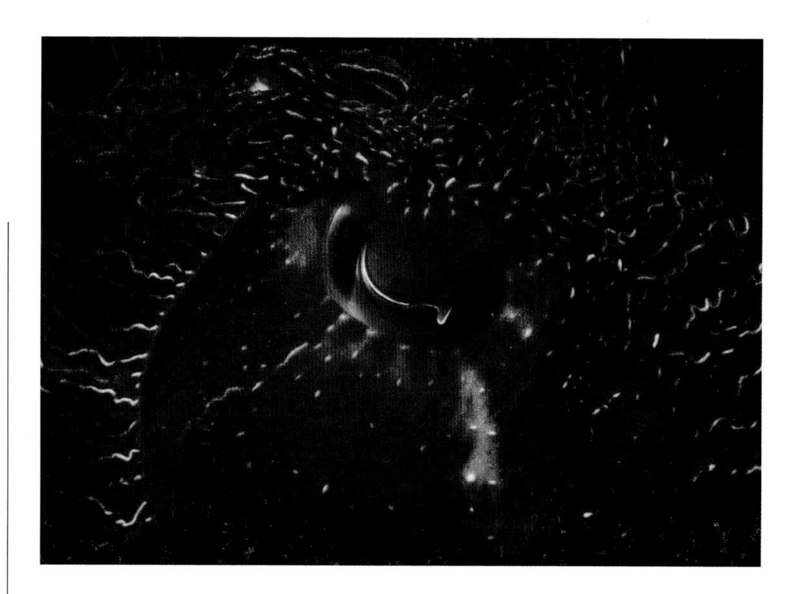

The W-shaped pupil of a giant cuttlefish contains a lens similar to that of a human but its focusing method is quite different, moving the lens towards or away from the retina, rather than altering the lens's shape.

Looking into my new friend's W-shaped pupils, I could only agree. Like so many divers before me, I got the distinct impression that the lights were well and truly on. In terms of complexity and behaviour, the giant cuttlefish and its fellow cephalopods are the most highly evolved marine invertebrates, having more in common with fish than molluscan relatives such as oysters, scallops and abalone.

"IN EVOLUTIONARY THEORY there's a rule that the more you strut, the bigger the behaviour, the more likely you are to get off without direct conflict and losing hunks of flesh," University of Melbourne zoologist Mark Norman told me from his office as we discussed the male giant cuttlefish's mating-season behaviour.

"They're really good at displaying – like 18-year-old testosterone-driven blokes," he continued, his description bringing to mind two macho cuttlefish I'd seen vying for a female's affections in NSW waters. Wearing their flashiest colours and flaring their large, fourth, outer arms to look as imposing as possible, they'd manoeuvred to glide with mirror-like symmetry side by side, until the less showy of the two admitted defeat and retreated.

I'd spoken to Mark after returning from Ulladulla, keen to compare notes on the giant cuttlefish behaviour Tony and I had observed during our dives. Mark had recently studied the mating behaviour →

The giant cuttlefish can grow to more than 1m in length and is the largest of the world's 100-odd cuttlefish species. Writer Pip Moran, pictured here, met this gentle giant in the cold waters off Ulladulla in southern NSW in winter, the season when they're known to gather in droves in the shallow reefs here to mate and spawn.

Cuttlefish mate head to head. After the male transfers a sperm package to a pouch beneath the female's mouth, she fertilises her eggs individually by passing them over the sperm-filled pouch.

of the giant cuttlefish in Spencer Gulf, South Australia. While looking for other marine species there, Mark had come across thousands of giant cuttlefish on a single reef, some of them bearing fresh scars.

"The extent of mate-guarding in Spencer Gulf was amazing," he said, referring to the males' extremely protective behaviour towards the females they'd just mated with. "It's the driving force behind male aggression and display." With good reason. Cuttlefish mate head to head, the male transferring a sealed sperm package to a pouch beneath the female's mouth with one of his arms. To fertilise her eggs, the female enters a suitable den and draws each ping-pong ball of an egg from her mantle cavity and passes it over her sperm-filled pouch. This means that the last, rather than the first, male to implant his sperm package prior to egg-laying is the reproductive winner.

"The females were laying their eggs in crevices and males were physically blocking the entrances to guard against other males and using high-pressure water from the funnels just below their heads, normally used for jet propulsion, to hose out the sperm packages and deposit their own," Mark said.

Coated in a sticky gelatinous substance, the newly fertilised eggs are hung from the cave roof or crevice in dense clusters. A cuttlefish will generally lay about 200 eggs. Females are thought to die shortly after spawning. Scientists believe the animals may live for just 18 months to two years, and although both sexes mature early in life, males are thought to begin mating earlier. "It may be that males have several seasons to breed, unlike females, which seem to lay their eggs in just one burst, then die of old age," Mark said, describing what scientists call "big bang" reproduction.

Lethargy follows spawning and the cuttlefish's body gradually deteriorates over the last weeks of its short life, easy pickings for predators such as the bottlenose dolphin, which feeds almost exclusively on the heads, leaving the bodies to float to the surface for scavengers such as the wandering albatross.

Meanwhile, protected inside individual rubbery casings, countless cuttlefish embryos quietly get on with the job of developing. Some four months later, they hatch as tiny 25mm replicas of their parents. Predation rates are high, however, and many don't survive beyond their first few hours.

THE CUTTLEFISH'S CHAMELEON qualities have long delighted visitors to their underwater realm. Its colours, I discovered, are produced by complex structures called chromatophores, embedded in the skin and unique to cephalopods.

"Each chromatophore contains a super-elastic, pigment-filled sac surrounded by a band of circular muscles wired directly to the brain," Mark explained. "When the muscles contract, the sac is pulled to a flat disc, making the extremely dense pigment visible. When the muscles relax, the sac folds up to a tiny dot of colour."

The giant cuttlefish has three types of chromatophore – yellow, orange/red and brown/black – each of which can be expanded or contracted independently. Enhanced by iridophores, mirror-like crystalline structures that reflect blue and green, and leucophores, the cells responsible for its white spots, the animal's arrays of colours and patterns number in the thousands.

The chromatophores aren't just used for kaleidoscopic mating displays, however. With an ability to change colour in less than a second, the giant cuttlefish is especially adept at camouflage, which is remarkable considering it's almost certainly colour blind. Many scientists believe that it sees contrast, rather than colour, to produce the body patterns that form the basis of its defence.

If its camouflage fails and the cuttlefish finds itself confronted by an enemy, it creates a decoy in the form of a mucus-bound blob of ink before retreating to safety. Secreted by a sac near the anus and discharged through the funnel, the ink may also be released in a large cloud – a smokescreen behind which the cuttlefish escapes.

All of this predator-avoidance, displaying, mating, guarding and spawning takes energy, and the fast-growing giant cuttlefish has a voracious appetite, feeding primarily on crustaceans such as crabs and prawns, other cephalopods and small fish. And in hunting, as in all of its behaviour, changing body patterns have a role, although one not yet fully understood. Some scientists believe that certain moving patterns and body postures may have some sort of hypnotic or distracting effect on its prey, which would certainly assist in its capture. Having watched a posturing giant cuttlefish make very short work of a rather large crab, I was keen to know more about its hunting technique.

Its prey within range, the cuttlefish draws its arms to a point, sometimes raising the first pair above its head in a V shape, then shoots out its secret weapon: two specialised feeding tentacles that are kept in pouches beneath the eyes. Having 'harpooned' its meal, the cuttlefish darts forward to engulf the victim in its arms, at the same time retracting its long tentacles. It then uses its parrot-like beak and radula, the rasping tongue, to break the prey into bite-size pieces.

SCIENCE IS SLOWLY TURNING the spotlight on one of our oceans' most colourful characters, but there's still much to learn. As Tony, in a fanciful frame of mind, had written in the field notes he has kept over the past winter: "At this time we're sending probes to Mars searching for signs of alien life, yet already an extraordinary creature exists in our oceans that we know so little about – the giant Australian cuttlefish. While under water I reflect on the fact that I am in its world – that I may as well be on Mars or some other planet, observing the life of an otherworldly creature."

After diving with this delightful chameleon of our southern waters, I too have developed a fascination for the giant Australian cuttlefish, one of our planet's very own 'aliens'. ■

Newly fertilised cuttlefish eggs hang from a cave roof in dense clusters. After four months inside the egg, the embryo emerges as a 25mm replica of its parents.

Hovering motionless near the sea floor, a giant cuttlefish raises two of its tentacles to create a V-shape. The function of this behaviour is unknown but is thought to be an attempt to mimic the surrounding kelp.

STORY BY **ROY HUNT** PHOTOGRAPHY BY **DARREN JEW**

SECRETS OF THE SEA LION

Researchers brave the aptly named Dangerous Reef to undertake groundbreaking research on the rare – and playful – Australian sea lion.

Issue 101 ◆ Jan–Mar 2011

SOME OF THE ISLANDS scattered across South Australia's Spencer Gulf are verdant, idyllic places. Dangerous Reef is not one of them. Rising from the ocean 35km east of Port Lincoln, the island is a wedge of black metamorphic rock scabbed with sun-bleached guano. Bleak, desolate and little bigger than a footy field, Dangerous Reef has no permanent fresh water and offers no shelter from the sun, rain or blasting easterly winds. But regardless of any perceived aesthetic shortcomings, this is a place of immense biological significance: the reef supports the largest surviving breeding colony of one of the planet's rarest marine mammals – the Australian sea lion (*Neophoca cinerea*).

I've come here near the end of the spring–summer breeding season with marine ecologist Associate Professor Simon Goldsworthy, who has been unravelling the secrets of the Australian sea lion for more than a decade. Awaiting our arrival is fellow seal expert Dr Brad Page – a giant of a man who, after spending the past couple of tempest-tossed weeks here in a leaky tent, has the wild look of a castaway.

Both researchers have been regular visitors to Dangerous Reef for the past seven years, as they've spearheaded a project for the South Australian Research and Development Institute (SARDI) that could help save the sea lion from extinction. Moreover, their unique work with the species is also amassing a wealth of information critical to the future of one of Australia's most biologically diverse and productive marine regions.

Brad leads us to a makeshift camp at the foot of the island's automated lighthouse. We pitch our tents on a tiny, nuggetty strip of guano, among boxes of scientific equipment and tinned food. I take a few steps beyond an imaginary perimeter for a closer look at our neighbours, but Brad abruptly pulls me up. Two of four female sea ⟶

Being mammals, sea lions are, of course, air-breathers. But they have a remarkable ability to hold their breath and have been recorded diving to depths of almost 300m, while remaining submerged for about seven minutes.

Dr Brad Page remains close to Imos 4, watching out for opportunistic attacks by potential male rivals until the 300kg male sea lion has recovered from sedation, administered during an operation to remove a satellite tracker fitted to the animal's back.

Australian sea lions are social animals that spend most of their lives in and around the breeding colony from which they originated. When not feeding at sea, they often sunbake on sandy beaches and rocks.

lions he's recently fitted with GPS trackers and miniature 'Crittercam' video-recorders are still out at sea. The devices will provide information about where and how the females hunt to support the dietary demands of their pups. The females could haul out at any time and Brad doesn't want to risk them being scared off before their precious footage and data have been recovered.

WHILE WAITING FOR THE tardy females, Brad takes us to find another sea lion of interest. On the island's lee shore, a 300kg male, known technically as Imos 4, reclines among his harem of females. He too is a research recruit. On his back, he's carrying a pocket-dictionary-sized box laden with scientific instruments and a satellite antenna. This bull has been transformed into a submersible data-collecting 'oceanographic observer'.

He represents the other side of SARDI's sea lion research project, which involves a team of seven males from different colonies gathering data across the Great Australian Bight. Very little is known about life below about 10m, but the use of these deep-diving sea lions is changing that. "Diving every eight or nine minutes, their capacity to sample their environment far exceeds what humans can do and they're doing it 24/7," explains Simon.

Male Australian sea lions have been selected over females for this role because they roam more widely. Unlike any other seal, the species reproduces non-annually and asynchronously: the breeding cycle at Dangerous Reef, for example, is a full six months out of phase with that of Lewis Island just 25km to the south-west. For males such as Imos 4, island hopping means 'staying in the game' year-round to maximise their reproductive potential.

Simon and I hunker down behind a rock as Brad creeps closer to Imos 4. As he gets within 10m, there's a barely audible pop from his tranquilliser gun and the target registers almost no reaction as the dart strikes. It carries a very precisely gauged sedative dose that won't render the sea lion completely unconscious. If his breathing needs help, an oxygen cylinder is available and an antidote is at hand.

Within minutes our boy looks floppier. Brad prods him gently to make sure he's sedated and nods to Simon, who then moves swiftly, cutting through dense fur to remove the device glued to the creature's back. Brad gently takes hold of a flipper, one of a sea lion's most sensitive parts, and leans close to the big, whiskery face to check his breathing. He's doing fine – and the muscle and fat he's piled on since his initial encounter with the research team, five months prior, indicates the backpack isn't interfering with his feeding.

The following morning, I'm scanning the water's edge for the missing females. I marvel as one mum emerges from the water, lifts her head, calls and, more than 30m away, a small pup in a group of several dozen replies almost immediately. Scent confirms the match-up as the pair draws close together and the hungry youngster homes in on a teat while Mum reclines on a rocky couch. Australian sea lions dive continually while at sea and must haul out on land to rest. Fur seals, on the other hand, can spend weeks at sea diving for fish.

When Brad and Simon were here in January, at the height of the breeding season, life in the colony was more frenetic and the researchers had their work cut out avoiding protective mothers as they marked pups to survey their numbers. The only way to work is to have one person marking while the other watches their back. "I got greedy one day," says Simon, recalling a momentary lack of focus. A little pup he'd almost tripped over presented a marking opportunity too good to miss. But just as he was making a grab for it, he felt as if he'd been whacked on the back of the leg with a cricket bat. The wound inflicted by the pup's mum needed 12 stitches.

DAWN BREAKS ON my third day in the colony and a flock of Cape Barren geese – common inhabitants of the islands off southern Australia – touches down in the mist. They're not the only new arrivals. On the rocks beneath the lighthouse – not 10m from our camp – is one of the females that we've been waiting for. After spending the past few days out fishing at sea she's finally returned to feed her pup.

Brad crawls into position along the ridge above her and she barely twitches as his dart hits home. Once she's settled, Simon approaches to

With a streamlined body and short, paddle-like forelimbs, sea lions are perfectly adapted for life in the ocean. A covering of fur over a thick layer of fat helps to keep them warm in cold waters.

cut loose the camera equipment. Within minutes, the pup that's been mewling pitifully throughout the procedure resumes feeding.

Usually researchers identify what seals eat by teasing apart their faeces, looking for squid beaks, crab claws and fish bones. This doesn't work for Australian sea lions because the prey is so ground up that few identifiable hard parts remain.

The value of Crittercams is that they answer the same dietary questions by providing real-life accounts of sea lions hunting. The video from one female's camera showed that she specialised in preying on a single species, spending her time pursuing octopuses across the seemingly featureless sandy seabed. Another female spent her first day wearing the equipment hunting rock ling in a coastal reef before switching to 'sit and wait' predator mode, diving down repeatedly to the same rock, where she would perch, cat-like watching over a sponge garden. Then she'd pounce on a passing leatherjacket.

Australian sea lions are benthic feeders – they forage on the sea floor. The video footage has revealed just how demanding a lifestyle choice this can be. Any pup growing up around here would need to acquire a range of hunting skills and an intimate knowledge of a feeding territory with very few landmarks. Simon believes that this explains why the Australian sea lion has the longest weaning period of any seal species: youngsters remain with their mums for 18 months learning this stuff.

THE NEXT MORNING IS my last on Dangerous Reef. Near the water's edge, there are a large number of pups. Most of them are now 3–6 months old and have formed little gangs of 30–40, banding together to spend their days playing and getting up to mischief.

Back in Adelaide a few days later, Simon and Brad begin the mammoth task of processing the data the sea lions have collected over the course of the season. Some of the information will play a part in determining how SA's Department of Environment and Natural Resources should zone the marine parks across the Bight.

Until now, key habitats and biodiversity indicators in Australia's oceans have been identified from a human perspective. This, Simon explains, has led to a bias towards habitats with complex structure, such as reefs, because they're known centres of biodiversity. Sea lions, however, perceive things differently. "They often target areas with very little structure that don't light up [for us on] our traditional anthropocentric mapping systems but that are often far more productive," Simon says.

Simon and Brad predict that, in the long term, a research partnership with Australian sea lions will greatly improve the management of marine ecosystems. As a top predator, the Australian sea lion is also a sentinel of climate change, with the species' diet and population trends reflecting broader shifts in marine food webs and productivity. "They are providing an enormous wealth of information," Simon explains. ■

CHAPTER FOUR

SURVIVAL AND LOSS

There's no way of sugar-coating it – Australia is in the throes of an extinction crisis. More than 450 species of Australian animal are currently at risk of disappearing forever, including about a third of our (non-bat) mammals.

Sadly, Australia already has the dubious distinction of hosting the world's highest loss of mammal species; since 1500, 35 per cent of all mammal extinctions have taken place in Australia. The problem started about 60 years after the arrival of European colonists, and from then on, we've lost one or two species per decade. That all adds up to a total of 27 of Australia's land mammals – more than 10 per cent of our original endemic land mammal fauna.

They're joined by 22 species of bird (although only one of those has been lost from the mainland), one species each of reptile, fish and earthworm, and four species of frog. It's very likely that several other species have disappeared without our knowledge.

Interestingly, where hunting and habitat loss are the main drivers of population declines and extinction elsewhere, in Australia the problem is strongly linked to inappropriate fire regimes, which increase the likelihood, extent and severity of wildfires, and the impact of feral animals, particularly introduced foxes and cats, but increasingly cane toads as well. Indeed, feral predators have been implicated in all but two of Australia's mammal extinctions.

One of those exceptions is the Tasmanian tiger, or thylacine. It's believed that the thylacine's woes began with the arrival of dingoes on the mainland, where they are thought to have become extinct about 2000 years ago. However, its fate was sealed when sheep were introduced to Tasmania in 1824. Thylacines preyed on the livestock, and in 1830 the Van Diemen's Land Company introduced a bounty. In 1888 the Tasmanian government followed suit and by the time its bounty scheme was ended in 1909, almost 2200 bounties had been paid. By then, it was obvious that the species was in trouble, but government protection didn't arrive until 10 July 1936, six years after the shooting of the last known thylacine to be killed in the wild and just 59 days before the very last known specimen died in captivity.

The yellow-footed rock-wallaby is another species that suffered a significant decline due to hunting pressure, but thankfully a 1912 act of parliament protected them before it was too late. By then, however, feral animals were also taking their toll and populations didn't bounce back as quickly as they should have. Fox baiting, particularly in South Australia and north-western NSW, has since helped to turn things around, but unfortunately the yellow-footed rock-wallaby isn't out of the woods yet and is still considered to be vulnerable to extinction.

Another species that has benefited from feral-animal control is the northern hairy-nosed wombat, Australia's largest wombat species. Although habitat loss and competition for food from introduced grazing animals, such as sheep, cattle and rabbits, have been the main reason for the species' rapid decline since European colonisation, the erection of a predator-proof fence around what was at that time their last sanctuary, Epping Forest National Park in central Queensland, in 2002, has been the key to their revival. However, they, too, are far from secure.

Occasionally, there's a small ray of light to counter this gloom, when a species that was long presumed to be extinct is rediscovered. In 1992 herpetologists working in SA rediscovered the pygmy bluetongue, which had last been seen in 1959. And in 2013 the first live night parrot to be seen since 1912 was found in south-western Queensland. And of course there are those who believe that one day we'll find a surviving thylacine population... ■

Previous page: In the 1880s yellow footed rock wallabies were said to occur "in droves of 60 or 70", but, sadly, hunting and introduced predators have greatly reduced their numbers.

On remote Codfish Island, off the southern tip of New Zealand, researchers prepare to extract sperm from a reluctant kakapo, one aspect of a breeding program that's desperately trying to ensure the survival of this unusual parrot.

Saving the northern hairy-nosed wombat

Story by **Ken Eastwood** Photography by **Jason Edwards**

Issue 72 Oct–Dec 2003

IF THERE'S A CLIFF called extinction, you can watch half a million African elephants stampeding towards it. They have time to change course. Five thousand tigers are much closer, slinking slowly towards the precipice, and 650 mountain gorillas are swaying dangerously close.

But an Australian marsupial – the northern hairy-nosed wombat (*Lasiorhinus krefftii*) – has three of its four paws hanging off the cliff edge. There are just 113 northern hairy-noses left, burrowed under a single 300ha strip of ancient creekbed in a small national park in central Queensland. The inbred population is skewed 70:30 towards males, so there are probably only 30 or so breeding females of the species left in existence.

No northern hairy-noses are kept in captivity and the last time a zoo tried, the wombat deteriorated rapidly and died seven months later of a twisted bowel.

Rise up in a mustering chopper above Epping Forest National Park (Scientific), 850km north-west of Brisbane, and you quickly see why the northern hairy-nosed wombat is doomed without our help. The park – a squashed pentagon of brigalow, gidgee and wooded grassland – is an island of dark green in a horizon of beige, cleared land. Barely a tree seems to stand outside the park's boundaries.

This area is the only place we know northern hairy-noses have lived since the early 1900s. During the 19th century, they were also found near St George, in southern Queensland, and as far away as Deniliquin, in southern New South Wales. Skeletal records suggest they were never as common as our two other wombat species: the southern hairy-nosed and common wombats.

Epping Forest was gazetted as a national park for the wombat's protection in 1971 and cattle were excluded 10 years later when the wombat population sank to 30 individuals. In 2002, after a pack of dingoes killed about 10 per cent of the wombats, 20km of 2m-high fence, costing about $400,000, was built around the habitat. The entire species is now held in one enclosure.

Apart from the wombats, a few kangaroos and a rufous bettong that hangs around the dongas in the well-established human camp, the most commonly sighted mammal at Epping Forest NP is a lanky, clean-cut bloke by the name of Alan Horsup. A conservation officer with the Queensland Parks and Wildlife Service, Alan has spent a total of more than two years living in this 3160ha national park, and another year out in the field studying rock-wallabies. "I've been married for 17 years, but we've only been together for 14 years of that," he says.

As the coordinator of the wombat recovery program, Alan has spent a significant amount of his time trying to help the wombats thrive – including supplying supplementary feed and water during times of drought. But the wombats stubbornly refuse any assistance, even avoiding areas where humans have been. "They're averse to anything foreign," Alan says. "We've tried hay, molasses, grain crops, carrots, everything. Even if there's terrible grass growing, they'll prefer that to anything we give them."

TWENTY YEARS AGO, their diet consisted almost completely of the 20 or so native grass species in the area – wire, bottle-washer, corkscrew and the beautiful golden beard grass. But increasingly, a prolific African species, buffel grass, is taking over the habitat. Wombats eat buffel when its leaves are young and tender, but it quickly grows into massive thick tufts, 1m-high by 1m-wide, outcompeting native grasses and reaching heights too tall for a 40cm-high animal to graze.

Alan reckons the buffel grass is one of the northern hairy-nose's biggest problems. "No-one's been able to put their finger on why the sex ratio in the population has changed to 70 per cent males," he said. "In the 1980s, when they were first trapped, the sex ratio was even. The change seems to correlate with the increase in buffel grass."

Wading through waist-high buffel, with an Australian hobby swooping on the sparkling locusts flinging themselves out of our way, Alan talked about the search for a site where the recovery team could translocate a population of the wombats if the population keeps growing. They're looking in southern Queensland, near St George. "One of the big criteria would be that it's buffel-free," Alan said.

Northern hairy-noses are the largest of the three wombat species, growing up to 1.3m long, and weighing up to 40kg. Unlike the →

Northern hairy-nosed wombat number 49, also known as Centauri, peers tentatively from the inside of a trap. The endangered marsupials in Epping Forest NP are caught every four years to assess their health.

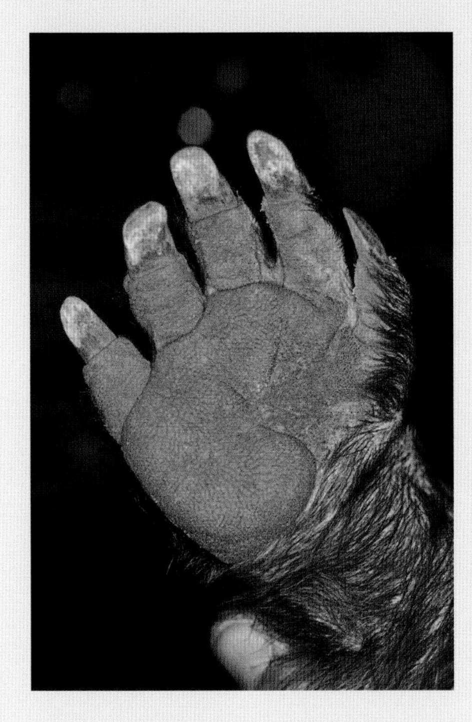

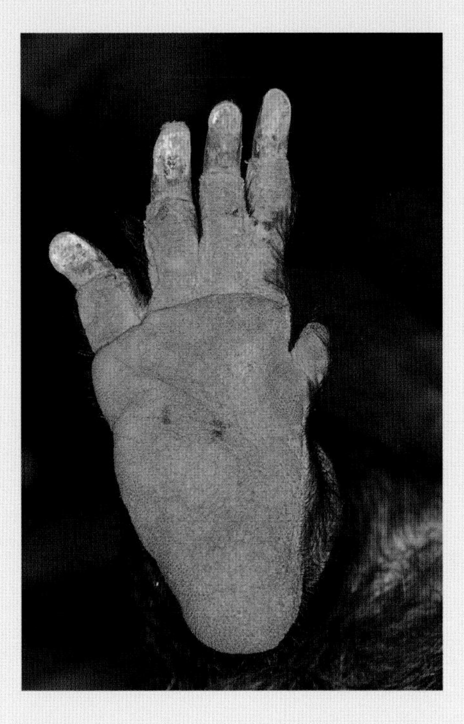

Surprisingly soft, the northern hairy-nose's front paw (far left) is fleshy, like a human palm. The toe and nail add an extra 3cm to its 7.5cm length. The back paws (left) are longer and more elongate. When digging their burrows, wombats use their front claws then push the loose soil backward with their hind feet.

common wombat's koala-like button nose, a very broad hairy snout dominates the northern hairy-nose's face. The wombat has perky, alert ears like a pig, and eyes that look too small for its body.

Wombats are the only marsupials to have constantly growing teeth, in order to keep up with the shearing and grinding of the silica-rich grasses they ingest. They have a very, very slow metabolism – it can take up to 14 days for food to pass through their system – but this means they gain as many nutrients and as much water as possible from each mouthful, and they don't have to forage very much. They generally spend no more than 3–4 hours each night out of their burrows. Compare this with some kangaroo species, which eat for up to 18 hours a day.

The rest of the time, the wombats are asleep, snuggled 2–3m underground in burrows up to 40m long. Burrows younger than 10 years tend to be very simple, with just one 50cm-wide tunnel that turns a few times, then suddenly ends. There's no wide sleeping chamber or other special features, and the ceiling often gets as low as 25cm off the deck. Older burrows have up to seven entrances and multiple layers, with intertwining tunnels.

While temperatures outside the burrow fluctuate between 10°C and 40°C, 10m inside it's a pretty constant 26°C. Humidity levels keep rising the further you go into a burrow. As northern hairy-noses spend so much time in their burrows, high humidity may help them to conserve water.

During the course of a year, northern hairy-noses use an average of five burrows over an area of about 5ha. They return to one burrow about half the time and 71 per cent of the time they'll be its only occupant.

Research supported by the Australian Geographic Society has shown that 12–18 months after they've given birth, females leave their burrow area. Strangely, they seem to end up in an area where their closest female relatives are – almost as if they seek their sisters out.

Back in the 1960s – before today's environmental correctness came into vogue – the Dennis family of Epping Forest cattle station, 3km north of the national park, used a bulldozer to dig out two northern hairy-noses. They kept the male, Darby, and female, Joan, as family pets in a concrete-floored pen in the yard. Years later, they caught another female in a paddock.

THE THREE WOMBATS survived for more than five years in their care, and Joan lived for more than 25 years. Every morning they fed Joan a wheat-derived chook feed called pollard – served warm in winter – and gave her couch grass and buffel at night. "She did really well on pollard," John Dennis says. "I think she did better on the pollard than she was when we found her. She was always shiny – a shiny coat like a cattle dog that's eaten too many eggs."

The family initially tried to keep Darby and Joan together, hoping they'd breed, but they fought too much – biting and the like – so were kept separately until Darby died of old age 10 years later.

Joan spent much of her time sleeping in a cubby, behind a hessian curtain, but would also go out and bask in the sun. She didn't like being patted, except by John's mother. "But the other female wombat turned out to be as quiet as a joey," John said. "They must have different temperaments."

When Joan eventually died, she was put in the family freezer so she could be preserved as a pickled specimen in the Queensland Museum: a pretty unceremonious end for one of the world's rarest pets.

While zoos across the country develop better ways to keep and breed common and southern hairy-nosed wombats, there's hope at the Rockhampton Zoo that the latter could be used as foster-mothers for northern hairy-nosed babies. This would potentially allow a northern mother to have more than the usual two offspring every three years. "At this stage, though, we don't even know what the right formula is to breed them," said Rockhampton IVF specialist, Glenn Druery. "But you've got to be positive about these things. You've got to start positive, anyway." ■

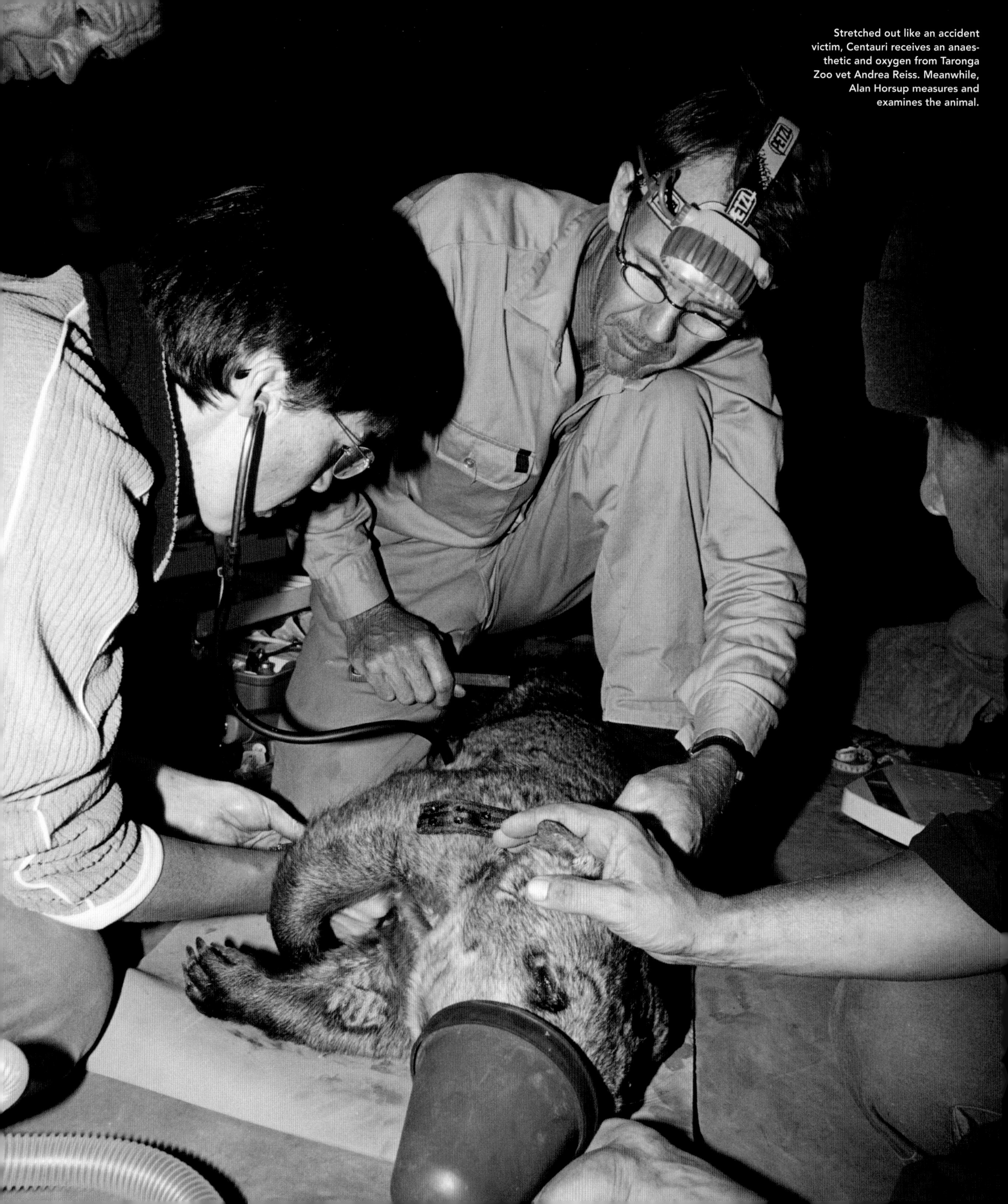

Stretched out like an accident victim, Centauri receives an anaesthetic and oxygen from Taronga Zoo vet Andrea Reiss. Meanwhile, Alan Horsup measures and examines the animal.

Secret sanctuary

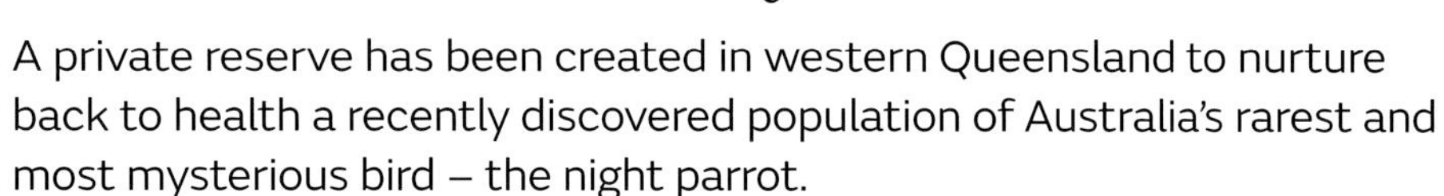

A private reserve has been created in western Queensland to nurture back to health a recently discovered population of Australia's rarest and most mysterious bird – the night parrot.

Story by **John Pickrell** Photography by **Steve Murphy**

Issue 134 Sep–Oct 2016

IT'S 7PM AND DARK, but still oppressively hot in this pocket of central-western Queensland. Here the tough *Triodia* grass, or spinifex, would usually only be illuminated by the moon and thousands of stars across the clear outback sky, but tonight the beam of a head-torch is methodically moving through the hummocks of spiky vegetation. The bearer of the light is wildlife biologist Dr Steve Murphy, and as he walks, he carries ahead of him a large, grey, boom mic. It's not really what you expect to see in the bush, but Steve – a fellow at Charles Darwin University and the world expert on night parrots – knows precisely what he's doing.

Shortly after dark, and before they leave roosts carefully snipped into clumps of spinifex, night parrots are most likely to call, and this is when you have the best chance of detecting these incredibly cryptic creatures. The most common call, composed of two high notes, is unmistakeable, "a sweet, ringing, parrot-like 'ding-ding'," says Steve, who adds that the parrots make at least seven other calls, including one that sounds like the croak of a frog.

These small, green ground parrots are so elusive that only three people, including Steve and his partner, fellow biologist Rachel Barr, have ever seen one alive. That's something that these scientists, together with Bush Heritage Australia, are very much hoping to change. With luck, dedicated conservation work led by Steve will bring this mysterious species back from the very cusp of extinction. And to this end he has already captured more than 100,000 hours of sound data using this manual method, as well as automated sound loggers left at strategic locations.

EUROPEANS FIRST DISCOVERED the night parrot in 1845, but it must already have been on a precipitous population decline, for shortly afterwards it disappeared almost completely. A specimen was taken in Western Australia in 1912, but then – save for a series of fleeting glances and claimed sightings – its existence wasn't confirmed again for 78 years, when a dead bird was discovered on a roadside near Boulia, south-western Queensland, in 1990 by Australian Museum scientists Wayne Longmore and Dr Walter Boles (the pair claimed a $25,000 reward for the rediscovery of a night parrot stumped up by AG founder Dick Smith).

The search for a live bird continued Australia-wide, with obsessive birders scouring remote locations in the hope of one day discovering another. Finally, many years of persistence – and an estimated 17,000 hours of searching – paid off for naturalist John Young, who got the first ever photographs and footage of a night parrot in a spot west of Longreach in 2013.

Soon after this, the Queensland government and Bush Heritage became involved in the push to conserve the small population. The charity purchased a 56,000ha chunk of the station on which the discovery had been made, turning it into their new Pullen Pullen Reserve in April 2016. Pullen-pullen is the name of the night parrot in the language of the local Maiawali people, and the reserve contains a number of culturally significant sites. According to Judith Harrison, one of just a handful of Maiawali alive today, her ancestors once used night parrot feathers in their headdresses for ceremonies. "That's what they did in the olden days," she says. "They used them for dress-ups – special ceremonies, not all the time." Judith described the rediscovery of the bird here as both spiritual and emotional, and she praised the conservation work to protect them.

Steve believes there's something unique about the landscape in and around the reserve that means night parrots have been able to survive better than in other parts of central Australia where they were once common. Part of this may be to do with the natural sparseness of the vegetation in this very arid region. Here clumps of spinifex are relatively widely separated, offering a modicum of protection from the huge, hot bushfires that have spread unchecked through much of the outback since Aboriginal people left the land, and its management through controlled burning ceased. Spinifex here forms large individual hummocks, some of which may not have burnt for more than 50 years, providing a "long-term, spiny, stable refuge", Steve says, and making these lands unusually suited to protecting parrots from the predators that stalk them.

The charity and scientists worked hard to keep the location of the reserve a secret, but following the publication of the details of the property online and in a newspaper in May 2016, the Queensland government created an exclusion zone. This means that birders or other people who encroach upon the site without permission face a fine of more than $350,000 or up to two years in prison. The night parrot has now also been added to a priority list of 20 birds targeted

A night parrot photographed at the Pullen Pullen Reserve by biologist Steve Murphy in 2016. Even he has only seen the bird a handful of times.

for urgent attention under the federal government's Threatened Species Strategy.

Steve says that because the night parrot is both beautiful and scarce, and because there has been so much interest in rediscovering it over the past century, there's now a real risk that poachers might attempt to acquire birds and eggs for the illegal trade in rare pets. With the help of experts at the Zoological Society of London, which has developed technology to prevent wildlife poaching in Africa, Bush Heritage is using camouflaged, solar-powered camera traps to monitor any people or vehicles detected at the reserve and send pictures by satellite link to station managers on site and the conservation group's Melbourne headquarters.

"We're very concerned that the disclosure of the location of the night parrot will lead to poachers and that's why we've taken this somewhat unprecedented step," Queensland environment minister Steven Miles told the ABC when the exclusion zone was announced. "For an animal as rare as the night parrot, poaching and disturbance are two of the greatest threats, and we're working to keep it secure."

Steve has now captured the bird on film several times. In 2015, using a mist net, they were able to capture a night parrot, take feathers for DNA analysis and attach a tiny radio-tracking device, which allowed them to uncover totally new information about aspects of its biology. They followed the bird for 21 days, discovering that, rather than being largely ground-dwelling as previously supposed, the species flies distances of up to 7km to forage each night. The scientists also now know that these particular birds at least aren't nomadic as was once thought, and each morning find their way back to the same roost to sleep through the day.

"Once we started the work here, a lot of the things we were finding were contradicting those earlier impressions and assumptions about night parrot biology," Steve says. "We know with absolute certainty that these night parrots have been sedentary in this spot since at least August 2013 and that covers periods of above-average rainfall and severe drought. They have persisted through periods of time here where conventional wisdom suggested they should have disappeared."

Steve has now detected night parrots at a number of locations within a 40km radius of the original discovery and he puts the overall population here at between 30 and 100 birds.

On one occasion this year, a bird froze when it was discovered, allowing Steve and Rachel to get within several metres of it and photograph it. This response to danger may partly explain why the species has fared so badly against introduced cats and foxes right across outback Australia.

Cats are by far the biggest threat to the birds at Pullen Pullen, and Bush Heritage has invested significant funds into high-tech 'grooming traps' developed by wildlife biologist Dr John Read. These computer-controlled traps produce the recorded calls of a variety of distressed birds and rodents at infrequent intervals, which has been shown to successfully attract wily felids.

When a cat crosses the path of an array of sensors on the trap, it triggers the device to spray it with fast-acting poison gel, which the cat then ingests when it licks itself during grooming. The traps have been programmed not to fire when other animals, such as dingoes, foxes and kangaroos, cross their paths, and cameras keep a detailed record of every time a sensor is triggered.

Rob Murphy, the charity's executive manager for northern Australia, is confident that with work to control cats and manage fire regimes at Pullen Pullen, they can return the population of parrots here to healthy numbers and may even in the future be able to consider the possibility of captive breeding, which is being attempted to aid the recovery of a related species, the western ground parrot, in south-western WA. But more than that, "we're hoping that there might be other populations still out there. And part of Steve's role is to do just that and find other populations," Rob says.

With a likely sighting of a bird in WA's Pilbara in 2005 and a dead night parrot found in 2006 in western Queensland's Diamantina National Park, it appears highly likely other populations are out there and the birds are simply so elusive that we're not spotting them. And armed with the new knowledge about the bird's call and nocturnal behaviour, searchers have a much better chance of detecting them. If more can be found and protected, the future for night parrots may become far less bleak than had recently been feared. ■

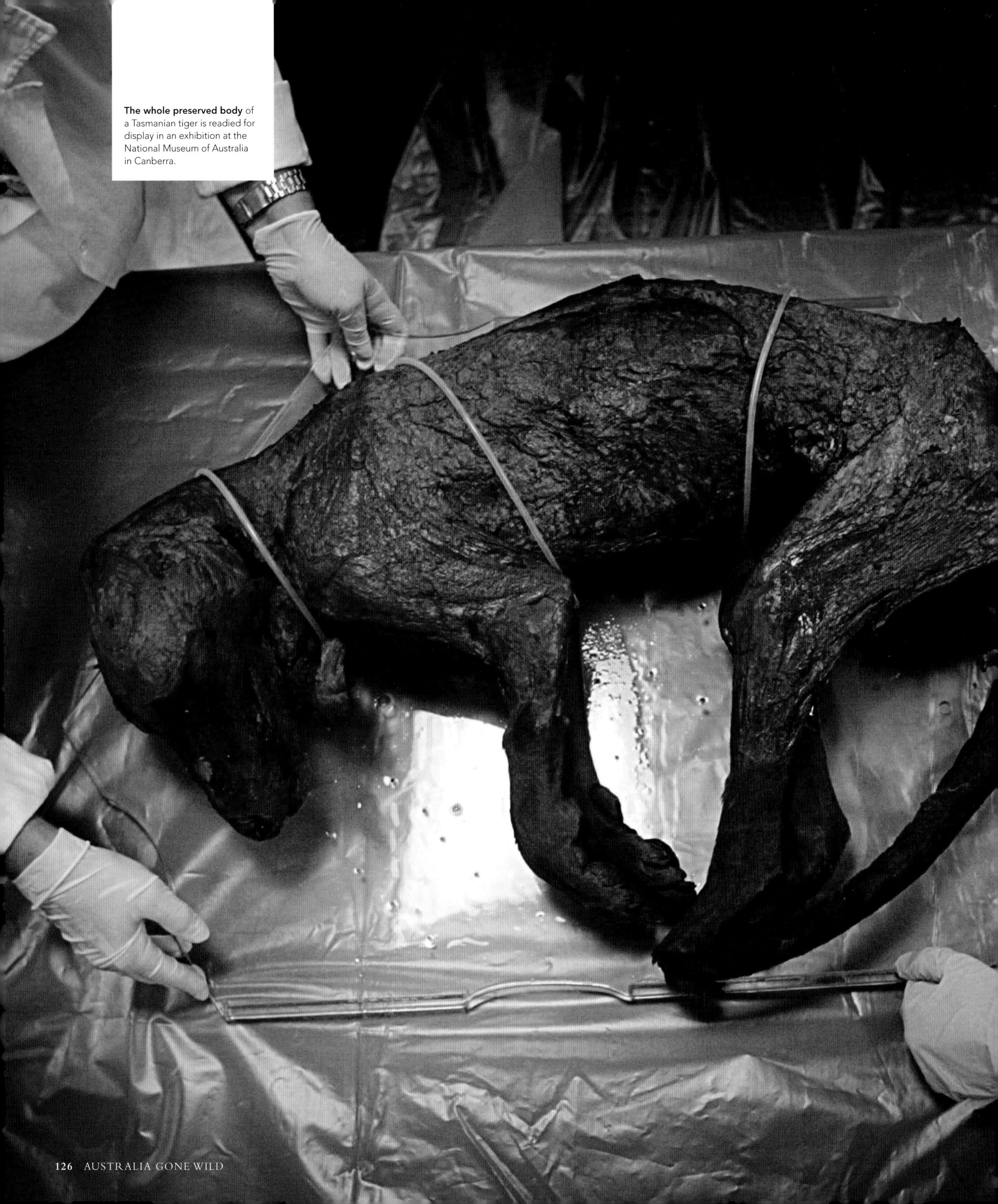

The whole preserved body of a Tasmanian tiger is readied for display in an exhibition at the National Museum of Australia in Canberra.

STORY BY ANDY PARK

TASMANIAN TIGER – EXTINCT OR MERELY ELUSIVE?

Issue 3 ◆ Jul–Sep 1986

SINCE THE TASMANIAN tiger was declared extinct in 1936, searchers have spent countless hours and hundreds of thousands of dollars looking for conclusive proof that it still exists. With no scientific evidence confirming its continued existence, but an abundance of eyewitness reports of sightings, many people think that the animal could reappear at any moment, while others consider it to be extinct.

Thylacinus cynocephalus (meaning pouched dog with a wolf's head) is the tiger's scientific name, but it has a string of aliases, including tiger, thylacine, wolf, hyena, zebrawolf and zebra-opossum. This animal was the largest carnivorous marsupial of recent times. It looked a bit like a dog with short legs and a long, stiff, kangaroo-like tail. Males were more solidly built than females, weighing up to 35kg and measuring some 60cm high at the shoulder, but their average weight was about 25kg.

The tiger's most distinctive feature, and the source of its most popular and enduring common name, was a series of about 15–20 black to dark brown stripes running across its back, from the shoulders to the base of the tail.

Being a marsupial – more closely related to a kangaroo than a dog – the tiger had a pouch, but it was quite different from other marsupials' pouches in that it opened to the rear. This meant that it wouldn't snag on obstacles as the tiger ambled through the bush.

Unfortunately, no scientific research was ever carried out on the life history or social behaviour of tigers, so even fundamental information, such as age at maturity, longevity, pair-bonding, responsibility for young, or even hunting range, is unknown. Hunting habits are better understood; the animals were predominantly nocturnal, typically hunting in the evening or at night. →

This beautifully romanticised lithograph of the thylacine by Henry Constantine Richter appeared in John Gould's *Mammals of Australia,* published in 1863.

FOSSIL RECORDS SHOW that tigers were once common throughout Australia and New Guinea, but disappeared from the mainland between 200 and 2000 years ago. Their extinction was most likely due to climatic changes and competition from the dingo, a more efficient carnivore that never reached Tasmania, where the tiger continued to survive.

Tigers were never particularly numerous in Tasmania – only four animals were collected during the first 17 years of the colony. They were also very shy of humans, but they were known to prey on livestock. By the mid-1820s, sheep were well established in Tasmania and the early settlers saw the tiger as a real threat to their blossoming pastoral industry.

In 1830 the Van Diemen's Land Company introduced the first bounty on tigers, which was augmented by a government bounty in 1888. By the end of the 1800s, at least 3000 tigers had been killed and the animals had become uncommon even in remote areas. Incredibly, the shooting and snaring continued. Captured alive, tigers were worth up to £150 and several zoos in Australia, the USA and Europe had the animal on display.

During the early 1900s, the tiger population crashed. Hunting pressure alone didn't account for this; an unidentified contagious disease, which also decimated Tasmanian devil populations, was blamed. In 1909 only two tiger bounties were paid and over the next 20 years the animals virtually disappeared. One of the last tiger killings occurred in May 1930, when a young animal was shot on a farm at Mawbanna, in the state's north-west.

In 1933 Elias Churchill snared one in the Florentine Valley and sold it to the Hobart Domain Zoo. It's thought that this was the same animal that died at the zoo on Monday 7 September 1936, the last tiger to have been indisputably alive. In the years since, no conclusive evidence for the continued existence of the Tasmanian tiger has been discovered. However, claimed sightings of the animal, not only within Tasmania but also throughout the mainland of Australia, including recent reports in far north Queensland, have proliferated.

THE TASMANIAN NATIONAL Parks and Wildlife Service (TNPWS) is officially responsible for monitoring all searches for the Tasmanian tiger and logging the continuous stream of eyewitness accounts. Because these are the only evidence for the tiger's claimed existence, keeping the lines of communication open between the TNPWS and the general public is vital.

The key figure in this public relations exercise is research officer Nick Mooney. Tall, square-jawed and incredibly fit, Mooney is more at home in the dense Tasmanian bush than in the confines of his Sandy Bay office. He deals with the public effortlessly, patiently listening to the accounts of sightings, then sorting through the details to determine which accounts are worth further investigation.

Several times a year, when a particularly good sighting is reported, Mooney races into the bush to investigate. His personal speciality is animal tracking, and in the basement of TNPWS headquarters he has amassed hundreds of plaster casts of tracks. "I've had a few good prints," he explained, pulling several out of a box to show me, "but nothing absolutely, positively concrete. The wallabies and devils are in such great numbers the few promising prints are always partially obscured – it's really frustrating."

Probably the best known tiger hunter of all is Dr Eric Guiler, retired Dean of Science at the University of Tasmania. A stocky human dynamo with sparkling blue eyes, Guiler follows the tiger trail with the grim determination of a modern-day crusader. His field trips in search of the animal would number in the hundreds, but a face-to-face meeting continues to elude him. "My colleagues on the mainland think I'm crazy," he explained in his lilting Irish brogue, "but the eyewitness accounts keep me going. There's no doubt in my mind it still exists."

MOST TIGER SIGHTINGS ARE quite sudden and unexpected and some are unnerving in their detail and accuracy. Consider, for example, this encounter reported by Hans Naarding, a wildlife researcher on contract to the TNPWS: "I had gone to sleep in the back of my vehicle, which was parked at a road junction in a remote forested area in the north-west of the state. It was raining heavily. At 2am I awoke and, out of habit, scanned the surrounds with a spotlight. As I swept the light-beam around, it came to rest on a large thylacine, standing side-on, some 6–7m distant.
My camera bag was out of immediate reach so I decided to examine the animal carefully before risking movement. It was an adult male in excellent condition with 12 black stripes on a sandy coat. Eye reflection was pale yellow. It moved only once, opening its jaw and showing its teeth."

The TNPWS kept this sighting a closely guarded secret for more than two years while their officers looked for further, conclusive evidence of the animal's existence. But once again they were unable to

Wilf Batty poses beside the Tasmanian tiger he shot on 6 May 1930 after he found it killing chickens in the hen house on his property in north-western TAS – the last thylacine to have been killed in the wild.

obtain even the most basic proof, such as a follow-up photograph, hair or even a clear set of tracks.

Naarding's sighting was called "the best in the history of the service" by TNPWS director Peter Murrell, but, while it was made in an obviously responsible manner by a respected researcher and recognised wildlife authority, it provides not a shred of acceptable scientific evidence. Director Murrell summed up his department's official reaction to Naarding's report: "We treated this incident as an excellent sighting with the usual follow-up investigation, but we are still waiting for a good, clear photograph."

ZOOLOGIST JEREMY GRIFFITH, who devoted four years of his life to diligently hunting for some sign of a tiger, is convinced it's extinct. "I believed the sightings and got totally involved," he explained, "even though I knew 80 per cent were totally fanciful, like one old bloke who had a tiger trapped in the Launceston tip – it turned out to be a greyhound. James Malley and I investigated an enormous number of 'sightings'. We walked and tracked most of their known territory and we never found a print that wasn't eventually explained as a devil or a wombat. It was my innocence that caught me out because I just couldn't believe that so many people could be mistaken. I was very gullible then."

Bob Brown worked with Jeremy in the office of the Thylacine Expeditionary Research Team. He investigated hundreds of tiger sightings but obtained no proof. "I'd love to say it exists," he says, "but the evidence clearly shows that it doesn't."

The overwhelming evidence points to extinction, for without supporting evidence, eyewitness accounts prove nothing. On the other hand, extinction is a very difficult thing to prove categorically. After all, the night parrot and the New Zealand takahe both disappeared for more than 50 years before being dramatically rediscovered – although neither was subjected to decades of intensive searching.

The tragedy of the tiger, put simply, is that its demise was so unnecessary. Naturalist John Gould warned of the fragile state of the tiger population during the mid-1800s, and in the early 1900s the Tasmanian Advisory Committee recommended that the animal be wholly protected. Unfortunately, the legislators of the day yielded to the political pressures of graziers and failed to act.

The tiger's story may yet help humanity grasp the irrefutable fact that modern civilisation radically changes the environment and extraordinary measures are necessary to preserve what's left of our natural heritage. How many more of our unique animals must disappear before we learn our lesson? ■

Yellow-footed rock-wallabies

Between and rock and a hard place.

Story by **Geordie Torr** Photography by **Esther Beaton**

Issue 60 Oct–Dec 2000

"OH, YOU'LL SEE WALLABIES." It was the tone of Col Morgan's voice that made me doubtful – the same air of confidence that makes me shudder when a set of directions ends with the words, "You can't miss it!" And, after all, my quarry – the yellow-footed rock-wallaby (*Petrogale xanthopus*) – is a threatened species. Col is the head ranger at Idalia National Park: 1440sq. km of steep escarpments and mulga woodlands 860km north-west of Brisbane. He knows the park like the back of his hand and reckoned I was guaranteed to see wallabies at a spot known as Emmet Pocket.

A rough hour's drive later, I was walking carefully along a sandstone escarpment, senses alert. Startled by a crashing in the undergrowth below, my heart leapt, then quickly sank as my binoculars revealed the grey back of a departing euro.

A bit further on, another noise. I looked up to see something wallaby-shaped standing in a dry creek bed about 50m ahead and my heart did the leap–sink thing again. Grey fur – another euro. I brought my binoculars up to make certain and just as I did, the light breeze parted a curtain of gum leaves to reveal, yes, a yellow-foot, sitting up and gazing at me. I stood stock-still and regarded the gorgeously marked marsupial as intently as it was regarding me. I took it all in – the white cheek-stripe, orange ears, forearms and hind legs, boldly striped tail and the soft, white fur on its belly.

I crept closer and the wallaby hopped a short distance, stopped and turned again to watch me. We repeated this pattern a few times before it finally pointed itself down the steep, rocky incline, its striped tail arched high over its back, and disappeared.

The next day, I returned to Emmet Pocket and soon saw why Col had been so confident that I'd see a yellow-foot there – within half an hour I'd spotted several, sometimes two or three together. Although yellow-foots are considered threatened in Queensland it isn't unusual to see more than one at a time because they're social, living in colonies that typically consist of a dominant older male and several females and younger males.

Unlike the skittish euros, which take off at the slightest disturbance, yellow-foots show remarkable composure in the face of a human intruder. Time after time, I found myself returning the gaze of a stationary yellow-foot perched atop an outcrop. I couldn't help thinking this calmness resulted from a confidence that when they take off into the rocks, nothing will catch them – a confidence born of agility and speed. Unfortunately, although these qualities are effective against their primary natural predator, the wedge-tailed eagle, they've offered limited protection against humans.

The Adnyamathanha, who've lived in the Flinders and Gammon ranges for centuries, call the wallaby *andu*. They hunted it extensively, but the exploitation was well regulated. The Europeans settlers weren't so forward thinking. Around the turn of the 20th century, tens of thousands of yellow-foots were killed for 'sport' and profit. The wallabies' habit of sitting up to investigate intruders made them sitting ducks, and populations dwindled. In 1912 the South Australian parliament banned the slaughter, but wallaby numbers didn't recover. This was odd – yellow-foots can breed continuously, so under favourable conditions their numbers can increase rapidly. But hunting wasn't the only scourge unleashed by Europeans. The reduced populations had to cope with predation from foxes and cats, and to compete for food with introduced grazers – sheep, rabbits and, most importantly, goats.

"AH JEEZ, another pair of pants gone," University of Sydney PhD student Steve Lapidge said as he surveyed the sartorial havoc wreaked by the still-struggling wallaby clutched to his chest. In 1997 Steve travelled through central Queensland looking for somewhere to release 24 captive-bred yellow-foots from the Queensland Parks and Wildlife Service breeding facility in Charleville, 680km north-west of Brisbane. That search ended here, at Lambert station, 140km north-west of Charleville.

Yellow-foots occupy some of the hottest and driest regions of any rock-wallaby, living in rugged country along the edges of tablelands and hills. Lambert fits the bill nicely. Flat-topped hills rise from parched plains, their slopes littered with debris that's crumbled from near-vertical escarpments. "We realised that this was great habitat for them," Steve had told me earlier. "So, we picked the sites and then started the feral-animal control."

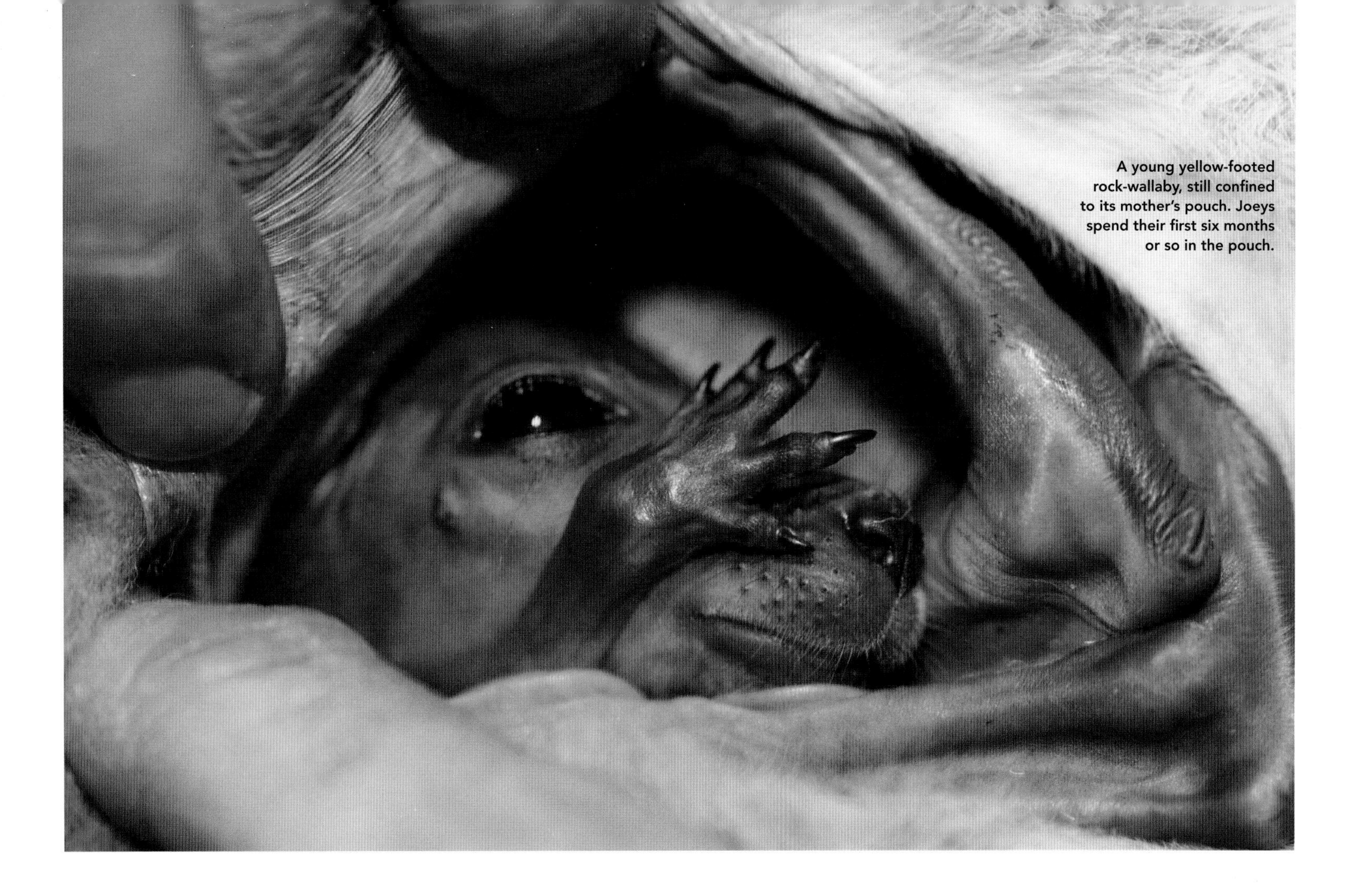

A young yellow-footed rock-wallaby, still confined to its mother's pouch. Joeys spend their first six months or so in the pouch.

Meanwhile, the 24 wallabies were divided into three colonies and placed in enclosures in Charleville. "We wanted to make sure the colonies had social cohesion before they were released," Steve said.

Six months later, the animals were released, and now Steve was back for one of his regular trips to check how they were doing. Cooing soothing words into his captive's ear, Steve waited until it had calmed down and then set about weighing and measuring it.

On the way to the next trap. Steve pointed to a hill about 6km away and explained that recently a subordinate male wallaby had left the safety of 'our' hill and made the perilous journey across the plain to the neighbouring hill. "There were signs of upheaval between him and another male while they were in Charleville," he told me. "But I was interested to see what happened. As predicted, he dispersed, which is what could have happened to some of the others if we hadn't checked the colonies' cohesion before we released them."

Steve pulled an unmarked, wild-born male from the next trap, kicking, scratching and tearing a hole in Steve's jumper to match the one in his pants. Running his hand over the wallaby's muscles, Steve remarked that it wasn't in very good condition. "He's been beaten up badly," he said, placing a radio-collar around its neck. The hill's dominant male was asserting himself, making the capture and collaring timely – this young male would soon be on the move.

Queensland's yellow-foots are fairly secure, but Steve's project will teach us lessons about releasing captive-bred groups that could prove useful in New South Wales, where yellow-foots are closer to extinction.

MY NOSTRILS filled with the smell of kerosene, my ears with a dull, rhythmic thudding and then we were airborne. Frigid air blasted through the open doorway over the white-helmeted head of NSW NPWS researcher Andy Sharp as the helicopter turned and headed south towards the Gap Range in Coturaundee Nature Reserve in north-western NSW.

We soon reached the escarpment, banked tightly then slowed to a crawl, tight against the rock wall. Flying past the cliff face, a wedge-tailed eagle kept pace with us. I carefully scanned the rock wall, but by the end of the survey run I'd only seen one wallaby. The chopper then banked and we headed back the way we'd come. After about 10 minutes we reached the Coturaundee Range and began the second survey; on this run I saw more than 10 wallabies.

"The aerial counts had been low and flat since about 1988," Andy later told me. Although about 40,000 goats had been shot off the park between 1986 and 1995, the wallaby populations hadn't responded. "Most of the other work around suggested that foxes were eating them, so we set up an experiment where we baited one range and left the other and watched the response." On the Gap Range, which has been left alone, wallaby numbers have remained low but stable, hovering at about 20–25. But on the Coturaundee Range, where more than 12,000 1080-laced baits have been laid, numbers have increased nearly 600 per cent to about 120–160.

Although counts on the baited range have plateaued, Andy thinks numbers are probably still increasing, with young animals dispersing out of the survey area. It's a gut feeling that proves accurate. A few days later, the team returns from a wedge-tail survey buoyant with an exciting discovery – a few small yellow-foots, almost certainly dispersing juveniles, were seen on a ledge above one of the survey routes. "That's made my day," said a beaming Andy. "I can go home now – the job's all done."

It's tempting to believe Andy's right – that the job really is done. But in reality it's going to take a lot of work and constant vigilance to get these appealing animals out from between a rock and a hard place. ■

STORY AND PHOTOGRAPHY BY **CHRISSIE GOLDRICK**

THE FALL AND RISE OF THE KAKAPO

By the mid-20th century it seemed inevitable the kakapo would be added to the long list of extinct New Zealand birds, but this peculiar parrot wasn't quite ready for its swan song.

Issue 115 ◆ Jul–Aug 2013

AROUND THE BREAKFAST table in our hut on Codfish Island, or Whenua Hou, the conversation invariably turns to sex. In particular, the nocturnal comings and goings of the residents of this remote isle. A high-tech surveillance network ensures that trysts between locals such as Sue, Lisa, Flossie, Jimmy, Ben and Lionel rarely go undetected. In fact, they are diarised, cross-referenced and discussed in depth.

Such seemingly prurient interest starts to make more sense when you understand that the resulting offspring of these alliances will be among the rarest and most valuable new arrivals on the planet. For these island dwellers are kakapo, a species teetering on the brink of extinction, and the observers are the Kakapo Recovery Team, whose members are hell-bent on slowing this strange green parrot's slide into oblivion.

A 1396ha speck off the southern tip of New Zealand's South Island, Codfish lies to the west of much larger Stewart Island. Islands and their unique geographic features have been inexorably linked to the evolution and fate of many endemic New Zealand birds. With no ground-living mammalian predators to threaten them, numerous flightless species developed here – among them 11 species of giant moa, all now extinct, and the kakapo.

Today, Codfish Island provides hope and a safe haven for the kakapo. It also acts as a hilly, windswept laboratory for the researchers who discreetly manage every aspect of their lives.

The kakapo is a very peculiar member of the parrot family, not least because it's the only one that has lost the ability to fly. Its scientific name, *Strigops habroptila*, describes its owl-like face and the softness of its feathers, while its common name, kakapo, means 'night parrot' in Maori. As that would suggest, it's a nocturnal creature that hides under logs and grassy tussocks during the day, emerging after dark to forage and mate. →

Although the kakapo is flightless, it often roosts in trees during the day, using its wings to 'parachute' to the forest floor to forage at night.

Kakapo Recovery Team members Jo Ledington (at left) and Deidre Vercoe check out the radio-transmitter attached to Blades, a large male kakapo on Codfish Island

So much about this bird remains shrouded in mystery, but its natural history is slowly being unravelled. We now know kakapo are very long lived and may reach 90 years of age or more.

Most other parrots form monogamous pairs that bind them for life, but the kakapo is a 'lek breeder', whose males perform elaborate courtship rituals to attract females to their 'leks' or communal display arenas. Females usually mate with several partners, and, in an evolutionary strategy almost guaranteed to result in failure, reproduction is inextricably and curiously linked to the irregular and infrequent fruiting of a single tree, the rimu.

I'VE JOINED THE Kakapo Recovery Team on Codfish Island during the breeding season. It's forecast to be a dud year because the rimu's fruit crop is diminished, but, undeterred by poor prospects, the team members are taking the opportunity to hone their methods for extracting and preserving kakapo semen. The sperm collectors, nicknamed the 'Love Team', are here every year at this time.

If any natural matings are suspected, the females in question receive a top-up, technical officer Daryl Eason explains. "Some of the birds will mate twice – sometimes with the same male or two different males, and they have a much higher fertility rate. We can't make them all mate several times, so we do it by artificial insemination," he says.

The donor males are specially selected to optimise genetic diversity, Daryl says. "It's a double-edged approach to improve fertility... and ensure that some of the founders get an even spread of matings." Kakapo were once abundant on the terrestrial predator-free idyll that was New Zealand before human settlement. But things changed rapidly when Polynesian colonists arrived 700–900 years ago, bringing hunting dogs and inadvertently introducing stowaway Polynesian rats, or kiore. Things took a turn for the worse when Europeans arrived in 1769. They brought a great wave of creatures (rats, cats, rabbits, stoats and weasels) that would sound the death knell for many natives.

Flightless, fearless, defenceless and exuding an attractive scent, kakapo were ill-equipped to deal with the deadly cocktail of predation and habitat loss. By the early 20th century, the only remaining kakapo were living high up on the wild, steep slopes of the Fiordland region in the south-west of the South Island.

A rescue plan by far-sighted early conservationist Richard Henry saw the world's first attempt to establish an island sanctuary for a threatened species. In the 1890s, Henry shipped more than 700 kakapo and kiwi to Resolution Island, between Dusky and Breaksea sounds.

But by the 1940s, all the birds were gone, wiped out by wily stoats, weasels and ferrets, which simply swam there. From the 1950s to the 1970s, kakapo were more or less considered doomed. That was until a sizeable, mixed-gender population was discovered on Stewart Island in January 1977. It was moved to predator-free Codfish Island in the '80s. Another 18 males were captured in Fiordland between 1974 and 1978, and some of these were also moved to Codfish, thereby launching one of the most ambitious species rescue efforts ever attempted.

Access to Codfish is, justifiably, strictly controlled, and the rigorous quarantine check prior to my boarding the flight here drove home just how hard-won its predator-free status is. Previous guests have included British author Douglas Adams and comedian Stephen Fry, both of whom came with zoologist Mark Carwardine. Mark's painful amorous entanglement with Sirocco (who attempted to mate with his head) was broadcast in the series *Last Chance to See*, and became an online sensation. This interest put the conservation effort on the map and made a celebrity of Sirocco, who now has his own Facebook page and Twitter account, and who acts as a charismatic conservation ambassador for his species.

On my first day in the field I join the Love Team as they effortlessly skip up steep, muddy tracks towards the top of the island. They come to a halt in a clearing, rapidly break out their bush laboratory and are soon ready to hunt kakapo. They pick up the signal of a radio-transmitter and dive into dense bush.

Within minutes, Jo Ledington spots her quarry as he climbs into the canopy of a tree. She follows him up and carefully snatches him off a bough, then places him in a hessian bag and we return to the clearing. He's identifed as Blades, a big male, and, as the researchers examine him, I'm invited to feel the dual air sacs located on either side of the parrot's chest. Blades looks me in the eye and holds my gaze rather defiantly – or so it seems to me – so I silently apologise for the intrusion. The two sacs are huge beneath the soft feathers. They need to be, for they produce the boom that's the most distinctive feature of the kakapo's unique mating ritual.

During the breeding season, males move to higher ground, where the vegetation is less dense, and band together to excavate a series of shallow bowls linked by tracks, which forms their lek. At night, they stand in their bowls and boom. This deep, resonant call – interspersed with a high-pitched "ching-ching" sound – is amplified by the air sacs and can be heard up to 5km away.

Although effective at attracting willing females, this elaborate display can't be solely relied upon to guarantee reproduction. DNA sequencing is used by the researchers to work out who is related to whom, and also to discover the best matches to avoid the problem of inbreeding. The team can then focus their artificial insemination efforts most effectively.

Daryl Eason explains that there's a particular problem with

Kakapo feet are enormous and zygodactyl (two toes face forwards and two backwards), which comes in handy for climbing trees.

inbreeding in the birds from Stewart Island, which has reduced their fertility rates and which is why improving them is their main focus.

Daryl and his coworkers make catching kakapo and extracting sperm look simple, but there's no doubt they're well practised at these difficult tasks. Today, we're collecting sperm to trial preservation methods, with the goal of successfully freezing it without reducing its viability. Just two kakapo have resulted from artifical insemination so far, both from freshly harvested sperm in 2009, the last big breeding year.

The Stewart Island founders are now dying off and their DNA desperately needs to be preserved – it has more genetic variation than that of the newer generation reared by the rescue program (the last Fiordland bird, named Richard Henry, died in 2010, but not before passing on his genes to Sinbad, Gulliver and Kuia).

WE REPEAT THE handling procedure numerous times over the next few days, as the team performs a series of health and equipment checks. Most kakapo succumb quietly to the disturbance. Others protest with loud "skraaarks" or throaty growls.

Each bird wears a small radio-transmitter on its back. Technology is integral to the rescue effort, opening a much-needed window onto the kakapos' secret world. The devices relay signals back to base camp, alerting rangers to activities such as visits to feeding stations, mating, nesting and, occasionally, deaths. The Kakapo Recovery Programme is labour intensive and costly, but clever technology is scaling back human intervention, while allowing the birds to live in a genuinely wild state.

Deidre Vercoe, program manager, is positive about the future. "The population has more than doubled since the program began in 1995 with 51 birds. There are now 124 and the age structure is a lot better. At the start it was 95 per cent old birds," she says. "Now it's almost reversed. We've been able to rebalance it so that the population is mainly made up of young, breeding-age birds and we've balanced out the sexes again, so that there's almost a 50–50 split."

There can be very few species that are managed as intensively as the kakapo. And, in the face of great conservation problems across the world, it might seem a luxury to devote so many resources to a single species that, in the long term, may already be genetically doomed because of its population bottleneck.

But to New Zealanders, the species is iconic, and the things that made it vulnerable in the first place – its inability to defend itself, its flightlessness and trusting nature – are all factors that have made it much easier to care for and study. The trailblazing conservation efforts for the birds are also providing invaluable information and techniques that can be applied to a whole spectrum of species under pressure. ■

CHAPTER FIVE

FERAL INVADERS

People began introducing foreign species to Australia several thousand years ago. It's thought that dingoes were first brought to the mainland by the Asian seafarers who traded with northern Australia's Aboriginal people (there's actually a school of thought that suggests that the bush fly may have come with them).

Over time, dingoes reached a certain equilibrium with Australia's ecosystems, to the point where they became a functional part of the natural ecological order as top-level predators. That process wasn't without its negative impacts, however. It's believed that the role that dingoes took on was previously played by the thylacine and that the former's arrival resulted in the latter's extinction on the mainland.

But it was the arrival of European colonisers at the end of the 18th century that opened the feral floodgates. For early European colonisers, Australia was an alien, unwelcoming place, full of strange plants and even stranger animals. During the mid-19th century, in response to a movement that had begun earlier in Europe, assimilation societies started popping up around Australia. Their aim was to import species that would make the settlers' new home feel more like their old one, while hopefully also making the land economically productive.

Suddenly, after millions of years of isolation, the continent was overrun with invaders. Most were either unsuitable or relatively benign, some were extremely beneficial, but a small number have had a catastrophic effect on the environment. Foxes and feral cats prey on ground-nesting birds and small mammals that evolved in the absence of such voracious predators; rabbits and goats denude and degrade the landscape, competing with native herbivores and causing erosion. Today, the damage caused by pest animals is believed to cost Australia about $720 million a year. And within New South Wales alone, more than 350 species, populations and communities are considered to be under threat due to the impact of pest animals.

Among the early imports was the Asian swamp buffalo, about 100 of which were imported by the British during the early 1800s. They were distributed among three settlements in northern Australia, where they were mostly used as draught animals. When the settlements were abandoned, the buffalo were left to their own devices and eventually spread out across the Top End, where they began to cause extensive damage, their numbers eventually passing 300,000 during the 1970s. A government program reduced the feral herd to about 30,000, and while it has since roughly tripled in size, it's now managed more effectively, reducing the environmental damage.

Horses arrived even earlier, coming over in 1788 aboard the First Fleet. And just as the Top End's buffalo will be forever associated with Crocodile Dundee, the iconic brumbies have entered our national folklore through stories and poems such as Banjo Patterson's *The Man from Snowy River*. Today, Australia's wild horses number at least 1 million, the world's largest wild herd. They're found in all of the mainland states and territories, having adapted to a wide range of habitats. Some argue that they've now become part of our cultural identity and deserve protection; others decry the damage that their hard hooves do to an environment more used to the soft pads of a kangaroo's paw.

A more recent foreign invader – one whose invasion is in fact still underway – is the cane toad, a big, fearsome-looking sumo wrestler of an amphibian that sports a pair of poisonous shoulder pads. Introduced in 1935 after north Queensland canefarmers complained about the beetles eating their crops, the toads ignored the cane-beetles, but proceeded to eat everything else that moved (even snakes). Anything that tried to return the favour was killed by the toads' toxins, leading to a series of predator population crashes in the newly invaded territory. They're still marching out in a destructive wave, now having reached as far west as Broome in Western Australia and as far south as Port Macquarie in NSW. A few hitchhiking toads have even established a colony in southern Sydney. ■

Previous page: Tempers flare as competition for water intensifies at Gilbert Springs, in central Australia. Dominant brumby stallions will defend their mares and offspring.

The cane toad's rapid colonisation of Australia can be largely attributed to its amazing reproductive rate, which is unparalleled among our native amphibians. They mate at any time of year and young female toads can lay up to 30,000 eggs in a single clutch, laying several clutches a year.

Some truths about cane toads

Loathed, feared, ridiculed and persecuted, these introduced amphibians have a heavy cross to bear. But do they deserve their terrible reputation?

Story by **Peter Meredith** Photography by **Esther Beaton**

Issue 44 Oct–Dec 1996

"DEPART FROM HERE, ye cursed creatures, in everlasting flames. Prepare to meet the devil and all his bloody angels." The damnation rang out over a small waterhole in north Queensland's sugarcane belt. It had come from the heart, even though the man who'd uttered it – Tip Byrne – might at times be given to gleeful sarcasm. I stood with him at the water's edge and looked out to distant cane fields. The afternoon was heavy with the impending Wet. Dark patches spread across Tip's shirt and sweat glinted on his brow under a thatch of brown hair.

His curse was directed at cane toads, no doubt hiding somewhere around the waterhole – the beasts introduced to Australia in 1935 to combat sugarcane pests and now spreading out of control across the top of Australia. Tip, canefarmer and mayor of Cardwell Shire – halfway between Cairns and Townsville – clearly remembers the day his father, James, also a canegrower, released toads at this very spot back in the late 1930s.

"There were eight or nine of them in an enamel dish – half males, half females," he said. "Within a month or two, the place was black with tadpoles.

"I thought Dad knew best. It was his idea because our farm was one of the worst affected by cane-beetle grubs in the shire. As we released the toads, he said: 'We've got these beetles now. That's the end of them bastards.'

"But we didn't have them at all. They had us. Within no time, the toads were all over the place but they had no impact on the beetle at all. It's been a complete bloody disaster."

THE CANE TOAD has leapt into Australian mythology like few other introduced animals, invading our national psyche along with the continent. It has had supernatural powers attributed to it – such as being able to survive freezing and being flattened by tyres – and in an odd way, Queenslanders have become tolerant, sometimes even proud of it. They've named a rugby league team after it, espoused its virtues as a pet and garden-pest controller and it has even spawned a string of lucrative cottage industries.

A native of South and Central America, it was introduced to Australia from Hawaii to control cane-beetles, whose grubs gnaw sugarcane roots. One hundred and one toads were imported to the Meringa Sugar Experiment Station at Gordonvale, 20km south of Cairns, in June 1935, on the assumption that since they eat lots of insects, they were bound to eat cane-beetles.

At the time, the sugarcane industry was influenced by information from Puerto Rico suggesting that cane toads were effective in controlling the cane-beetle. From Gordonvale, the offspring of the original toads were sent to cane farms up and down the coast, to the joy of farmers but in the face of strong protests from some wildlife experts. What happened next was a classic case of a biological control going horribly wrong.

Not only did the toads fail to control the pest, they also showed an amazing capacity to reproduce – a female can lay up to 30,000 eggs at a time – and spread. It's the speed and efficiency with which they've spread across Queensland and the Top End and into Western Australia that has prompted widespread fear and loathing of cane toads. They are seen as disgusting, poisonous aliens that are devastating native animal populations as they march across the country. Having never set eyes on one, I'd come to Queensland to find out if they really were the repulsive scourge everyone said they were.

My first encounter with cane toads was at Tilpal, a property north of Rockhampton, when I opened a plastic crate. There they were, a mass of jumping amphibians, the alleged bane of our environment. Squatly built and sandy to dark brown in colour, they felt cool and rubbery. Their striking eyes gazed unblinkingly from faces fixed in expressions of injured dignity.

These were the study specimens of CSIRO technicians Geof Bartram and John Libke, who were gathering information for a study of cane-toad feeding habits and their impact on native animals.

During my visit to Geof and John's study site in the Shoalwater Bay Military Training Area, just before the onset of the Wet, I saw toads in all stages of their life cycle. By day, while Geof and John set pit traps to catch small native creatures beside a lily-decked waterhole,

Tiny toadlets leave the waters of their birth soon after metamorphosis from tadpoles. At this stage, they are known as metamorphs and grow very quickly, as much as 1mm every day.

Such is the toad's compulsion to breed that this particular male has clamped himself onto photographer Esther Beaton's foot. This gripping embrace is known as amplexus and can last for several hours.

I walked around its edges through hordes of tiny, hopping toadlets (known as metamorphs) recently emerged from their tadpole stage and looking like cute, dark-hued froglets.

At night, the toadlets went into hiding and the adults emerged from wherever they'd been sheltering from the heat and headed for the waterhole to soak up moisture through their skin. Since adults are partial to any bite-sized morsel that crosses their path, be it an insect, small mammal, native frog or even their own young, this change of shift is probably essential for the toadlets' survival.

Under a crescent moon, Geof and John caught toads by hand. As the toads sat on the banks or in the soupy shallows, the men would lock on to them with their torch beams, approach quietly and lunge. The toads were then taken back to Tilpal for "processing".

This involved, among other things, marking the animals for recapture by clipping one or more toes off, and injecting them with trace amounts of a radioactive isotope to help determine how much they were eating – information that will later show whether the toads compete with native species for food.

ALTHOUGH MANY SCIENTISTS believe the cane toad is a serious threat, at least one is convinced that the alien's impact may be exaggerated. Bill Freeland, deputy director of the Parks and Wildlife Commission of the Northern Territory, told me that no data from Queensland or the Gulf of Carpentaria area beyond Borroloola had shown that a single species had become extinct or rare as a result of cane toads. He also confirmed that there seemed to be no great impact on frogs.

Michael Crossland, of James Cook University, in Townsville, has discovered that many native predators – particularly the larvae of frogs – are poisoned by eating toads in their aquatic stages (during which, like adult toads, they are highly toxic), but a surprising number suffer no apparent ill effects. And even though some native animals (goannas, quolls, snakes and birds) have reportedly been poisoned after eating adult toads, many more savour them with impunity – including keelback snakes, ibises, cranes, crows, frogmouths and kites.

"People talked a lot about the effect of cane toads on creatures like goannas," Bill said. "We did some work over four years – before and after cane toads arrived in the Borroloola area – and found that, yes, within a matter of months populations of the big goannas crashed by about two-thirds. However, within 12 months they had started to come back and data from the final year indicated that populations had totally recovered."

What appears to happen is that a certain percentage of goannas never eat cane toads. Those that do are poisoned, leaving only those that don't to reproduce and pass on their dislike of toads to later generations. "It's natural selection, evolution, happening within a very short span of time after the toad invasion," Bill said. "Not only are we not losing species but there seems to be some really interesting biology going on. The reality is that the toads are a'comin' and so far the impacts don't seem to be horrendously major."

FOR THE MOMENT, at least, whether we like it or not, it looks as though the cane toad is set to become as much a part of the Australian landscape as the rabbit. Its amazing resilience was amply exemplified on the last night of my Queensland visit.

A week previously, I had visited a drought-shrunken farm dam outside Townsville. In the last of the dam's putrid water, I found a single emaciated toad sheltering in a half-submerged log. The place looked like amphibian purgatory. The day before my departure, however, storms had turned the dam into a brown sea, and instead of a lonely, sick toad, more than 3000 wallowed in the shallows. Around the dam, countless other toads – as well as native frogs – were engaged in frenzied mating. So urgent was the desire to breed that toads were jumping onto photographer Esther Beaton's shoes, seeing them as potential mates. The atmosphere was of a joyous celebration of life.

Cane toads are supreme survivors, and for that they have earned my admiration. It's not their fault that they're surviving on the wrong continent. As for a toad's character, surely this tenacity is the very essence of it. If, like me, you find all of nature extraordinary, you can't help but marvel at such a fierce will to endure. ■

Australia's 1 million feral horses have adapted to a range of landscapes, many towards the north. Populations can grow at a rate of up to 20 per cent a year in a good season.

STORY BY **AMANDA BURDON** PHOTOGRAPHY BY **JASON EDWARDS**

WHERE THE WILD HORSES ARE

Historic icon, convenient resource or environmental vandal – brumbies are both revered and reviled across our continent.

Issue 130 ◆ Jan–Feb 2016

ALL THE ABORIGINAL STUDENTS perched on the steel fence around the dusty arena want to ride a piebald horse called Allan. A three-year-old desert brumby, he's steady and surefooted, with just the right amount of spunk to test new riding skills; he's also the unlikely poster boy for a unique learning program.

"Before we started offering the Certificate II in rural operations, most of these kids didn't have a good attendance record," says horseman and mentor Chris Barr, a teacher at the Ntaria School in Central Australia. "Now it's up by 500 per cent and the horses are a big part of that."

Twice a week the class travels to the remote outstation of Ipolera, south-west of Ntaria (Hermannsburg), to catch and gently break in wild horses, build fences, sleep out in swags and learn how to make saddles and bridles. One student was recently offered a job on an indigenous-run cattle station to the north, and several others see a future on horseback. "It's wonderful seeing the growth in these young people as they work with the horses and learn from them," Chris says.

Several communities are now working with the Central Land Council (CLC) to develop feral-horse management plans, which include mustering horses for sale as part of small-scale local enterprises. Before that, steeds that make up one of the largest wild populations in Australia were often left to die of thirst or starvation in the summer heat.

There's no such problem in Kosciuszko National Park, where cooler year-round temperatures and summer snowmelt sustain lush grassy plains and whispering creeks within the headwaters of the Snowy, Murray and Murrumbidgee river systems. Here, wild mobs, now estimated to be →

Immortalised by poet Banjo Paterson, mountain brumbies now have the run of grassy Currango Plain, in Kosciuszko NP. But even Paterson wrote of the horses being "a great nuisance to stock owners".

4000–8000 strong, provide a thrilling sight for horse trekkers threading their way with Peter Cochran through shadowy forests of black sallee and mountain gums.

To Peter, a High Country cattleman, former member of Parliament and ardent brumby advocate, there's a spiritual connection between families such as his and the Snowy Mountains brumby. "It's a deep bond between the animal, the land and the people, and we are very protective of the brumbies," he says.

WILD HORSES ARE deeply embedded in our national psyche and roam the landscapes of our imagination, made famous by writers such as Elyne Mitchell (*The Silver Brumby*) and Banjo Paterson (notably *The Man from Snowy River* and *Brumby's Run*). An introduced species first brought with European colonisers, they're said to carry the bloodlines of horses exported to the British Army in India and the loyal beasts that carried our Australian Light Horse Brigade.

Now numbering at least 1 million, our national herd – the world's largest wild population – can grow at a rate of up to 20 per cent a year. Our largest populations today are in the rocky ranges and arid plains of the Northern Territory and tropical grasslands of Queensland. They also favour the temperate ranges of New South Wales, subalpine and alpine areas of both NSW and Victoria, and the arid northern pastoral zone and Coffin Bay in South Australia. In Western Australia, they're found in the Kimberley, east Pilbara and the northern goldfields.

But are they wild horses or feral pests? Even to describe them as a feral animal, instead of a brumby, raises the hackles of supporters such as Peter Cochran. "We would like to see the state government acknowledge that the Snowy Mountains brumby has a permanent place in the park and to legislate to protect it. The horses symbolise freedom and are a part of Australia's cultural identity," he says.

However, according to the NSW National Parks and Wildlife Service, the hard-footed beasts are having a significant negative impact on the sensitive alpine and subalpine environments where nationally threatened sphagnum moss bogs support delicate creatures such as the she-oak skink and corroboree frog. There's also concern about the horses' role in degrading water sources, spreading weeds and compacting soils.

"Horses are a majestic, beautiful animal in the right place," says ranger Rob Gibbs. "But a lot of time and taxpayers' money is being spent trying to manage them. There are simply too many horses causing too much damage."

Rob believes that wild horse management is "tangled up with the dispossession and lingering resentment that cattlemen feel about losing their High Country grazing leases". Peter Cochran contests that the horse populations didn't "begin to explode" until wilderness areas were declared.

Horses have cultural, social and tourism value, but people have to realise "that value comes at a cost", says Rob. "These ecosystems simply didn't evolve with large, hard-hoofed animals. But it's very difficult for native animals and ecosystems to compete with the romanticism of *The Man from Snowy River*."

On one thing most people do agree. Australia's wild horse population needs to be reined in. The question is how and by how much. Seasonal 'passive trapping' in national parks in NSW and Victoria,

Twice weekly, students from Ntaria School in Central Australia travel to the remote outstation of Ipolera to catch and gently break in wild horses, and learn to make saddles and bridles.

Beauty is in the eye of the beholder when it comes to Australia's wild horse population. Horses arrived with the first European colonisers; their feral descendants now number at least 1 million.

whereby horses are lured into trap yards with food and then trucked out, is both expensive (costing about $1000 per horse) and labour intensive. It's also limited to more accessible areas.

About one-third of the horses trapped are collected by non-profit organisations that prepare them for re-homing and domestic life. Member groups of the Australian Brumby Alliance (ABA) have found homes for about 960 horses in NSW, Victoria, Queensland and WA during the past decade. Thousands more have made the trip to an abattoir. Even so, passive trapping has barely kept pace with annual reproduction rates.

Aerial culling – which was outlawed in NSW after the shooting of 600 horses in Guy Fawkes River National Park in 2000 – is the most contentious option of all. Although this method is still used periodically in remote regions, a public raised with domestic horses largely finds the idea unpalatable.

Ecologist Dr Dave Berman, who has studied wild horses around Australia since 1984, believes they pose one of the greatest land-management challenges of our time. "They need to be tackled on a national scale and that approach needs to be holistic," says Dave.

"We can't just say that they are a pest; the history and mythology is important, too," he continues. "They are lovely animals but they are causing damage. There are too many horses breeding too quickly. We need to work with all the interest groups to find an agreed approach and consider all the methods available to manage our feral horses."

ONE THING WORKING in their favour, however, is the fact that Australia's wild horses have proven themselves to be adaptable and easy to train. Revered for their stamina, agility and surefootedness, former brumbies compete in a variety of arenas, from endurance riding and pony club competition to bush racing and showjumping.

But the ABA is keen to see the identification of a "viable, sustainable population number that will not overtax the landscape... When brumby numbers are kept in check they help the land," says ABA president Jill Pickering. "Their manure serves as a fertiliser and their cropping reduces the fire risk."

Catherin McMillan, a portrait artist and brumby enthusiast from the NSW South Coast, prides herself in having owned a number of these "heritage horses" and currently has one in training. "Once they bond with you, they will jump through fire for you," she says. "They are intelligent and so willing to please, and very patient with kids. More people are starting to see brumbies as an asset and asking where they can get one."

Attitudes – but of a very different kind – are also changing in the central deserts, according to CLC spokesman Sam Rando. There was a huge outcry when an aerial cull was first mooted in May 2013 on Tempe Downs station, south-west of Alice Springs, to protect waterholes and cultural sites from feral horses. Some 24,000 people signed a petition in opposition.

"People were saying they should be captured and trucked to the coast and adopted out. They seemed to think that trucking was a benign option, but a lot of horses are killed or injured in the yards or during transport," Sam says. "Indigenous people don't like to see horses shot, but they see the degradation of country and horses starving or dying from a lack of water, and believe that shooting can be the more humane option, which has been supported by independent veterinarians. There is a lot of romantic, wishful thinking; the reality is much more difficult."

WHATEVER YOUR VIEW, wild horses are now an established part of the Australian landscape, just like feral donkeys and camels, deer and pigs. Land managers concede that they could never rid the country of all horses, even if they wanted to. That suits horse advocates, who regard them as noble emblems of the toughness and fighting spirit that characterises Australians.

For Antoinette Campbell, whose husband is Banjo Paterson's only great-grandson, taking part in one of Peter Cochran's riding treks through the Snowy Mountains was the fulfilment of a lifelong dream. "To read Banjo's poetry and then experience the horses in the High Country, one can't help but feel an amazing connection with these magnificent animals and the rawness of the plains that are their home," she says. ■

Buffalo rising

Enduring symbol of the NT's frontier days, the buffalo is now a growing part of Australia's live-export and restaurant meat industry, and a valuable dairy animal.

Story and photography by **David Hancock**

Issue 82 Apr-Jun 2006

THE DOUBLE-DECKER, triple-trailer road train started to unload in the early-wet-season humidity of Darwin. Wild buffalo from Arnhem Land came off first. The powerful, heavy animals charged down the ramp, sweeping their large, curved horns from side to side, hammering a clear warning on the metal panels: beware!

Several animals stopped, their eyes filled with a mixture of bewilderment, fear and defiance. Others got stuck in the race because their horns were so broad. Stockmen waved their hats in the air or used 'jiggers' – electric prods – to get them moving. The big-horned beasts eventually strode up the alleyway to the cattle ship with their heads turned sideways. "They'll quieten down after a few days at sea," said Michael Swart. "Here come the farm animals – you'll see the difference as plain as day."

The farm-bred buffalo were younger, smaller and quieter. Their horns were short and blunt and they moved along the race without fuss. The stockmen kept their hats firmly on their heads – no jiggers needed here. It was hard to believe they were of the same species as the wild buffalo.

Michael, vice-president of the Northern Territory Buffalo Industry Council, explained that the load represented two ends of the modern-day buffalo industry: mature animals from a wild harvest and young, domesticated stock. If you were comparing them with cattle, you'd say it was a case of feral scrub bulls versus docile, moon-eyed yearlings.

All were bound for Asia, where buffalo meat is prized because it is lean and suited to absorbing exotic flavours in cooking. The bigger animals would be destined for the 'wet' market – village and roadside stalls that sell fresh meat, while the smaller animals would go to small feedlots or herded around palm oil plantations for several months – all slaughtered in the Muslim fashion (halal).

Suntanned and natty in his small, Bavarian-style hat, Michael represents nearly three decades of sweeping change in the buffalo industry. Once a professional buffalo contractor, he is now a farmer and leader of an industry with much hope and potential.

In the 'old days' – the 1970–90s – the Swart brothers, Michael, Jeffrey and Andrew, roared through the bush in cut-down, four-wheel-drive vehicles called bullcatchers that were reinforced with thick bullbars and steel panels to prevent wild buffalo from goring the occupants. Accompanied by helicopters buzzing low over the herds, they drove at breakneck speed through the scrub, chasing and then shunting buffalo into portable yards.

The operation was often an affair of swirling clouds of bull dust and bullcatchers bouncing out of wallows, swerving past large trees and crashing over saplings. Flimsy fences, or 'wings' – star pickets strung with two strands of wire covered with hessian, channelled buffalo into yards concealed under trees or close to a river bend.

This was frontier living at its best, and one with a long history in the Top End.

BETWEEN 1825 AND 1838, the British brought about 100 Asian swamp buffalo from Kupang in Timor to northern Australia. At the settlements of Fort Dundas, in the Tiwi Islands, and Fort Wellington and Victoria Settlement, on the Cobourg Peninsula, buffalo were used as draught animals and for milking and cultivating crops. All three settlements were abandoned by 1849, but the imported animals remained. Sambar deer, Banteng cattle and Timor ponies didn't wander far from Cobourg, but pigs and buffalo spread through Arnhem Land and the Top End's northern wetlands.

By the early 20th century, buffalo were spread across the Top End and an industry had developed around their incredibly tough hides. Buffalo bulls were shot from horseback. Their hides were salted, exported and used to make machinery belts, cavalry saddles and footwear.

Employing Territorians of European, Chinese and Aboriginal extraction, the hide industry waxed and waned until the 1950s, then collapsed as synthetic materials came into widespread use.

Buffalo stream ahead of Donny Stewart's airboat during a wet-season muster at Carmor Plains station, about 125km east of Darwin. An innovation from the USA's Florida Everglades, airboats permit movement across nearly impassable wetlands.

Dust and leaves fly as helicopters and modified 4WD "bullcatchers" pursue wild buffalo towards mobile yards in Arnhem Land. Buffalo generally move in family groups – a trait exploited by musterers.

The government was left trying to manage the Top End country overrun by buffalo.

By the 1960s and '70s, NT floodplains were black with buffalo and it wasn't unusual to find a stray wandering through the suburbs of Darwin or Nhulunbuy, on the Gove Peninsula. Buffalo were seen as far afield as the Victoria River in the west and Wave Hill in the south. During this period, buffalo were mustered or shot for the Australian pet-meat industry, or for export to the USA and Europe as game meat, but there was no formal management system in place.

Buffalo numbers reached a peak in about 1972, when it was estimated between 300,000 and 400,000 roamed the Top End. The tough and adventurous lifestyle associated with these large, dangerous animals attracted plenty of colourful characters. The buffalo became the symbol of the Top End and was further romanticised in movies such as *Crocodile Dundee*.

However, under buffalo domination, some areas became dust bowls and many rivers ran thick with silt created by erosion. Buffalo swim-channels (watery tracks across wet-season floodplains) were held responsible for the intrusion of salt water that poisoned and killed paperbark forests.

Buffalo trampled rainforests and their grazing knocked out many trees and stripped the floodplains of native grasses that held sediments together; their tracks and wallows caused erosion and they spread weeds such as mimosa. In times of drought, tens of thousands of buffalo died. The survivors ate up any remaining fodder.

Everything changed during the late 1980s, when the NT implemented the federal government's Brucellosis and Tuberculosis Eradication Campaign (BTEC) and systematically mustered or shot more than 300,000 buffalo on country west of Arnhem Land. Technically, BTEC was an animal-health program designed to eradicate feral animals that carried TB and thereby threatened Australia's billion-dollar beef industry. Among its consequences was that buffalo husbandry got a start as a niche industry.

Buffalo farms were established on pastoral leases between Darwin and Kakadu and millions of dollars were poured in to electrify fences, manage pastures, develop selective breeding programs and to seek markets in Asia and Australia. Meat from young, domesticated buffalo, called TenderBuff was sold to restaurants around Australia.

Top End swamp buffalo were crossed with larger, quieter riverine (European) buffalo in order to develop animals that gain weight quickly and are suitable for the buffalo dairy market. Some of the world's largest dairy herds – in Europe and Pakistan – are comprised of buffalo. Today, buffalo dairying services a small but growing niche market in Australia.

AT THE END of the BTEC cull a herd of just 30,000 buffalo remained in the wilds of southern Arnhem Land, ensuring that there'd be a genetic pool for future expansion of the industry. Since then, numbers have grown to more than 100,000, providing potential for remote indigenous communities to earn income from a burgeoning export market and from trophy hunters who pay thousands of dollars to shoot a bull buffalo with big horns.

However, growing numbers also pose a danger to the pristine Arnhem Land environment and cultural (rock art) areas and not all traditional owners welcome the animal.

Despite the dramatic changes that have taken place within the industry, the wild buffalo days still strike a nostalgic chord with long-time Top Enders. Terry Baldwin, a former shooter, musterer and station owner, wants to establish a Buffalo Hall of Fame on the Arnhem Highway between Darwin and Kakadu. "They were thrilling and dangerous times and I was fortunate to be part of it," said Terry. "I want the Buffalo Hall of Fame to showcase the Top End's amazing history and show how Asian, European and Aboriginal people all worked together. It will be a tribute to a magnificent animal and some really remarkable people." ■

STORY BY AMANDA BURDON PHOTOGRAPHY BY JASON EDWARDS

OUTCAST

Pest or endangered species? Villain or environmental saviour? The dingo, Australia's 'native' dog, often finds itself in no-man's land.

Issue 136 ◆ Jan–Feb 2017

THE CORRUGATED-IRON shearing shed is all that's left of the days when flocks of sheep grazed the stony plains of Mt Willoughby station, north of Coober Pedy, in northern South Australia. Cattle are now king here on the edge of the Great Victoria Desert. But 84-year-old Bill Lennon's memory is long. He spent his childhood roaming this country, shepherding with his maternal grandparents, mother and siblings.

"We lit little fires at night to keep the dingoes away," says the Antikarinya Aboriginal elder. "But those old dingoes didn't bother us. My grandmother and grandfather each had a dingo. In the night-time, if there was danger around, they would warn us and protect us.

"They are one of our totems," he continues. "When an Aboriginal man goes through the law he might become a perentie man, an emu man, a kangaroo man or a dog man. Those dingoes watch over the dog men and make them spiritually strong. They are part of our Dreaming."

Outside the East Gippsland town of Omeo, in north-eastern Victoria, attitudes towards dingoes are very different. Beside the road to Benambra, a prominent gum tree drips with about 30 dog carcasses in various states of decay. Many closely resemble the archetypal dingo – lean, golden animals with broad heads. Others are brindle, black, and spotted – more like domestic pets.

To the sheep and cattle producers who live around here there is no distinction. Any dog that poses a threat to stock is shot on sight. Most farmers bait extensively in autumn and spring with the poison 1080.

Before they installed electric fencing and carried out extensive baiting, Penny and Fraser Barry, of Bindi station, just south of Omeo, were losing as many as 1500 sheep a year. "We went through 15 years of losses; we were fighting for survival," says Fraser. "I was spending 100 per cent of my time on dogs, up all night trying to shoot them. I was physically and emotionally exhausted." →

The dingo is well adapted to the Australian continent and roams widely, ever-watchful for potential prey and people.

FEW ANIMALS DIVIDE opinions quite like the dingo. Loved as a mysterious outback icon, or loathed as a marauding killer – it depends on which side of the fence you sit. In all but its most far-flung territories, the dingo is now near indistinguishable from feral dogs or hybrids of the two. In fact, cross-breeding probably poses the greatest threat to the purebred dingo.

Legislation deems the dingo (*Canis lupus dingo* – thought to be descended from Asian domesticated dogs) a pest on private land in every mainland state and territory except the Northern Territory. Across the 60 per cent of SA outside the dog fence, dingoes aren't even protected in national parks, but baiting is restricted to ensure its survival as a 'wildlife species'. In Victoria, the dingo is listed as a threatened species and protected in national parks, but is fair game on private land or within a 3km buffer of public land boundaries to safeguard livestock. The same rule applies in New South Wales, Queensland, SA and Western Australia, where land managers are legally required to cull them.

"Not all dogs will, but any dog has the potential to kill livestock," says Greg Mifsud from the Invasive Animals Cooperative Research Centre. The National Wild Dog Action Plan, an industry-led, government-endorsed initiative, advocates a landscape approach to controlling "wild-living dogs, including dingoes, feral dogs and their hybrids". It supports aerial and ground baiting, trapping, fencing, the use of guardian dogs and shooting where necessary.

"The annual cost to the Australian economy in sheep and cattle losses from wild dogs and control efforts is in the hundreds of millions of dollars," says Greg. "It's an emotionally charged issue. We are not about obliterating dingoes; we recognise their place in national parks. We want to provide long-term opportunities for production and dingo conservation."

Second-generation dingo scientist Dr Ben Allen, an ecologist with the University of Southern Queensland in Toowoomba, says that there's little evidence to prove the widely touted theory that dingoes could help halt Australia's biodiversity collapse by suppressing feral cats and foxes. However, there is good evidence to indicate that dingoes control kangaroo numbers.

"I wouldn't be baiting routinely in arid and semi-arid cattle production areas; it often has no benefit and can sometimes make matters worse," Ben says. "But nor would I inhibit landholders from controlling dogs if they needed to. Dingoes can be benign one minute and your worst enemy the next."

Wild dogs are, unequivocally, public enemy number one for sheep producers. "Sheep and dogs will never get along and sheep graziers will need to fence, bait and have guardian dogs," Ben says.

THE DINGO IS nothing if not adaptable. Dr Guy Ballard, an ecologist with the NSW government's Vertebrate Pest Research Unit and the University of New England, has studied them for a decade. "They are incredibly successful animals that can live at high-altitude on high, bony ridges, in rainforests and in the harshest deserts," he says.

"They roam towns, and live around airports, caravan parks and rubbish tips," he continues. "They do whatever they need to survive. Modern dingoes are very much a product of the Australian landscape."

As Jim Benton well knows, his quarry is opportunistic, resourceful and highly intelligent. As one of 18 wild dog controllers employed by Victoria's Department of Environment, Land, Water and Planning (DELWP), he spends his days setting and checking traps throughout East Gippsland.

"Sometimes I have caught the dog in a week, but a cunning dog can take months," he says. "The longer they go, the smarter they get. I've seen 30 sheep killed in one night. If we cut back on our work, numbers explode."

Still, Jim accords dingoes respect. "They are only dogs, doing what's natural," he says. "And only the strongest survive. If they weren't territorial, they would be impossible to catch. But even a cunning dog will come unstuck, and they do die of old age eventually."

Victoria has one of the country's most active baiting programs, says state manager of the DELWP's wild dog program Barry Davies, and it has been very successful in reducing stock losses. Like elsewhere in the country, property owners are also increasingly using cluster fencing, electric fencing and guardian animals – including dogs, alpacas and donkeys – to protect their flocks.

SA landholders Caroline Thomas and John Knight, whose property adjoins Mt Willoughby, are keeping an open mind. They are opposed to baiting dingoes, both philosophically and in order to meet their organic beef certification requirements. "We are letting nature take its course," Caroline says.

"There will be some losses during dry years but we will try to manage stocking rates to ensure the cattle are strong enough

At the Australian Dingo Discovery and Research Centre in Melbourne, Lyn Watson (at right) and her team of volunteers care for 40 pure-bred dingoes and their litters and conduct community education.

Dingo breeding season is in March–June, with an average litter containing five pups, such as these youngsters at the Australian Dingo Discovery and Research Centre.

to defend their calves from dingoes. Ours is what you would call predator-friendly production."

John says dingoes play an important role in maintaining long-term ecological stability. "On evidence, it is better for us to suffer cattle losses (about 30 a year during a drought) than kill dingoes indiscriminately and cause chaos in the dog population," he says. "However, we are vigilant and watching all the time to see if this is the best approach."

Dr Arian Wallach, an ecologist with the University of Technology's Centre for Compassionate Conservation in Sydney, is in no doubt. After five years exploring the relationships between dingoes and other wildlife on Evelyn Downs and Mt Willoughby, she says she firmly believes that killing causes an increase in dingo densities and predation, because their hierarchy is disrupted.

She believes that natural dingo function can improve native pasture and cattle growth, and, ultimately, a producer's bottom line. "I am encouraged to see small pockets of predator-friendly production in Australia, where the focus is shifting from controlling dingoes to protecting livestock," she says.

First-time property owners Jake Fennell and Frankie Lumb say that refraining from baiting is simply not an option on 3812sq. km Wintinnna. None of their immediate neighbours bait, due to organic beef production or spiritual beliefs.

"When the dogs are thick, we could lose 25 per cent of our calves, but we bait all the time with factory baits and get a delivery of injected baits yearly to blanket the property," says Jake. "We have seen dingoes chewing on the back legs of calves, their tails and lips, and then had to put them down. When you have a few dogs hunting together, no cow is good enough to protect her calf."

CROSS-BREEDING, control measures and habitat fragmentation are bringing the dingo into closer contact and conflict with people. It saddens Lyn Watson, from the Australian Dingo Discovery and Research Centre on the outskirts of Melbourne. She wants to see dingoes taken off the pest list and protected nationally.

"We don't recommend them as pets, but the wave of anti-dingo sentiment sweeping Australia makes me think that people are going to have to keep them as pets if the species is to survive," Lyn says. "These are magic animals – and they are Australian and we are killing them. They are our top predator, the equivalent of Australia's lion, and they are responsible for keeping our biodiversity intact."

Despite 200-odd years of dingo control, many scientists believe that there are more dingoes now than ever before. In many cases, the provision of rabbits, livestock and watering points (which attract macropods) has enabled this opportunistic species to expand its range. "Dingoes are still here and numbers are still increasing, even though we have eradicated them from about 15 per cent of the continent," says Ben Allen. ■

Australians abroad

Cane toads, rabbits, lantana...the destruction caused by species introduced to Australian shores is well known. But what about the impact of our natives overseas? How damaging have our flora and fauna been to other ecosystems?

Story by **Tim Low**

Issue 139 Jul–Aug 2017

Australia's common brushtail possum (left and right) has become a serious challenge for New Zealand. An estimated 30 million are now spread across the length and breadth of our South Pacific neighbour, causing environmental and agricultural havoc.

AS AUSTRALIANS, WE LIKE our brushtail possums, tolerating their thefts from kitchen bowls and gardens, but over in New Zealand these same animals provoke dismay. They were taken there during the 19th century as fur-bearing animals, with a claim that an acre of bush with possums would return more profit than an acre of grass with sheep. Soon they were targeting orchard fruit, pitting farmers against trappers. The good and bad of possums was debated in parliament as part of a national argument that raged for decades. No-one defends them today when, in densities of up to 25 per hectare, they denude and kill rainforest trees, damage gardens and farms, and spread tuberculosis to cattle.

Australia's ongoing wars against rabbits, foxes, blackberries and the like can encourage the idea that introduced pests are an especially Australian problem. What we don't hear about much are all the Australian species misbehaving overseas, often on a vast scale. Every continent except Antarctica has unwanted Aussies stealing land and water, attacking crops and displacing native species. In several places the most despised pests are Australian.

On the South Island of New Zealand a few red-necked wallabies were liberated in 1874, and with no predators to curb them they proliferated until, come the 1960s, there were 500,000 or more, teeming over 1 million hectares, fattening on crops and sheep pastures. Hundreds of thousands have since been poisoned and shot.

Australian species do best in those parts of the world with a congenial climate and substantial trade links. Along with marsupials, New Zealand has acquired some of our plants, frogs, lizards and several birds, including magpies that kill the native birds. Smaller arrivals include blowflies, cockroaches, termites and redback spiders.

Southern Florida has a balmy subtropical climate and now has weedy Australian umbrella trees, she-oaks and 4000sq.km of paperbarks taking over the Everglades. England is so cold that its Australian contingent, which includes wattles, as well as millions of barnacles, is centred in the south. Australian carpet beetles, having traded a diet of dried animal skins for textiles, occur as far north as Yorkshire, and Australian spider beetles, pests of stored grain, get by in Scotland, but only because they live indoors.

The Australians that thrive abroad are often very hardy. Redback spiders can go most of a year without eating, which helps explain how they've colonised Japan, Belgium, Iran and other places after travelling inside furniture or machinery. Eucalypts, wattles and she-oaks are widely grown because they do better than most plants on degraded, drought-prone lands. Hawaii's tree ferns are icons of local rainforest, but Australian tree ferns are so much hardier they are installed in gardens instead and their spores float for kilometres into national parks. Some slopes they have claimed are so steep that herbicides are shot at them from helicopters. Yabbies and redclaws are tougher than most crustaceans so they are widely farmed and thrive when they escape.

SPECIES FROM EVERYWHERE are spreading today in a world changing dramatically from globalisation. People and products have become more mobile and so have many species. Some scientists now say the Earth has entered a new, humanised age, the Anthropocene, and the travel of species, unprecedented in the planet's history, is part of that. It means, for example, that Australian crayfish crawl around in the Sea of Galilee and rock-wallabies hop about near Honolulu. The world's biggest stands of Australian paperbarks are probably those growing today in Florida, from back when their seeds were broadcast from planes. I have driven for 20 minutes past walls of them lining the highway.

Globalisation means that Australian species threaten biodiversity in many places. Sweet pittosporum trees claim the habitat of an endangered bullfinch in the Azores and redback spiders attack endangered chafer beetles in New Zealand. It means the Cootamundra wattle, native to a small area in inland New South Wales around the town of Cootamundra, now grows wild on every continent except Antarctica.

The Anthropocene means that Australian plants now feed many foreign animals. Baboons eat wattle seeds and hummingbirds are changing their migration routes to exploit eucalypt nectar. In Borneo, I saw wattle trees stripped by elephants that had eaten the bark. In Africa, the spread of kangaroo paws and banksias is abetted by sugarbirds and sunbirds pollinating the flowers. The new weedy habitats are never as rich as those they displace. Wattles form monocultures in place of Africa's fynbos, the world's richest shrublands, famous for their lavish flowers.

The ongoing spread of unwanted species, from Australia and elsewhere, justifies good quarantine and a commitment to biological control. An Australian insect was one of the world's first biological control targets, when in 1888–89, Australian ladybirds and parasitic flies were taken to California to quell an Australian bug, cottony cushion scale, that was accidentally carried abroad. Its appetite for sap had brought the Californian orange industry to its knees. More recently, biocontrol agents have been enlisted with varying success against wattles in Africa, paperbarks in Florida and the psyllid bugs that leave eucalypts in California so sickly they drip sticky sap on parked cars.

The success of Australian species abroad is one reason to shed forever that old image of Australia as a land populated by wildlife that is primitive and inferior. Our species, whether they are liked or loathed, command considerable respect. Eucalypts have shown this by becoming the most widely grown trees on Earth after pines, valued for their hardiness and vigour. Brazil alone has 5000sq.km of plantations. The tallest tree in all of Africa is a Sydney blue gum in South Africa, more than 80m tall, and the tallest flowering tree in Europe is a karri eucalypt in Portugal.

Birds of prey favour lofty trees so I wasn't surprised when, in Zimbabwe, I saw black eagles nesting high up in a solitary eucalypt planted beside miombo woodland. It was yet another reminder that Australian species have made their presence felt all over the world. ■

CHAPTER SIX

ECOSYSTEMS

Australia may be the smallest continental land mass but it's also the world's largest island and the sixth-largest country. It has a land area of almost 7.7 million square kilometres, a figure that rises to nearly 13.6 million square kilometres if you include our overseas territories.

This vast nation is a land of climatic extremes – from a highest recorded temperature of more than 50°C to a low of –23°C, from droughts to flooding rains – and, consequently, of varied habitats, from the deserts at the centre, both sandy and stony, through tropical savannah, temperate woodland, alpine heath, buttongrass plain and coastal heath to rainforest in all of its forms, from tropical lowland rainforest to misty upland cloud forest and moss-draped cool temperate rainforest. And if you want to go extraterritorial, you can add polar tundra.

Home to some of the oldest rocks on the planet, Australia is a land of ancient landforms: rugged gorges, flat-topped mesas, stony plains, uplifted sea floors and extensive cave systems, and while compared to other parts of the world it boasts few mountains worthy of the name, it does have Uluru, the world's largest stone monolith. These landscapes are criss-crossed by a vast network of waterways, from mighty rivers such as the Murray and Murrumbidgee to creeks, lakes, waterholes and peaceful billabongs. These sections of river that have become cut off from the main channel often act as vibrant oases, supporting hundreds if not thousands of species: crocodiles patrolling the shallows, white-bellied sea-eagles the skies, archerfish shooting down insects with powerful jets of unerringly aimed liquid, dragonflies hawking for prey of their own, their wings a barely discernable blur.

Perhaps surprisingly, however, it's the desert regions that harbour some of the most diverse ecosystems in Australia. A single sand dune can support about as many lizard species as the whole of western Europe, so when you consider that there are almost 1 million square kilometres of sand-dune deserts in Australia, it's clear that that adds up to a lot of lizards – not to mention snakes, frogs, birds and mammals.

This diversity is believed to be underpinned by the humble spinifex, which provides both shelter for a myriad of creatures and food for termites, which themselves sustain a large proportion of the local animal community.

In a country this vast, it's perhaps unsurprising that even today there are still regions that are little explored. Take Cape Melville, a remote peninsula on the eastern side of the Cape York Peninsula, where a jumble of giant black boulders shelters a range of unusual species found nowhere else, many of which were only discovered within the past 20 years; a 2013 survey turned up five new vertebrate species. Effectively cut off from the rest of the mainland by the Melville Range, Cape Melville can be considered an island of habitat, and it's this isolation that has led to the high levels of endemism found there.

And then there are Australia's actual islands – all 8222 of them – each an ecological experiment, with individual ecosystems built using whichever organisms managed to cross the surrounding seas (or perhaps a long-ago-inundated land bridge). They are also evolutionary laboratories, where outlandish creatures have been able to develop in isolation – the bright-red land crabs of Christmas Island, the gargantuan black tiger snakes of Mount Chappell Island off Tasmania, Ball's Pyramid's giant flightless stick insect. And many are made special by what isn't there – the lack of predators on some islands allow certain species to prosper, such as the robber crabs of Christmas Island, which are among the world's largest invertebrates. ■

Previous page: A desert spadefoot toad emerges from sand in the Central Desert region. This species has been found as deep as 1m below the dry desert ground. It survives drought by aestivating.

A comb-crested jacana, or Jesus bird, carefully picks its way across floating vegetation on McCreadies Billabong, Labelle Downs Station.

STORY BY **CONRAD HOSKIN** PHOTOGRAPHY BY **TIM LAMAN**

CAPE MELVILLE'S LOST WORLD

An expedition by helicopter to an isolated mountain plateau on the Cape York Peninsula resulted in the discovery of a whole new ecosystem.

Issue 132 ◆ May–Jun 2015

DIRECTLY AHEAD WAS a dark mountain of boulders and rainforest rising up from the plains. We'd flown two hours from Cairns – one over the lush rainforest of the Wet Tropics to Cooktown and the other over woodlands and sandstone escarpments as we followed the coast north. Looming in front of us was our destination, Cape Melville – an isolated range barely visited by biologists. We approached in the helicopter to explore the uplands, which had long been a goal of mine.

A decade earlier I'd driven to Cape Melville and stood on the beach looking up at a wall of jumbled boulders, wondering what was at the top. I climbed a fair way, but was knocked back by the heat and the scale of the rocks. I needed a chopper.

Many years later, that wish was fulfilled, but thick cloud stopped us landing in the uplands and instead we explored boulder fields in the lowlands. On the last morning of that trip I was woken at dawn by a brief shower. As the rain eased and the water flowed through the rocks deep into the mountain, I became aware of a strange rattling call. I quickly got up and climbed down among the boulders. After squeezing through crevices, I found a distinctive new species of microhylid frog. Shortly afterwards we departed, having had but a tantalising glimpse of Cape Melville's secrets.

A COUPLE of months passed before I had the opportunity to return, this time with Dr Tim Laman, an American photographer and ornithologist. As we approached, it became clear that conditions were ideal and I'd finally be able ⟶

The Cape Melville leaf-tailed gecko, a spectacular species discovered during the surveys, is known from an area of the uplands just 100m across.

The Cape Melville boulder-frog is one of the region's eight endemic vertebrates. It only emerges from the depths of the boulder fields during wet weather.

to explore the uplands. Flying over the boulder fields, we could see the top of the range was roughly a plateau, with more upland area and rainforest than expected. There were areas of well-developed forest that seemed to be growing on earth not boulders; I was very excited.

Landing on a giant rock, we swiftly unloaded under the motion and noise of the spinning rotor. As the sound of the departing chopper faded, we stood in the quiet and surveyed the incredible scene. An expanse of forest lay ahead, with hoop pines and black boulders, and wisps of cloud sticking to the highest ridges. It looked like a lost world and I was eager to find out what secrets it held.

Cape Melville is a peninsula dominated by the Melville Range. This sits alone, rising from the plains of drier forests to the south, and bounded on its other sides by the sea. The nearest significant rainforest is 200km south in the ranges of the Wet Tropics or in the McIlwraith Range, 130km north-west on the Cape York Peninsula. Getting there by car from Cairns is an easy drive to Laura and then a long, tough drive through Rinyirru (Lakefield) National Park to Cape Melville National Park, where you finally pop out on the beach at Bathurst Bay – where I'd stood a decade earlier.

Despite its incredible geology, the range remained largely unheard of until 1978 when a local Aboriginal man named Wodyeti told botanists about an unusual palm. The plant was described as the foxtail palm (*Wodyetia bifurcata*), found only on the boulder fields of Cape Melville, and it caused a stir due to its beauty and the subsequent smuggling of seeds for the nursery trade. The foxtail is now a fixture along esplanades from Cairns to Florida, and has an artificial distribution many times larger than its natural range. Another plant, the Cape Melville nightshade, was also discovered to be endemic, as well as three vertebrates: the Cape Melville snake-eyed skink, the Cape Melville tree frog and the Cape Melville boulder-frog, discovered in 1998, '97 and '98, respectively.

After setting up camp we began exploring. We only had a few days and there was plenty of ground to cover. That afternoon and evening we found interesting species but nothing unexpected. I started to wonder if Cape Melville was too small and too harsh for rainforest creatures to have survived here for hundreds of thousands, if not millions, of years of isolation. After all, the plateau measures just 6 x 3km, and rainforest-dependent creatures that can't cross gaps in vegetation would have needed rainforest here that entire time. I began to think that perhaps the three known endemics and the new frog was the sum of unique vertebrates, a number of unique species on par with any other mountain in Queensland.

THE NEXT MORNING we woke early and headed higher, onto a ridge. It looked different up here – moister, mossier and rockier. As we walked through an enchanting area of boulders under low rainforest, a small lizard leaping between two boulders caught my eye. There in front of me was an undescribed skink – golden and long-limbed. It was a new species of *Saproscincus*, a genus of lizards found in rainforests to the south. I subsequently named the species the Cape Melville shade skink (*Saproscincus saltus*, 'saltus' meaning 'leaping'). It is the most northerly member of its group and, with its bizarrely long limbs and flattened body, the only one that's adapted to living among rocks.

This was an exciting start, but only the beginning of what was to be an incredible day of discovery. Shortly afterwards, I caught a large lizard in thick leaf-litter at the base of some boulders and a small, fast skink, which was active on the leaf-litter.

These would ultimately be described as the Cape Melville bar-lipped skink (*Glaphyromorphus othelarrni*) and the Cape Melville rainbow skink (*Carlia wundalthini*), respectively. The species names for both were chosen in collaboration with the bubu gudjin, the traditional owners of this land.

As evening fell we stepped out of the rainforest and onto the boulder fields. The view was magnificent. Behind us were rocky peaks and misty rainforest, and in front of us immense slopes of boulders sweeping down to the ocean. We climbed down into them to search for the new frog that I'd found on the previous trip. The rocks were incredibly rough, removing skin with the merest brush against them. And the gaps were treacherous – we regularly found ourselves stepping across chasms that disappeared into the black depths. A wrong move would be serious.

Before too long it was evident that frogs were common here. We found some emerging from deep in the boulders to forage for invertebrates on the surface rocks. I subsequently named this species the blotched boulder-frog (*Cophixalus petrophilus*, with 'petrophilus' meaning 'rock-loving'). The species survives the long dry season deep in the boulders, where it's cool and moist, and emerges in the wet season to feed and breed near the surface. They are also 'terrestrial breeders' – eggs are laid in moist rocks and the clutch is guarded by the male. The tadpoles develop entirely within the eggs, and after a month or so little frogs hatch out and disappear into the depths of the boulder field.

Working our way off the boulders and back into the rainforest, we headed up a gully. Looking ahead I saw red eye-shine coming from a tree growing among boulders. We had seen plenty of Cooktown ring-tailed geckos (impressive lizards large enough to eat frogs and other geckos), but the way this one appeared to be sitting, head-down and

One of the distinctive features of the beautiful Cape Melville rainbow skink is the orange colouration taken on by breeding males.

motionless, suggested something much more exciting. I scampered up the boulders and there before me was a creature with long spindly legs, huge eyes and an elaborately frilled tail – a new leaf-tailed gecko!

Although I'd hoped that Cape Melville might harbour such a species, I could hardly believe it was true. The Cape Melville leaf-tailed gecko (*Saltuarius eximius*, with 'eximius' meaning 'extraordinary' or 'exquisite') received international fame when it was chosen by the International Institute for Species Exploration for its annual list of the top 10 species discovered globally.

THESE 2013 SURVEYS of Cape Melville revealed five new vertebrate species, a number of range extensions and some invertebrate and plant species that have yet to be resolved. In terms of vertebrates, the endemic species count went from three to eight, the highest known for any mountain in Australia.

That's on top of the two known endemic plants and no doubt more species awaiting discovery – and all within an area about the size of Sydney's city centre. For reptiles and frogs, the species diversity in the rainforest at Cape Melville isn't all that high. However, it's the distinctiveness of the species here that sets Cape Melville apart. Why are there so many endemic species? And why are they so unusual? The answer to both those questions involves the rock.

The Melville Range is small and not particularly high – about 600m above sea level at its highest – compared with other rainforest refugial areas such as the Wet Tropics, where many mountains exceed 1000m. The upland area is important for rainforest persistence because, historically, rainforest contracted to cool, moist peaks during globally dry periods. But what Cape Melville lacks in scale, it makes up for in rock.

The deeply layered rock of the boulder fields would have retained cool, moist conditions through even the toughest times. And they would have kept out fire. Therefore, the massive pile of rocks at Cape Melville acted as 'lithorefugia' – cool, moist refuges where rainforest-associated lineages could persist through time. These isolated lineages have split into numerous species over millions of years.

The reason Cape Melville species look so different from relatives in rainforests to the south or north can be attributed to the rock, too. There are some consistently distinctive features among the Cape Melville endemics that are likely to be adaptations to this environment, particularly with respect to movement across and between rocks. The lizards have relatively long limbs and flat bodies, and the frogs are large and have huge hands and finger-pads. Even the unusually large eyes of the leaf-tailed gecko and boulder-frog could be the result of living in the dimly lit crevices.

And what does the future look like for these unique species? Cape Melville NP is now jointly managed by the Queensland Parks and Wildlife Service and the Cape Melville, Flinders and Howick Islands Aboriginal Corporation. But despite formal protection and the fortress-like boulder-field slopes surrounding the uplands, there are still threats to this unique environment.

Some invasive species have found their way to the top. Pigs are the most conspicuous example and efforts continue by the park managers to reduce these impacts. Introduced diseases are also a potential threat; on the survey trips we were always very careful to ensure that all our clothing and gear was clean and sterilised. It's my hope that Cape Melville's remoteness and ruggedness, along with careful management of invasive species, will protect it into the future. ■

A day in the life of a billabong

Documentary filmmaker Ben Cropp stays sharply focused as he dodges salties to record the extraordinary life on this hidden billabong.

Story by **Ben Cropp** Photography by **Nick Rains**

Issue 87 Jul–Sep 2007

BEFORE DAWN, with the stars still ablaze in the sky, I carefully set out to walk 100m to the tinnie. I hold the torch level with my eyes and swing it left to right. A red eye blinks to the left of the boat, another to the right. Crocs. I count 17 in total. I'm on McCreadies Billabong at Labelle Downs Station, 80km south of Darwin, with my niece Tanya. It's late in the dry season and we plan to stay four weeks to make a documentary.

Like many billabongs, McCreadies (pronounced 'McEddies') is a banana-shaped lagoon, a cut-off part of a river – the Reynolds River in this case. The diverse area around this billabong has 3000 plant species and 300 bird species. Add to that the myriad insects, fish, turtles and reptiles, and you have one of the richest and most fascinating ecosystems in the world.

As Tanya and I motor slowly up the billabong, the dawn chorus finds voice and breaks the silence, trees slowly emerge from their shroud of mist and streaks of orange colour the sky, as if a great paintbrush is sweeping across it.

At dawn, tendrils of mist rise off the billabong in spiralling wisps. Birds flock across the sky, heading in from their roosts elsewhere to feed on the billabong. Trees glow golden as the sun emerges, lighting up a darter's plumage as it dips its head and plummets into the water. An expert hunter, it stalks fish among the weeds, stabbing its prey with lightning speed.

As I watch the darter manipulate a fish down its throat head first, I spot an estuarine croc slinking through the weeds. I keep my camera rolling on the darter, when the water suddenly erupts and the bird disappears. We spot the croc climbing up the bank, the darter grasped firmly in its jaws.

These estuarine crocs, or salties, are the kings of this billabong. They can live in both salt and fresh water and grow to 7m – as long as a car with a trailer. Their jaws can crush victims with three times the bite-strength of a tiger shark – 40 times what I can chomp.

At about 8am, hundreds of pelicans and little black cormorants come together in a mass feeding frenzy. It starts with a few cormorants finding a shoal of fish, and when they pop up with wriggling catches, hundreds of others swoop in. This is the cue for all the roosting pelicans to rush in.

Cormorants are great divers. Pelicans aren't, so bully pelicans steal baby catfish, grunter and barramundi from the cormorants. If a cormorant refuses to hand over the fish, the pelican grabs the cormorant by the neck and roughly swings it around on the surface until the unfortunate bird surrenders its catch.

Wading birds such as egrets and ibis also seem to lose more than half their catch to other thieving birds, especially whistling kites. The kites hover overhead, and the moment a wader gets a fish, they swoop down and harass it into dropping its catch.

ABOUT MIDDAY, with the temperature and humidity taking their toll, I drift out in the tinnie to catch dinner. Barramundi is the prized sport and table fish up here and I've never seen a lagoon with so many. They run in schools, so are easy to catch.

All barramundi are born male. They mature at four years of age and generally have just a few years to fertilise the females before changing sex. They can grow to nearly 50kg. Barramundi don't breed in the billabong. In the Wet, when the floodplain lies 2m under water and the billabong's outline is lost in a broad sheet of water, the barramundi swim down to the mouth of the river to spawn. Before the end of the floods, the young swim back.

High on a nearby perch, two white-bellied sea-eagles scan the water for dinner. Down one comes, so graceful with its 2m wingspan. It plucks a barra from just beneath the surface. A whistling kite swoops in to try to intimidate the eagle, but it's no match.

The most amazing fish in the billabong is the archerfish, which shoots insects down with a jet of water. When a moth or other insect settles on a branch above the water, the archerfish rises to just below the surface and shoots, knocking the insect into the water, where it can be easily gulped down.

The most graceful fisher is the long-legged jabiru, or black-necked stork. We see one uncharacteristically jumping around a bush as if walking on hot coals, and discover that it's trying to break off branches to build a nest. Close by is a big, sunbaking croc, and the jabiru is scared – it rushes in, quickly tugs at a dead branch and leaps back, failing to break off even a twig. Eventually it flies off.

We moor the boat and a 2m saltie surfaces with a 3kg barra in its jaws. It crawls up on the bank beside the boat. It crunches and crunches for some 15 minutes, slowly reducing the fish to a soft and floppy mess, then flips it around and swallows it head first.

Another species that's quite common here is the freshwater crocodile. It rarely grows to 3m and has a narrower snout and smaller, finer teeth than its saltwater cousin.

MacCreadies Billabong teems with life and is constantly changing. It's rich in diversity both below and above the water.

Freshies feed by lying at the water's edge and snapping at any movement close by. They generally catch smaller prey than that taken by salties, and are considered almost harmless to humans, but could give a nasty bite if cornered or trodden on. I want to get some underwater shots of freshies. At first I use an underwater camera on a pole. It works okay, but the footage isn't as good as I'd like, so, with lots of second thoughts, I enter the lagoon in an area where we haven't seen any estuarine crocs, only freshies.

Under water, it's awfully spooky. During my brief swim, hugging the edge of the bank, I see a freshwater croc up ahead, lying among some sunken tree branches. I approach to within a metre. It moves away and the swirl of its tail stirs up the debris, before it disappears into the gloom.

Adrenaline courses through me and my heart beats rapidly. A large shape looms up. I flinch and when it comes into full focus I see it's a giant catfish, 1.5m long and maybe 30kg in weight. I swing back towards the bank and see a barra cruising along. Then a whole school rushes past. I lose my cool and leap out of the water.

WADING BIRDS ARE STILL fishing towards the end of the day, taking terrible risks when feeding near sunbaking crocs. I've filmed crocs taking a wild pig and a wallaby. In both cases, the croc slammed the victim on the water's surface to break bones and soften it up so it could be pulled apart. Crocs don't chew; they bite, crush, shake, roll, tear and then swallow.

In this period at the end of the Dry, freshwater crocodile hatchlings begin to emerge. Each mother lays 13–20 eggs in a sandy bank and covers them up for their 10-week incubation. Goannas can smell and dig up freshly laid eggs, and only about 30 per cent of the eggs make it to the hatchling stage.

When the hatchlings break through their shells underneath the sand, they struggle upwards. First their little heads then their bodies emerge, before they scamper for the water. Kites swoop down and big barra lurk in the water. About 90 per cent of the hatchlings die during their first year.

Comb-crested jacanas lay their eggs in the Dry. Sometimes called Jesus birds, these birds appear to walk on water. They're one of the only animals capable of walking on the floating, unstable carpet of water lily leaves, their enormous feet and claws distributing their weight over a wide area. Jacanas lay 3–4 eggs on a lily pad. The eggs look exposed, but predators can't see them from under water, lizards can't walk on lilies and the mottled-brown colour of the eggs hides them from sharp-eyed raptors.

Late in the day, we witness some of the first rains of the Wet. Thunder and lightning crack across the floodplain as monsoonal storms sweep in from the Timor Sea. The welcome rains are light at first, falling on ground that hasn't seen a drop for eight months.

In the coming days and weeks, the rains will become a flood and the billabong – a tranquil pool during the Dry – will spill into the surrounding forest, joining it once again to the river of its birth. ■

Life in the furnace

It takes a special kind of plant or animal to live in Australia's deserts, which are among the harshest and most extensive in the world.

Story by **Karen McGhee**

Issue 115 Jul–Aug 2013

IT'S EARLY MORNING on a midsummer's day in the Simpson Desert, just east of the Queensland–Northern Territory border, and the air temperature is already on its way to passing 40°C. With jerky movements like a mechanical toy, a thorny devil emerges from the spinifex before almost disappearing, its blotchy colouration perfect camouflage against the red sand and desiccated plant debris.

There's no obvious water about, but the spiky little lizard pauses at the edge of a claypan. Almost imperceptibly, liquid begins to travel via capillary action – as if sucked through a series of tiny drinking straws – upwards between rows of scales running along the devil's legs and body to its mouth.

Professor Chris Dickman, a University of Sydney terrestrial ecologist, has witnessed this scene repeatedly during the 24 years he's been overseeing the Southern Hemisphere's longest-running desert biodiversity study. But he still marvels at the devil's extraordinary survival prowess in one of Australia's most challenging environments. "A bizarre appearance, weird behaviour and an incredibly specialised diet of only little black ants," he observes, "make the thorny devil one of our standout desert survivors."

AUSTRALIA'S 10 OFFICIAL deserts cover 1,371,000sq.km, each receiving less than the desert-defining average maximum rainfall of 250mm a year. But, because much of the harsh interior suffers such crippling spells of aridity, twice this area – nearly 40 per cent of Australia's landmass – could be categorised as desert.

Average annual rainfall is well below 250mm in the Simpson. As for much of the inland, the timing of falls is notoriously unpredictable and there's a broad cycle of flood-creating deluges every decade or so, then years of very light and occasional showers. This pattern is fundamental to life's limits here and inextricably entwined with another key feature of our deserts: fire.

Each flood stimulates a rapid vegetation build-up that dries off during succeeding years to become fuel for huge wildfires that engulf millions of hectares of Australia's parched interior. "That's very much a defining thing about Australia's deserts," Chris says. Nowhere else do desert fires burn with such frequency, intensity and coverage.

This places unique stress on Australia's desert flora and fauna, says Alice Springs-based botanist with the NT government's flora and fauna division Dr Catherine Nano. For her, the desert's survival superstars include native grasses, peas and daisies, which occasionally burst into life en masse, creating short-lived carpets of flowers and foliage. "They're superb at evading drought by having long-lived seed banks that survive decades at least – but possibly hundreds of years – waiting for the dual opportunity of a fire event and rainfall," Catherine says.

Living inside termite mounds ensures that these tiny insects can survive the extreme heat of the desert by creating their own cooler and more moist environments on the inside.

Fire clears enduring hummocks of drought-hardy spinifex – slow-growing, long-lived, shrub-like grasses with tough herbivore-resistant leaves reinforced by silica and roots that reach 3m down to tap subterranean water. Spinifex is endemic to Australia. Its roots help stabilise the sand and soil that covers more than one-fifth of the continent and it's the major vegetation of the country's five biggest deserts – the Great Victoria, Gibson, Great Sandy, Tanami and Simpson. Spinifex flowers only after heavy rain and some species' seeds need fire to germinate. It creates crucial habitat for desert fauna. But, although hardy arid-zone kangaroos, known as euros, will nibble soft new shoots, very few animals eat mature spinifex. Termites are the major exception. These insects occur in enormous numbers in arid Australia and are critical food for many desert dwellers. Indirectly, at least, spinifex ultimately underpins many of the continent's desert food chains.

Beaked geckos, for example, eat termites and little else. Belying their fragile appearance, geckos are ubiquitous arid-zone →

Thorny devils are superbly adapted to their desert home. At night, dew condenses on their bodies and in the morning they brush up against dew-laden grasses. The tiny grooves between their scales then channels this moisture into their mouths.

Greater bilbies are omnivores that usually build multiple burrows within their home ranges. Like so many desert dwellers, they forage after dark for food items that are also the animals' water source.

inhabitants and their diversity across Australia's deserts is among the world's highest. These small-bodied, big-eyed lizards shun high daytime temperatures and harsh ultraviolet radiation by sheltering in old spider burrows, surfacing only every few weeks at night to gorge themselves on termites.

During a fire, spinifex roots remain protected underground, poised to throw new shoots upwards after the flames have passed. Above ground, after the foliage has burnt away, there's a brief blank canvas, free of competing vegetation when, following a deluge, long-dormant seeds awaken and rapidly sprout, and grow into adult plants that then flower and shed new seed. The precise triggers aren't fully understood for all species, but research shows that, for at least some seeds, water laced with dissolved chemicals from charred vegetation is important.

DESERT VEGETATION SURGES trigger sequential explosions of animal life. First come insects. Then, about six months after a big rain, seed-eating native rodent populations begin peaking.

The plains mouse is one rodent that's rarely seen in desert dunes during drought years but is everywhere after inland floods, its numbers rapidly exploding out of small core populations that survive dry periods in holes and cracks on gibber plains and cracking clay soils. 'Gibber' is the Australian term for desert pavement – a surface made of small, closely packed rocks. It covers about 10 per cent of Australia's land area and desert ecologists are finding that it supports important drought-refuge habitat for species with boom-bust population cycles.

About six months after native rodent numbers explode, populations of mouse-sized insectivorous marsupials, including several dunnart species, can take off. Dunnarts also shelter underground by day – in burrows abandoned by rodents and large invertebrates such as scorpions – where daytime temperatures are lower and humidity is higher, emerging only at night. When food is scarce, dunnarts enter torpor – a short-term hibernation-like state, during which body temperature and metabolic rate drop to reduce energy consumption.

Mulgaras – aggressive, carnivorous, rat-sized marsupials – also rise in numbers after floods. Dunnart burrows can flood during big deluges, but mulgara refuges rarely do. Mulgaras do their own excavations and carefully position entrances in complex, metre-long tunnels halfway up sand dunes, to drain during rain. When water levels rise too high, mulgaras seal their burrow entrances with sand plugs.

The grey falcon has a vast range that covers Australia's deserts. It uses thermals to hunt, mostly for other birds, and breeds once a year. There are thought to be fewer than 1000 individuals left in the wild.

The hairy-footed dunnart shelters from the heat of WA's arid regions in burrows during the day. It hunts at night, catching the insects on which it relies for energy, nutrients and water.

Rabbit-sized greater bilbies once occurred across Australia but their numbers have been decimated, partly by feral predators. There are, however, still good populations in the Great Sandy Desert around central Western Australia, says Dr David Pearson, a desert ecologist with the WA Department of Parks and Wildlife. Like many desert animals, bilbies mostly extract the moisture they need from their food and have highly concentrated urine to reduce water loss. However, they aren't quite as good at this as spinifex hopping mice, which use their specialised kidneys to produce near-solid urine – the most concentrated of any mammal anywhere.

Bilbies use strong front limbs and claws to dig deep, twisting burrows, where they remain by day, emerging only at night to forage. "They go down in a corkscrew so things like goannas can't dig them up," David explains. They're also often situated under termite mounds, for insulation.

Australia's supreme mammalian desert burrowers are marsupial moles, which rarely appear above ground. Rather than create tunnels, they 'swim' through sand using spade-like front feet, well-developed shoulders and a calloused nose and forehead. Weighing less than 60g, they're thought to have such low oxygen requirements they can survive on the air between sand grains.

SURPRISINGLY, ABOUT 40 frog species occur in arid Australia. Some of them are among the desert's best underground dwellers, including the desert spadefoot toad and desert trilling frog. Both are thought capable of surviving long droughts underground, possibly years at a time, by 'aestivating' – reducing their metabolic rate and energy needs to bare survival levels.

As little as 5–10mm of rain infiltrating the top sand layers can bring them briefly to the surface, where they forage and rehydrate before returning underground. "They'll only breed after really big rains when the claypans fill," Chris Dickman says, "and then they go nuts and it's almost impossible to sleep with the din of calling frogs!"

Birds and lizards mostly buck the desert trend for nocturnal living. One notable exception is the letter-winged kite. The world's only night-hunting raptor, it preys on nocturnal mammals by moonlight. It often subsists in low numbers in desert refuge areas, but highly specialised adaptations allow it to breed quickly when conditions are right, so it booms when there's plenty of prey about.

Another specialist arid-zone resident raptor is the grey falcon. Endemic to Australia, it treats the continent's deserts as one huge home range that it patrols from on high across vast distances. Research suggests a single continent-wide population of just 1000 individuals, making it one of the world's rarest birds.

THERE'S A STRONG link between trees and birds in Australia's deserts and any vegetation with height is well used for roosting and nesting. Some trees cope with desert conditions by being slow growing but long-lived and one of the most extreme exponents is the waddy-wood wattle, which lives 500 or more years. It's found in just a few places east and west of the Simpson, on dry stony plains and slopes and in old river channels.

Other acacias, collectively called 'mulga', are widespread throughout Australia's central and eastern desert areas. In southern and western arid areas they're replaced by 'mallee', eucalypt species that grow with multiple stems originating from an underground lignotuber. All have complex root systems with deep taproots to exploit underground water, and fine lateral roots that take advantage of surface water from sporadic rainfall. 'Stem flow' architecture makes these trees look like upside-down umbrellas, with branches arranged to direct rainfall straight down into surface roots.

As with birds, about a quarter of Australia's reptile species are found in our deserts. But, unlike the birds, these 200 species are all residents – the most diverse assemblage of desert reptiles in the world. They include geckos, dragons, skinks, snakes and goannas, including the perentie. At up to 2.5m, this is Australia's (and one of the world's) largest lizards – an aggressive carnivore that eats almost anything and tops many desert food chains. ■

STORY BY **EMMA YOUNG** AND **JUSTIN GILLIGAN**

INTO THE ABYSS

The world of the deep sea is a cold, dark, highly pressurised and largely unexplored frontier populated by strange, unearthly creatures.

ISSUE 101 ◆ Jan–Mar 2011

YOU WOULD HAVE THOUGHT Dr Ron Thresher was describing a mission to a distant planet. "Everybody was crowded into the control room to see what it would look like. We had no idea what we'd find," the CSIRO marine and atmospheric research scientist recalls. "Imagine a light shining out. It's all dark, apart from the occasional sparkle. Then we saw a fine-silt bottom and a couple of weird-looking black things crawling along, then a huge, transparent, tulip-shaped creature about a metre high. It was a very strange world. You got the impression you were in a place [far from] home."

Ron is talking about a location just 4km from his research vessel – 4km straight down, that is – off Tasmania's southern coast. It was the deepest dive ever undertaken in Australian waters. Carried out by a remotely operated submersible named *Jason*, the dive represented an exploration of a hidden world where temperatures hover around 1.2°C and the ambient pressure – up to 1000 atmospheres – could crush a standard submarine. In January 2009, *Jason* made 14 dives into this frigid, eternal darkness – research excursions that are still transforming scientists' understanding of one of our planet's most inaccessible regions.

While there isn't any technical definition, the 'deep sea' is often considered to begin about 200m beneath the surface of any ocean. Below this depth, there isn't enough light to drive photosynthesis – the process by which plants convert light into energy.

Australia lays claim to more than 10 million square kilometres of ocean, with an average depth of 2500m, so we have a lot of deep sea. In fact, it's Australia's – and the planet's – largest habitat. Yet, it's also our most poorly understood. Exploring such an enormous, remote and hostile environment is logistically very difficult, of course, and extremely expensive. "It costs a bundle to go down there to take a look," Ron acknowledges.

Jason's Tasmanian mission into the deep →

Food is difficult to come by in the deep sea. The threadfin dragonfish uses its fearsome and numerous teeth – which even protrude from the roof of its mouth and tongue – to help ensure it snares a rare meal with the first bite. This specimen – from the collections of Museum Victoria – was captured in the Tasman Sea in 2003.

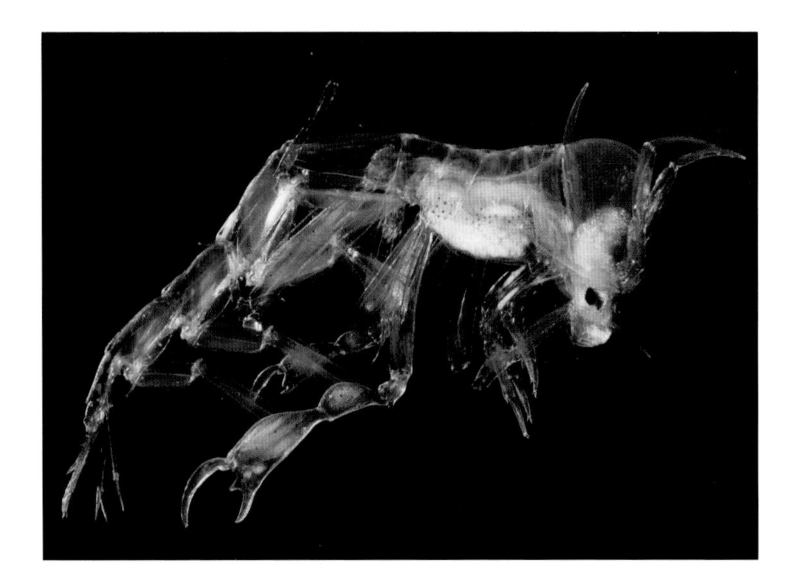

The pram bug lives a strange existence. It devours the interior of the jelly-like barrel salp and lives in the hollowed-out chamber, pushing it along for use as a mobile shelter.

Found worldwide to depths of 700km, making them among the deepest-living large animals, Dumbo octopus can grow to 2m. They're named after the Disney character for their elephant-ear-like fins.

was a collaboration between the CSIRO, the US National Science Foundation and several Australian museums and universities. While the team spotted strange creatures, the project's main aim was to locate and collect deep-sea corals.

Oceanographers have discovered that, during the past 15–20 years, the deep ocean has become slightly warmer. But to identify whether this is due to human-induced climate change or natural variability, and whether the warming is likely to have any negative effects on the coral, a very long record of past temperatures is needed. That's exactly what *Jason*'s samples are providing.

Ron's initial results suggest that deep-sea temperatures have indeed varied naturally in the past. And the corals have survived, suggesting they're more resilient to temperature changes than some scientists have supposed. There has also been concern that the rising acidity of the world's oceans, caused by an increase in dissolved carbon dioxide, would lower the availability of carbonate to such an extent it would restrict coral growth. All corals – including deep-sea forms – need carbonate to make their skeletons. The good news, says Ron, is that so far the data demonstrate that deep-sea corals can tolerate very low carbonate concentrations.

WHILE TASMANIA'S deep-sea corals are providing insights into the global phenomenon of climate change, other researchers are focused on investigating what lives deep in our oceans, uncovering some weird and wonderful life forms in the process.

Surprisingly, given the harsh conditions, there seems to be incredible biodiversity in the ocean depths. The decade-long international Census of Marine Life, completed in October 2010, identified 5722 species that can only be found at depths of 1km and below, and 17,650 that only live below the 200m mark.

Meanwhile, recent work by marine scientists at the Monterey Bay Aquarium, in California, USA, suggests the 'gelatinous blob' is by far the most common body form in the deep sea and therefore – given the size of Earth's many deep-sea regions – on the planet.

It makes good sense to be jelly-like if you're living in the cold, with food difficult to come by, says Adrian Flynn, a University of Queensland PhD student researching deep-sea fishes. "Most things that live in the deep sea are living on a metabolic knife edge," he says. "The way to deal with that is to have a very, very slow metabolism. You don't move much, so there's no point putting a lot of energy into muscular body forms and bones and things, because you won't be swimming around. So, a lot of species have a way of life that is basically to float and wait."

And when food does come along, you want to make sure you get it. As a result, many species, such as anglerfish, have developed very impressive sets of teeth to make prey capture highly efficient. Adrian is focusing on a deep-sea group called lanternfish. Each night, an estimated 600 million tonnes of these fish migrate from their day-time haunts – at a depth of about 1km in each of the world's oceans – up to the surface waters, where they feast on zooplankton. Such nightly vertical migrations are a common behavioural adaptation among deep-sea species.

By feeding on tiny animals at shallower depths, lanternfish also help to transfer energy from the sun-lavished surface to the deep sea, where they, in turn, are preyed upon by other animals, such as deep-sea squid. Adrian has also found that at Macquarie Island, midway between Australia and Antarctica, lanternfish can be an important food source for surface dwellers such as elephant seals and penguins.

Another remarkable, but common, deep-sea characteristic seen in lanternfish is that they come equipped with bioluminescent 'headlamps' for communicating in the inky darkness. No-one yet knows exactly what messages their flashes convey, but it's believed that they play a role in choosing mates and helping individuals to remain with their schools.

In May 2010, Professor Justin Marshall, one of Adrian's University of Queensland supervisors, spearheaded research using specially designed cameras to explore the sea floor 1400m down at Osprey Reef, 350km north of Cairns. The cameras emitted red light –

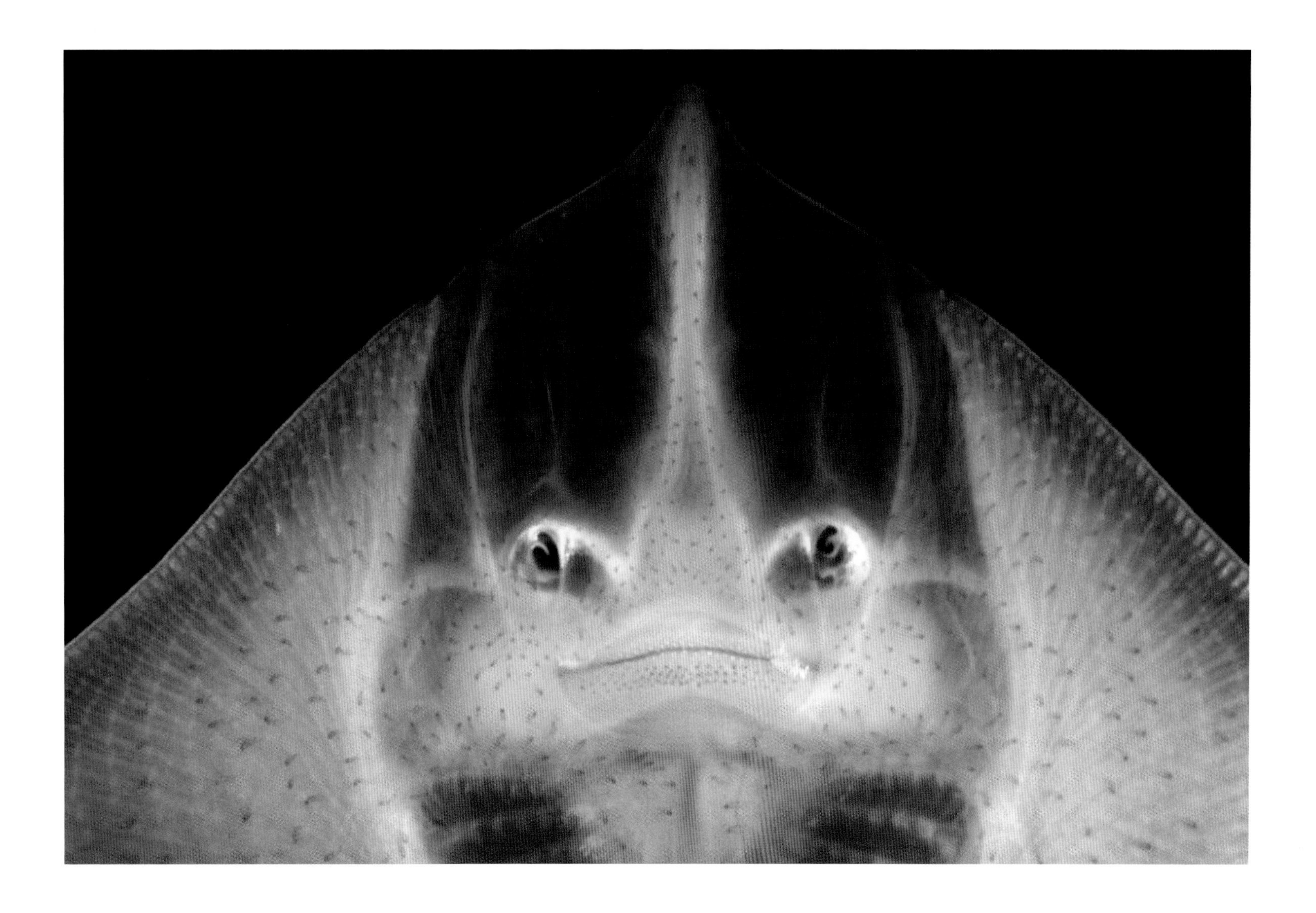

What look like eyes on the underside of this rough skate are actually nostrils. Living at depths down to 1500m in the south-west Pacific around New Zealand, its skin is spotted with large pores that help to detect the vibrations and chemical signals of its prey.

undetectable by almost all deep-sea animals – so that they could film in natural conditions. Justin and his team found a host of bizarre species, including six-gilled sharks, *Atolla* jellyfish and snake-like halosoar fish hunting along the sea floor.

But one of the ongoing aims of Justin's work is to discover more about how deep-sea animals use bioluminescent organs to communicate. "There's a whole secret language going on down there," he explains. The team hopes that further research trips will help decode it.

EXPEDITIONS SUCH AS THOSE into the depths off Osprey Reef are certainly helping scientists to understand the kinds of animals that live in the deep sea. But a better understanding of their distribution around the world will be essential if this huge habitat is to be managed properly, says Dr Tim O'Hara, a marine invertebrate specialist at Museum Victoria, Melbourne.

Certain deep-sea features, such as underwater volcano peaks and sulfide-spewing hydrothermal vents, are known to be hotbeds of marine biodiversity. But plenty of animals also live across the vast expanses of sea floor. "Some areas of the deep-sea floor can be as diverse as rainforests," Tim says.

It isn't clear, however, how deep-sea habitats, and the animals they support, change around the world. "On land, we know where deserts turn into rainforests and how temperate Australia is different from tropical Australia, but in the sea these patterns haven't been put together," Tim explains.

He has undertaken the ambitious task of analysing expedition collections to map the distribution of brittle stars (relatives of starfish) off Australia's east coast, from the equator to the South Pole.

Already, Tim has found that only 10 per cent of the brittle star species living at that depth off New Caledonia, for example, are also found off Tasmania. Why two almost environmentally identical locations with no physical barrier between them would share so few species in a group with larval young dispersed by currents is still unclear.

In fact, research on the deep sea is throwing out as many questions as answers. "On the one hand, there's the lure of the unknown, just to find out what's there," Ron says. "Then, if you're trying to manage the deep sea for conservation purposes, it would be nice to know what you're managing. And then there are lots of questions – what drives productivity in the ocean, and [how] the ocean works? When you start seeing wholly new communities down there, it gives you a new insight into how these things link together." ■

Islands of life

From the Torres Strait to subantarctic latitudes, nature still rules the roost on most of Australia's 8222 islands.

Story by **Tim Low**

Issue 83 Jul–Sep 2006

PERCHED ON A CLIFF by the water's edge, I watch the boobies returning from sea. It's early evening on Christmas Island, 1800km north-west of mainland Australia, and hundreds upon hundreds of these big bony birds are passing by, so close at times I could almost touch them if I tried.

There are larger frigatebirds as well, sweeping by on black, scythe-like wings, and noddies, much smaller and flapping faster as if in haste. Into the night this great host continues, without a sound, or none that I can hear above the coconut fronds crackling in the wind and the sea surging below. I'm moved by this mighty parade and find myself thinking: "Only on an island could I experience something like this."

Australia is blessed with 8222 islands. Each is a little world unto itself: a unique experiment in life, an opportunity for animals and plants to operate differently. Islands – especially remote ones – are shaped by unusual rules. The ecosystems are simpler, the dynamics are different.

On islands, predators are often absent, so certain animals can go about their business without fear. During the Age of Exploration, European mariners were often struck by the fearlessness of animals on remote islands. When Matthew Flinders was exploring south of the Australian mainland in 1802 and encountered relaxed kangaroos, he astutely deduced that he had found an island, and bestowed upon Kangaroo Island, South Australia, the name it bears today. Nowadays, many an Australian camping ground boasts tame marsupials, but none can match KI's laid-back roos. When I was there, one confiding matron let me slide my hand deep inside her pouch.

Seabirds roosting on islands were often so easily caught that sailors assumed they were stupid. While the birds on some islands are no longer so 'friendly', close encounters on others still occur. On Lord Howe Island, 580km off the New South Wales coast, you can cry out to the providence petrels and they'll sweep down to your feet and let you pick them up. King penguins on subantarctic Macquarie Island also display a striking lack of fear. There are protocols about how close to them you can go, but no rules to keep them away from you. When I was there, if I strolled up a beach they would eye me cautiously, but whenever I stood still I soon had my own little fan club, a coterie of the curious, bleating in my face and nibbling my fingers.

Islands are classed as one of two types: oceanic or continental. Oceanic islands are born at sea, as rising volcanoes, uplifted oceanic crust or old submerged mountains coated in a veneer of coral and sand. The variety of life on such islands is always limited because everything on them had to get there by flying, floating or swimming.

When biologists first explored Christmas Island – a classic oceanic island – their tally of vertebrate animals was tiny. There were only six forest-bird species, five mammals, six reptiles and no frogs. That's a paltry score for a 13,500sq.km patch of tropical forest. Frogs are as rare on oceanic islands as pirate treasure, because salt spray on their damp skin soon kills them, so they rarely survive voyages at sea on logs or debris.

Most of Australia's islands are continental. They're slices of the mainland that were stranded by rising seas 12–6000 years ago, after the most recent ice age. For example, Fraser Island, 200km north of Brisbane, abounds in frogs, because their ancestors didn't have to cross any ocean to get there. Most continental islands are far too small to conserve the original wildlife – so larger animals such as kangaroos, dingoes, emus and koalas are usually missing – but Fraser is large enough to retain a rich continental fauna.

WHEN SMALL CONTINENTAL ISLANDS lack predators they often attract nesting seabirds and a distinctive community develops. Their numbers on some islands are astonishing. Each summer 440ha Babel Island, off Flinders Island in Bass Strait, hosts more than 5 million short-tailed shearwaters, or muttonbirds.

Over time, some island birds that feed safely on the ground lose interest in flying and become bigger instead. This happened on Mauritius to the dodo. On Lord Howe Island, a diminution of wings took place on a woodhen and much larger white swamphen. White isn't a great colour for a plump bird on the ground, and when British colonisers arrived, the Lord Howe swamphen soon went the way of the dodo. Thankfully the woodhen population has survived.

Christmas Island isn't suitable for flightless birds because it's crawling with crabs. Nowhere else in the world do so many big crustaceans scuttle about in a tropical rainforest. There are red crabs, blue crabs and their much larger nemesis, the robber crab. It's a snapshot of the world we might have had if animals with backbones had never evolved – one ruled by clanking segmented arthropods. Robber crabs, with their lurid colours and weird moving parts, are Christmas Island's biggest animals after seabirds, reaching the size of soccer balls and a weight of 4kg. The largest among them are probably 50–60 years old, an age that few mammals or birds reach.

Robber crabs – some of the biggest animals without backbones to

At up to 1m long, robber, or coconut, crabs are the world's largest land arthropods, the group that includes insects, spiders and crustaceans. This one is pictured on Dolly Beach, Christmas Island.

walk the Earth – highlight the fact that size-shifts, both up and down, often occur on islands. The Komodo dragon – the world's biggest lizard by far – and the dodo are famous island giants. On some islands even the plants are giants. The Macquarie Island cabbage could win all the ribbons at a country show if it actually looked like a cabbage. It has metre-long leaves, if you count the stalks. Its gigantism is attributed to the stable humid climate, rich soil fertilised by seabirds and lack of herbivores.

DURING THE MOST RECENT ice age nearly all of Australia's continental islands ceased to exist – they merged back into the mainland. The relatively short span since their re-emergence has limited their opportunities to develop separately.

Only a few oceanic islands have remained completely isolated and they are by far the most distinctive. Christmas Island, Lord Howe Island and Norfolk Island, 1700km north-east of Sydney, are three priceless jewels, each carrying a bevy of unique species. The 250 Christmas Island specialties include a fruit pigeon, frigatebird, owl, butterfly, blind cave scorpion and even a mosquito. Lord Howe has more than 100 unique plants, including tree ferns and palms. Norfolk boasts 45 unique plants as well as a parrot, warbler and two white-eyes.

Macquarie and Heard are also old oceanic islands of immense worth. Although their birds, seals and most of their plants are found on other subantarctic isles, you only have to run your finger round a globe to see how scarce and tiny such islands are. The latitudes they occupy are mostly cold and empty sea. Subantarctic land is the rarest real estate of all and its ecological values are enormous.

Australia's other remote islands are the coral cays in the Indian Ocean and Coral Sea. The Cocos (Keeling) Islands lie more than 2000km north-west of mainland Australia, while Ashmore Reef and Cartier Island sit well north of Derby in Western Australia. East of the Great Barrier Reef, there are 46 tiny cays in the Coral Sea Islands Territory. These cays, as well as those bestriding the Great Barrier Reef, are formed of infertile sand and coral rubble. Rising only a few metres above sea level, they're too small and unstable to support diverse communities, but as breeding sites for seabirds they're outstanding. In the north of the Great Barrier Reef, a cute native rat – the endangered Bramble Cay melomys – is confined to one island just 340m long and less than half as wide.

Australia's islands are places to celebrate and admire, but they're sometimes places to mourn as well. The attributes that make them so special also render them vulnerable. Tiny Norfolk and Lord Howe islands have each lost more birds to extinction than all of mainland Australia. Christmas Island has lost to disease two giant native rats. It's no coincidence that an island specialty – the dodo – became the world's symbol of extinction. ■

CHAPTER SEVEN

REPTILES AND AMPHIBIANS

With so much of the continent being hot, arid and sandy, it's perhaps unsurprising that Australia is a country where reptiles rule. Indeed, when it comes to reptiles, Australia is a land of superlatives.

It's home to more reptiles than any other country (more than 910 known species, which is more than three times the total found in North America) and more skinks as well (about 400 known species), and the level of endemism is higher than anywhere else (more than 90 per cent). We share the continent with the world's largest reptile (the saltwater crocodile, which can grow to a length of 7m and weigh more than 1 tonne) and the most toxic land snake (the inland taipan, whose venom is believed to be so toxic that a single bite could kill at least 100 adult humans).

Australia has almost 200 known species of snake, 25 of which are considered to be potentially deadly. However, one of our best-studied reptiles is a non-venomous snake. A long-running study of the water pythons of Fogg Dam in the Northern Territory has uncovered another Australian-reptile superlative – the snake population that lives on the floodplain represents the highest known biomass of predators in any ecosystem on Earth.

While it's the snakes that often engender a lurid fascination, Australia is truly the land of the lizard. Among them are instantly recognisable iconic species such as the frill-necked lizard of the north, the thorny devil of the central deserts and the widely distributed blue-tongues. And of course there are the geckos, of which Australia boasts about 140 known species, and which gave rise to our legless lizards, the pygopodids, of which there are another 35 species. Such is the incredible diversity of lizards in Australia that a single hectare of grassland in central Australia can play host to 40 or more species. Indeed, the most diverse assemblages of lizards on Earth are found in these spinifex deserts.

As with the reptiles, Australia's amphibians are remarkably diverse and show extremely high levels of endemism, with about 230 described species, almost 95 per cent of which are found nowhere else. They vary in size from the 14mm slender-bodied javelin tree frog to the white-lipped tree frog, the world's largest tree frog, which grows to a length of 135mm.

Although they reach their highest diversities in the continent's moister margins, frogs have also managed to colonise the desert regions; some 40 species are found in the arid centre. In order to cope with the harsh conditions and the unpredictable rainfall, several species spend much of their time underground. The water-holding frog, for example, creates a cocoon around itself by progressively shedding layers of skin and can remain underground for as long as five years.

Among Australia's frogs are a number that have evolved some unorthodox reproductive strategies. Several have done away with the free-living tadpole stage, the eggs hatching into tiny, fully formed froglets, while the male marsupial frog, which lives in the high country on the New South Wales–Queensland border, carries its developing tadpoles in special hip pouches. However, perhaps the most unusual were the two species of gastric-brooding frog. These rainforest-stream-dwelling amphibians, found in central-eastern and south-eastern Queensland, were only discovered in 1973 and 1984. They shared a very peculiar – and indeed, unique – reproductive strategy that involved the female swallowing the eggs or young tadpoles and rearing them in her stomach. Sadly, neither species has been seen since the 1980s and both are presumed to be extinct.

They're joined by two other extinct species and, rather worryingly, five that are considered to be critically endangered. For a long time, the cause of these declines and extinctions was a mystery – particularly because most occurred in pristine rainforest habitats, but it's now believed that the culprit is chytridiomycosis, an infectious disease caused by the chytrid fungus. ■

Previous page: The southern angle-headed dragon is an arboreal species found only in rainforests and rainforest margins in eastern Australia. Its closest relatives are mostly found in New Guinea.

Once abundant in swamps and scrub on Australia's east coast, the green and golden bell frog has undergone a significant decline in NSW, reduced to fewer than 50 recorded locations, most of which are home to small populations of fewer than 20 adult frogs.

A hatchling olive ridley turtle bobs on the sea surface. Hatchling sea turtles are beset by myriad threats and it's estimated that only about that only one in 1000 will survive to adulthood.

STORY BY **SORREL WILBY** AND **KAREN MCGHEE**

MARINERS MOST ANCIENT

Australian biologists are battling to understand a decline in the success of sea turtle hatchlings before it's too late.

Issue 123 ◆ Nov–Dec 2014

SEA TURTLE REPRODUCTION is protracted and arduous. That's becoming very clear on this balmy summer night on remote Raine Island – at the Great Barrier Reef's northern end – where for more than 90 minutes I've been watching a huge female green turtle shovel about a tonne of sand with her flippers.

'Tears' have been streaming from her eyes and she finally volleys about 100 leathery eggs into the chamber that she's created above high-water. She covers them with sand and – emitting a few deep-pitched grunts – turns to drag her massive form back to the water.

Female green turtles return to lay eggs near the beach where they were born. They don't reach sexual maturity until their third to fourth decade, meaning this mother-to-be – one of about 500 nesting on Raine tonight – may have hatched on this beach sometime in the 1980s, possibly earlier.

The average nesting female weighs about 130kg, has a top shell that's at least 1m long and usually spends more than five hours out of the water digging her nest and laying her eggs. By dawn's approach, all have slipped back beneath the gentle Coral Sea shore break, transforming from lumbering terrestrial misfits into agile aquatic divers.

A TREELESS 32ha low-lying coral cay, Raine is a seabird haven and supports the world's largest green turtle rookery, where thousands of adult females return in any one year.

Sexually mature females lay only every 2–8 years. They must reach a fat threshold before they can breed, explains biologist Dr Ian Bell, a senior conservation officer with the Queensland Department of Environment and Heritage Protection (DEHP) threatened species unit team that operates on Raine. The females on the beach tonight would have spent the past few years building up their body fat. Energy from that fat would then have gone into developing hundreds of yolky follicles that are released as eggs, in batches, from their ovaries during the 3–4-month breeding season.

"Once she's built up her reserves, a female →

Under cover of darkness, a female flatback turtle deposits her eggs into the chamber that she has dug on a sandy beach on Crab Island off Cape York Peninsula in the Torres Strait, QLD.

green turtle will move from her feeding grounds to a courtship area, mating with two, three, four, perhaps even eight different males over the course of several weeks," Ian says.

Each female stores all of that sperm in her oviducts, maximising breeding potential by enabling females to mix the paternity of broods, ensuring genetic diversity; evolutionary pressure for survival probably begins before conception as the sperm of different males compete to fertilise the eggs.

"When she's ready to lay her first clutch, she'll pop off 50 follicles from each ovary," Ian says. "These then travel down into her oviducts, where they are bathed in sperm. They are now fertilised eggs that begin to develop their shells. The embryos develop for six days to pinhead size, then sit there, in suspended animation, inside each of the eggs until they are laid."

It takes two weeks to prepare a clutch of eggs for laying. And each female will lumber up onto the shore six times, on average, during the breeding season, digging a new nest for each new clutch of about 100 eggs. As the eggs emerge they are covered in transparent slime.

"When that mucus drains away, there is an oxygen and gas exchange across the shell membrane," Ian says. "And that's when the little embryos recommence their development, when they are there, in the sand."

GREEN TURTLES ARE ONE of seven types of sea turtle. The others are the hawksbill, flatback, loggerhead, leatherback, olive ridley and Kemp's ridley turtles. All but the latter occur in Australian waters. Northern Australia is the flatback's stronghold, home to the species' only recorded nesting locations.

As cumbersome as these air-breathing reptiles are on land, sea turtles are sublimely adapted to marine habitats. Adults swim at speeds of up to 25km/h, surfacing to breathe every 30 minutes or so. Turtle tears are another adaptation to marine life. The reptiles get all their moisture from sea water and their food, and 'cry' constantly to expel excess salt via glands behind their eyes. Tears play a crucial secondary role for females when they nest. Without flooding eye secretions, their vision would be quickly impaired by the sand they flick up.

Eggs are left unattended to incubate in the sand. Within about two months, the home-alone offspring rip through their shells using a special 'tooth', just as birds do. Temperature is the main determiner of sea turtle gender. For successful incubation, a nest's temperature must be 25°C to 33°C; temperatures at the low end produce males, at the high end, females. Some beaches produce predominantly male hatchlings, others females, and the sex ratio varies among species and populations. For Raine's greens, females are favoured two to one.

"At 29°C, it's going to take about 55 days for those eggs to hatch," Ian observes. "The hatchlings will break out of their shells and the ones at the top will start to dig." It's thought that during incubation the embryos may absorb scents from their surroundings to develop an imprint of the unique 'signature' of their beach, which will help breeding females return in future decades.

"They wait just below the sand surface – maybe up to 3–4 days – until they feel the temperature change in the sand [usually after dark], then they burst out of the sand and race towards the sea," Ian continues. "Assuming they avoid being attacked by birds or hungry crabs en route, they then battle their way through the breakers."

They keep travelling en masse – relying on the safety-in-numbers principle that at least some will survive – to face a posse of sharks and other carnivorous fish. Any survivors of this harrowing journey will have used the last of the yolk they've absorbed for energy and swim frantically out to meet an open-ocean current.

Researchers used to call the next few years of sea turtles' lives "the lost years". Decades of tagging research have now told scientists a lot about this time but there's still much to learn: nobody is exactly sure where small green turtles go or what they do until they are about dinner-plate size, which is when they reappear in the coastal feeding grounds. Feeding grounds for greens (the only primarily herbivorous sea turtles) are places with plenty of seagrass or algae.

For every 1000 sea turtle hatchlings, just one is likely to survive myriad natural hazards across several decades to eventually breed. Yet as arduous as a sea turtle's life seems to be it works, because these reptiles have been around for more than 110 million years.

IN SPITE OF THEIR evolutionary longevity, five of the seven species of sea turtle are now categorised internationally on the IUCN's Red List of Endangered Species as endangered or critically endangered. Australia's own lists designate our populations of loggerheads, olive ridleys and leatherbacks as endangered, and our green, hawksbill and flatback turtles as vulnerable to extinction.

Worldwide, human-induced threats include excessive harvesting, especially of adult turtles; loss of eggs from human consumption or feral predators; coastal development with associated loss of nesting and feeding habitats; oil spills; coastal lighting that confuses hatchlings; and boat traffic. In Australia, significant turtle numbers are claimed by ghost nets – deliberately discarded or accidentally lost fishing nets that drift with the currents, indiscriminately snaring and drowning air-breathing animals such as turtles.

Overlaying all other threats is the unquantifiable impact of climate change. No-one is quite sure what it may mean for sea turtles, but a

A flatback turtle, a species endemic to Australia and southern New Guinea, swims over a coral reef. Flatbacks are carnivorous, feeding mostly on soft-bodied prey such as sea cucumbers, soft corals and jellyfish.

global 1°C temperature rise might feminise populations or increase the mortality rate. One of Australia's leading turtle researchers for the past four decades, Dr Col Limpus, chief scientist for the DEHP's threatened species unit, is hopeful about sea turtles' ability to make it through climate change but less optimistic about the other human-induced challenges they face.

"Green turtle population [numbers] in eastern and northern Australia go up and down together from year to year, and it's predictable," Col comments at Mon Repos Conservation Park, near the Queensland coastal town of Bundaberg. There's a popular nesting site for loggerheads here that Col has personally been monitoring since the late 1960s. "It's driven by the climate. You get a big El Niño event and 18 months later you will have big numbers of turtles nesting. You get a La Niña event, and 18 months later you'll have very few turtles nesting.

"When you have a drought, you don't have the run-off from the rivers," he continues. "You have fewer cyclones. The seagrass and algal pastures are not knocked about and you have lots of turtles go into breeding condition. It's not a new phenomenon."

Col believes there are two ways turtles could respond to rising temperatures. One would be through changes to breeding cycles and incubation, which could take hundreds of years to take effect. The other is by females choosing alternate nesting beaches as they begin their adult lives. And that, says Col, is already occurring.

Various protective measures and interventions – such as predator controls on Queensland's Cape York Peninsula and the successful annual relocation of more than 50,000 otherwise doomed loggerhead eggs – have already helped some turtle populations recover from other threats. But sea turtle species still hover precariously on endangered species lists. To researchers, failure to improve their conservation status isn't worth considering.

The consequences of sea turtle extinctions would have far-reaching impacts says Ian Bell, explaining that a major decline of green turtles from the northern Great Barrier Reef, for example, would precipitate the collapse of other food webs.

For Sally Eagan, DEHP's manager of strategy and policy for threatened species, the potential impact is heart-wrenchingly simple. "The world will be a much poorer place," she says. "Imagine getting up in 100 years and showing your child pictures of turtles...and saying, 'The world used to be full of these.'" ■

Geckos: the eyes have it

Story and photography by **Steve Wilson**

Issue 59 Jul–Sep 2000

THE BEAM of my head-torch swept back and forth across the heath, carefully following the slender, woody branches, lingering on the bunched sedges and taking in the patches of bare sand. Finally, there it was. I'd waited 20 years to see that dull-red glow.

As I moved closer, the glow faded and a lizard took shape – a striped gecko, clinging securely to the foliage with adhesive fingers and toes. Thanks to a simple pattern of bold, narrow lines it was nearly invisible in the tussock. Slowly and deliberately a flat, pink tongue emerged to lick clean the clear spectacles covering its lidless eyes before it turned and retreated into the dense thicket.

In the appeal stakes, geckos have what it takes. Their large, unblinking eyes and soft, velvety skin create a frail, newborn look that seems to strike a chord. And their wry smiles and delicate, padded feet certainly don't do their charm any harm.

For years, I only knew how to find geckos by day. I dug holes, turned rocks, peered behind loose bark and found the odd ones crossing roads at night. But in Marchagee Nature Reserve, a tiny island of sand, sedge and banksia in the cereal sea of Western Australia's wheat belt, about 250km north of Perth, I learnt how to use a head-torch. Now I was back to celebrate that memorable evening back in the late 1970s when one of nature's greatest secrets was revealed to me: gecko eyes reflect light.

Some geckos have evolved state-of-the-art camouflage – colours and intricate patterns designed to perfectly match their backgrounds. But the head-torch exploits a loophole in their disguise. With the beam coming from between my eyes, the light bounces back.

Geckos thrive in warm, dry climates, and Australia has about 170 species at the latest count. So where are the hot spots? Old woodlands with dead trees, peeling bark and hollow limbs are ideal. So are granite and sandstone outcrops with flat slabs, crevices, caves and overhangs. Rainforests are generally poor in species, but contain a small core of spectacular specialists.

It seems surprising that these soft, often translucent lizards seem to do best in some of the harshest Australian deserts. We tend to think of desert dwellers as heat tolerant and drought resistant, but geckos excel at avoiding extremes. Inside prickly spinifex hummocks, in vertical spider holes, or mere centimetres under sand or stone hot enough to roast them, they find humid, stable environments.

Southwards into cooler climates, the variety of geckos drops sharply. There are none in Tasmania or south-eastern Victoria and only a handful across the rest of southern Australia. But some of these hardy, cold-adapted varieties have much to teach us about the history of our climate and forests.

WHEN I VISITED Pelican Island, I was taken aback by this bleak little 50m-long outcrop off the southern WA town of Denmark. The weather wasn't looking promising either, but, ever the optimist, I stowed my camera bag behind a lichen-encrusted boulder, safe from the squalls of horizontal rain, and went looking for geckos. Hiding places are scarce, yet within a few minutes the large, plump lizards turned up under old birds' nests and in rock cracks and the meagre gaps where grass presses against stones.

According to WA Museum herpetologist Ken Aplin, there are two similar kinds down on that coast. The marbled gecko is common and widespread across southern Australia, while a poorly known close relative lives only in the moister areas of the deep south-west. "The south-western endemic gecko is about 20 per cent bigger, is genetically distinct and breeds at a different time of year. If you want to see both side by side, have a look at Pelican and Rabbit islands."

Ken thinks these larger geckos, currently unnamed, offer some important clues about past climate changes. "Their core habitat is the karri forests, but they still cling to isolated moist pockets along the southern coast and offshore islands." Ken believes they were left behind when the forests contracted, and, based on their distribution and evolution, he estimates that about 500,000 years ago, wet forests extended east to the area where Esperance now stands, 600km south-east of Perth.

In some places, the two species live within 500m of each other but something keeps them apart. "The habitats look similar but the bigger geckos probably rely on extra moisture," Ken told me.

Scarcely more than a good footy kick from Pelican Island lies Rabbit Island, two or three times Pelican's size and graced with →

Geckos' wide, a unblinking eyes are one of the keys to their appeal, but few can rival the splendid golden orbs of the western spiny-tailed gecko.

Not all geckos are secretive bushland dwellers. Young Hannah Couper watches a native house gecko scuttle up a Brisbane windowpane with gravity-defying ease.

a smattering of trees, and some shrubs, tussocks and rock outcrops. There I found a thriving population of the smaller and more slender marbled geckos.

ON THE OTHER SIDE of the continent, spectacular species are still being discovered and named. Tucked away in land-bound islands, these lizards are providing researchers with evidence about the changing face of Australia's rainforests.

Few reptiles are as effectively designed for invisibility as leaf-tailed geckos. Intricate, lichen-like patterns, spiny flanks and broad, flat tails combine to seemingly fuse the lizards onto trunks and rocks.

When I was a kid, there were only two known kinds: one on the sandstone cliffs and caves around Sydney and another in rainforests between northern New South Wales and northern Queensland. Now, thanks mainly to research by herpetologists at the Queensland Museum in Brisbane, 17 species have been named.

The discoveries mean much more than just a bunch of exquisite new geckos. Each species is confined to a rainforest or rock formation and their inability to cross habitat boundaries has created fertile ground for the evolution of different species. "No other vertebrate group demonstrates the breakup of our early rainforests as effectively and spectacularly," museum curator Jeanette Covacevich told me. "Each isolated rainforest block seems to harbour its own species, probably derived from some common ancestor that lived when the forests were joined."

In mid-eastern Queensland, three species of leaf-tailed gecko live in adjacent forest blocks. Following the directions of the museum's resident gecko expert, Patrick Couper, I made my way to the summit of Mt Blackwood, 30km north-west of Mackay. Behind a dense wall of tropical vegetation lay a still, solemn land of boulders and rope-like vines festooned with moist, delicate mosses. This is the domain of the Mount Blackwood broad-tailed gecko, discovered during the early 1990s and known only from Mt Blackwood and its sibling peak, Mt Jukes.

Just 15km to the north-west of Mt Blackwood, Mt Ossa can be seen clearly. The country in between is low and flat – now mostly sugar cane and a patchwork of gums and paperbarks. Across that gap, among the tumbled boulders of Ossa Creek, live different leaf-tailed geckos. They have the same extravagant form – slender, spidery limbs, clawed, angular toes and broad, flat tails – but they are much bigger and more prickly. And 30km to the west, in Eungella National Park, the geckos are even larger and spinier.

This pattern of different species inhabiting isolated patches of habitat speaks volumes about climate change, expanding and shrinking

Sizing up its prey, a golden-tailed gecko prepares to leap. Thanks to its keen eyes, sure grip and impressive agility, there isn't much chance it'll miss. All geckos are hunters, catching a variety of insects and spiders.

forests, and the seemingly trivial breaks that are, as the lizards demonstrate, real boundaries between separate and unique communities. Who knows how many unique species we could lose if we don't conserve these forest fragments?

GECKOS ARE BUSY gobbling moths and cockroaches under the porch lights in virtually every rural dwelling in northern Australia. These swift, nimble, ghostly pale lizards skitter with gravity-defying ease over smooth walls, ceilings and windowpanes.

A colony of robust velvet geckos inhabits my home in Kurwongbah on Brisbane's outer northern outskirts. The fattest stake out the garage and front-door lights, and with arched backs and waving tails they defend their prime real estate against all comers.

Like all geckos, these domestic varieties have a voice – usually a squeak or wheezing bark emitted only when facing rivals or predators. But among the hardy household natives, a noisier feral interloper has become increasingly vocal. Asian house geckos, ubiquitous in tropical dwellings worldwide, probably invaded Australia as stowaways.

They are among the few geckos that call day and night to stake their territory. For years their distinctive chuck...chuck...chuck was only heard around Darwin. Herpetologist Paul Horner from the Northern Territory Museum of Arts and Sciences remembers when native house geckos called dtellas were common there. There are still plenty in the surrounding bush but they have been replaced in the suburbs. "The oldest Asian house geckos in our collection date back to 1964, although they were probably established here well before then," he told me.

Asian house geckos now extend well beyond the NT. Queensland Museum staff watched their spread through Brisbane, beginning in the early 1980s. "Workers opened shipping containers and little grey lizards ran out," technician Greg Czechura told me. "Initially, they kept close to the wharves, then reports filtered in from along the Brisbane River and the city. When they turned up in outer northern suburbs we checked the street directories and found they were following arterial road links!" By the mid-1990s, Brisbane's Asian house geckos were common but patchy. They have since exploded across the city, becoming permanent fixtures on just about every wall with a crack to hide in and a light to attract insects.

Darwin, Brisbane and an increasing number of northern communities will forever ring to the call of the imported product. They have certainly reached my house, but as I open the front door each evening, it's reassuring to see the grey nose of a native velvet gecko slide discreetly behind the light. Hopefully, these big-eyed little Aussies will continue to claim the night for years to come. ■

Australia Zoo's crack croc team subdue a 5m saltwater crocodile that has been trapped in the Wenlock River on the Steve Irwin Wildlife Reserve on Cape York.

STORY BY **CHRISSIE GOLDRICK**
PHOTOGRAPHY BY **RUSSELL SHAKESPEARE** AND **CHRISSIE GOLDRICK**

WILD CROCODILE RIVER

On a remote nature reserve at the northern tip of Australia, Steve Irwin's memory continues to inspire efforts to understand and conserve his beloved reptiles.

Issue 122 ◆ Sep–Oct 2014

MANY HANDS MAKE light work of hauling the heavy steel trap out of the Wenlock River and up a sandy bank. The cage clears the brackish water and scrubby shoreline vegetation, and, along the pull ropes, necks are craning to catch a first glimpse of its contents. But this is no time for gawking; the clock's ticking, the sun's warming rapidly and hearts are racing as a crack squad of khaki-clad wildlife workers launches into a well-practised routine.

Inside the trap, a huge estuarine crocodile (*Crocodylus porosus*) appears docile, momentarily mesmerised by the unfamiliar sights and sounds. Ropes are threaded through either side of the trap and looped around the creature's top jaw. Once the chief wrangler is satisfied the ropes are correctly positioned, she crouches in front of the trap and issues the instruction to raise the gate.

A collective intake of breath hushes the small crowd of onlookers as we nervously watch Terri Irwin coax the creature out into the open. The lull is brief. Suddenly the crocodile springs from his metal prison and unleashes his fury, trying desperately to extricate himself from the ropes.

The ground beneath my feet vibrates with every roll as the hapless creature thrashes and writhes, binding the ropes ever more tightly around his snout. He expends all of his available energy with his efforts to escape and eventually just gives up and quietens down.

This is the moment the jump crew has been waiting for. Once again, Terri issues the instruction and they leap forward as one, landing on the crocodile's back, swiftly taping his jaws shut and fitting a blindfold over his eyes. It's time for the drama to cease and the science to begin. →

The Wenlock River is one of Australia's most biodiverse waterways. The river is fed by a series of perennial springs that flow up through the porous bauxite that underlies the surrounding area.

Juergen, a 4.7m male crocodile, has his left foot photographed for later measurement. Juergen was first captured in 2012 and comparisons of his foot length will provide information about his growth rate.

THE WENLOCK River flows through the Steve Irwin Wildlife Reserve (SIWR) in Cape York, one of four conservation properties in Australia Zoo's portfolio. It's here, since 2007, that the world's most comprehensive crocodile study has been taking place. I'm spending a few days with the team led by Professor Craig Franklin, director of research for the SIWR. The group, which includes Terri Irwin and her children, Bindi and Robert, spends a month here in the middle of the dry season each year to monitor the river's crocodile population.

The reserve was acquired in July 2007 after the federal government signalled its wish to honour Steve Irwin's memory by renaming a national park after him. Terri requested a more hands-on memorial to her husband. "I said that we would like to proactively manage a property so that instead of just setting it aside in Steve's name, we could do some positive things with it," she says. That property turned out to be Bertiehaugh Station, a 1350sq.km pastoral lease 55km north-east of the bauxite mining hub of Weipa.

Barry Lyon, a seasoned Cape York park ranger, had tracked crocodiles in the Wenlock River previously, so when it came to deciding upon a property, Terri sought his advice. "It was very near and dear to Steve's heart because of the crocs, and Barry was the one who said it should be this place," Terri explains.

Once they had purchased the property, Barry came on board to help run it and to develop a management plan. "Through Barry's hard work with a number of scientists, we've learnt that this place is so much more valuable than we ever anticipated," Terri says. It was the Wenlock's rich aquatic biodiversity, not least its high density of crocodiles, that originally drew them here.

Ultimately, however, it was a series of permanent freshwater springs associated with a bauxite (aluminium ore) plateau that would secure its status as a 'strategic environmental area' under the Queensland government's Cape York Regional Plan.

The plan seeks to balance environmental protection with sustainable economic development on the peninsula, and the designation ended a pre-existing bauxite mining option on about 15 per cent of the reserve, including the plateau.

Not a great deal is known about the hydrology of the vast bauxite deposits that typify much of this remote area of Cape York. However, initial observations of the lush oases sustained by those perennial springs indicated that they might be a previously undocumented ecosystem type, possibly found nowhere else.

The eight springs, known locally as the Coolibah Springs complex, are inextricably linked to the geology of the plateau. The porous bauxite acts like a giant sponge, filtering rainwater down to a deep sandy aquifer during the wet season and transmitting it progressively throughout the dry season to the springheads, where it eventually flows down to the Wenlock River.

According to Dr Marc Leblanc, a French–Australian hydrologist who specialises in semi-arid regions: "It's pretty rare to find a large, permanent spring system in this climate, and very rare to have a spring that sustains such incredible ecosystems...all of them a little bit different, which makes it a very significant place in terms of what we call its eco-hydrology." The plant communities vary from spring to spring, but each hosts rare or threatened species.

But at this time of year, it's typically croc researchers who are most conspicuous around Coolibah Camp, where an airy tin shed serves as general HQ. Joining Craig Franklin in the field each year are brothers Dr Ross Dwyer – a colleague from the University of Queensland – and Dr Hamish Campbell from the University of New England. I sit with them around the dinner table the night before I'm scheduled to head out along the Wenlock to check crocodile traps with the rangers.

I'm excited by the prospect, but keen to understand the method and purpose of the research first. "It's the largest and longest telemetry study on crocodiles ever to be conducted," Craig says. "We'll be tracking more than 100 crocodiles here for the next 7–10 years."

The work is significant for the management of crocodiles that live close to human populations and therefore pose major safety risks.

Following capture, Juergen sits within his floating trap, which has been hauled ashore. Once his jaws are secured with ropes, the jump crew will hold him in place while his mouth is taped shut.

"In Queensland, problem crocodiles were translocated up until about 2008. Our research demonstrated that crocodiles will return to the same area once removed. Now translocation is no longer employed as a management strategy and crocodiles are removed permanently to farms," Hamish says.

How crocs navigate, how far they travel, whether they maintain permanent territories, and how social hierarchies operate are among the questions the researchers seek to answer. The team has mapped out a detailed picture of the Wenlock River group, observing that in these pristine rivers, populations remain stable and balanced. Large, dominant males control movements in the river, and smaller males are forced to migrate, which accounts for some of the epic oceanic journeys recorded.

This has important implications for the practice of removing the biggest crocs from waters near human populations. "We don't know the effect that removing these large males might have on the dynamics of a river," Hamish says. "If, from an area near people, you remove a large male that was controlling the movement of smaller 2–3m males, it could cause more of these smaller animals to move into that area." Larger numbers of highly mobile young males pose a greater risk to humans, and so it's vital to solve these puzzles quickly.

IT'S WHY, next morning, our big, beautiful saltie has been dragged from the river and is now lying under the weight of eight of us: Craig works quickly. First he scans for a tag. It's a recapture. "Juergen" has been trapped twice before. He's measured, has blood taken and the acoustic tag is checked and replaced under local anaesthetic.

Meanwhile, I'm awestruck to be touching a wild crocodile and I'm surprised by the soft texture of the scutes on his back. Juergen doesn't move at all during the ordeal and, all along his massive 4.7m body, the team remains silent and respectful, trying hard not to disturb him too much. Soon it's time for the release; it's the riskiest part of the process and those not directly involved, including me, are moved to a safe distance. The blindfold and jaw tape are removed and the jump team gets ready to flee. Juergen, once free, will be at his most dangerous and could move in any direction. Hearts are once again pumping as everyone prepares for the call to release.

The order comes and the team scatters, the jaw ropes come away, and, after a brief hesitation, Juergen heads down the bank, disappearing beneath the coffee-coloured water. It's a textbook operation. Steve Irwin taught his people well. They have perfected a method that eliminates the need to tranquillise the animals, and it's a technique that has been adopted by other crocodile researchers around the world. ■

The lizard of Oz

The frill-necked lizard is one of the great symbols of Australia, along with the kangaroo and the koala. But until now little has been known about the lifestyle of this most distinctive animal.

Story by **Rick Shine**

Issue 28 Oct–Dec 1992

SQUINTING IN THE sun's glare, I strained to focus on the small, slender gum tree by the roadside. For the third time, Billy Moore pointed at the tiny sapling 10m away, and again he spoke: "Blanket lizard." His patient tone suggested he wasn't in the least surprised to discover I was effectively bush-blind, like most non-Aboriginal people of his acquaintance. I was discovering how a spectacularly distinctive reptile, measuring almost 1m from nose to tip of tail, can be so beautifully camouflaged as to be almost invisible to the untrained eye.

Billy had spotted the "blanket lizard", better known to most Australians as the frill-necked lizard (*Chlamydosaurus kingii*), as our four-wheel-drive vehicle lurched along a dusty track about 20km from the town of Jabiru in Kakadu National Park. Frill-necked lizards – "frillies" for short – are predominantly tree-dwellers and extremely shy. To hide when clinging to a tree trunk, they sidle around it so that only the tips of their slender long toes are visible to a keen-eyed observer. In theory, therefore, the easiest way to find a frilly is to look for these toes poking around the tree trunk. In practice it's not so easy, especially when bouncing along a bumpy road at 30km/h. But to the Gagudju people, the bemmung – an Aboriginal reference to the folds of skin around its neck – is a particularly sought-after traditional food. Trackers such as Billy are extremely adept at toe-spotting from a distance.

The frill-necked lizard, with its huge Elizabethan ruff of loose erectile skin behind its head, is one of the most distinctive animals in the world. It must surely qualify as one of the great Australian symbols, along with the kangaroo and the koala. Tourist shops are full of plastic models that have become popular souvenirs, yet until I began my investigations in 1985, no-one had researched anything about the ecology and behaviour of this celebrated species. There wasn't a single scientific paper on the frill-neck's biology.

This lack of research is surprising, because frill-necks are common, often abundant, in the tropical savannah and woodlands of northern Australia. They were even found in the suburbs of Brisbane before urban development destroyed their habitat. So why haven't they been studied? Mostly, it seems, because reptiles in general have attracted far less scientific interest than our "warm and cuddly" mammals. This is a real pity, because Australia's reptiles are every bit as unique and distinctive as our better-known marsupials.

What would we want to know about frillies? Well, the obvious first question is: Why do they have such enormous frills? Display structures in the neck region, like skin folds and 'beards', are widespread among lizards, but no other species has anything approaching the size of this magnificent ornament. Indeed, the frill must be one of the largest display structures, relative to body size, in any animal species.

THE FRILLY'S THREAT display is truly remarkable. The lizard stands on its hind legs, gapes widely to reveal some impressive teeth, and erects its large frill by means of U-shaped bones in the throat region. This complex combination of bone and cartilage works rather like the spokes of an umbrella. The frill itself can extend to be larger than a dinner plate, covering a diameter more than four times the width of the lizard's body. The combined effect of this display is enough to startle any observer.

While there's no doubt that the frill is used as a threat display to deter attacks, can this be its only function? It has been suggested that it also works as a parachute, allowing the lizard to glide from trees, or that it channels sound into the creature's ears, improving its hearing. Others have speculated that the frill's folds are used to store food, or to aid in body temperature control, acting either as a parasol, a solar panel or a heat-dissipating structure, like an elephant's ears.

In fact, our behavioural observations revealed that frillies mostly use their extraordinary display structures not for zooming through the air, holding food or keeping cool, but for warning off other members of the same species. Male frill-necks grow much bigger – averaging more than 250mm from snout to vent – than the females, which average about 200mm. And males have bigger frills than females as well. If you sit quietly and watch an adult male frilly in the wild during the mating season, you can see it wave its frill to let other males know that a particular area has been claimed. These lizards live in relatively open woodland and have terrifically keen eyesight, so the spectacular display can probably be seen by every male frilly for hundreds of metres around. We never saw females or juvenile males use their frills in this way. Even the males stop displaying outside the mating season.

However, male territorial displays are certainly not the only function of the frill. Females raise it to rebuff unwelcome suitors, and both sexes raise it to repel possible predators, such as birds of prey. But we saw no evidence that the frills are used to control body temperature. And, sadly, we never saw frillies parachuting, or 'listening' with their frills, or storing food in their folds.

For its size, a large male frill-necked lizard has one of the largest display structures of any animal species. Research suggests the main function of the spectacular frill is social display, with males using it as a 'flag' with which to proclaim their territory.

One of the strangest stories about the frill, however, involves its consequences for how these lizards move around. To carry this elaborate display organ, frill-necks have exceptionally long and slender necks that give them the flexibility to lean far enough backwards to balance on their hind legs, even when walking slowly. Most other lizards would fall over if they tried this. Walking on two legs raises the frill-neck's head high off the ground and may give it a better view of its surroundings. Many other species of lizard raise their front legs off the ground if they run quickly. The water dragon of eastern Australia is perhaps the most familiar example. In species such as the water dragon, however, the two-legged stance comes only after an initial four-legged burst, and only at relatively high speeds. If the lizard slows, it drops on all fours. Thus, lizards may run on two legs, but they always walk on four – or so I thought.

I FIRST SAW A FRILL-NECK walking around on two legs while I was sitting in a hide in Kakadu, watching a large adult male that I had located the previous afternoon. I set up the hide early in the morning, while the lizard was still hidden in the foliage of his tree. Not long after he came down the tree's trunk to bask in the morning sunshine, he noticed a large caterpillar on the ground. He immediately descended tailfirst, turned around on reaching the ground, then hauled himself upright and sauntered over to the caterpillar – on two legs! He stopped a few times to drop down on all fours, to display and to pick up his food, but stayed upright on two legs the rest of the time. In order to keep himself upright he had to lean backwards, so that the weight of his head was over his point of balance, the hind legs. The result was so comical I had to stop myself from laughing out loud. This usually proud, distinguished and rather fearsome-looking beast resembled a fat little prince as he waddled about on his hind legs, a worried gleam in his eyes and a rather middle-aged look about the paunch that hung forward where his belt should have been.

Over the next few weeks I saw many frill-necks wandering around on two legs rather than four. Occasionally, as I sat quietly in the hide, one would casually 'motor' past my hiding place like a miniature cyclist. Frill-necks thus qualify as one of the very few animal species that routinely walk around on two legs. Many animals hop on their hind legs, but very few – apart from humans – walk that way. And frillies can only manage that athletic feat because of their long, flexible neck, which in turn exists only because of their remarkable frill.

Even without their frills these lizards are interesting, and there are many other questions to ask about their natural history. The answers to those questions may, in the long run, prove vital in planning conservation policies for this remarkable species. I hope frill-neck numbers remain high, but their disappearance from southern Queensland over the past 30 years suggests that we need to keep a close eye on their wellbeing. In several areas, the invasion of cane toads seems to have been followed by a decrease in frilly abundance. Should northern Australia's frill-neck population show signs of widespread decline, as has happened in southern Queensland, then the more we know about this magnificent species, the better will be our chances of ensuring that we don't lose this iconic reptile from tropical Australia. ■

Snakes alive

Land of plenty for water pythons.

Story by **Geordie Torr** Photography by **David Hancock**

Issue 74 Apr–Jun 2004

I'M SURROUNDED BY PYTHONS. Thousands upon thousands of them. To my right stretches the flat, brown expanse of the Northern Territory's Adelaide River floodplain; to my left is the lush oasis of Fogg Dam, 50km south-east of Darwin.

The dam is a popular tourist destination, but little do the day-trippers know that sheltering within cracks in the floodplain soil and floating in the dam is the highest known biomass of predators and prey of any ecosystem on Earth – higher even than Africa's fabled Serengeti Plain.

Beside me stands Thomas Madsen, a biologist from the University of Sydney and one of the people who uncovered the truth behind this incredible biological bonanza. Thomas and I are on the road that runs along the raised dam wall, a road that Thomas knows very well, having driven along it more than 10,000 times.

Thirteen years ago, Thomas came to Fogg Dam to study water pythons and their primary prey, the dusky rat. The project had been initiated a few years earlier by Sydney University's Professor Rick Shine. Rick began heading out to the dam after a tip-off from renowned Australian herpetologist Harold Cogger. "It just seemed so exciting to see so many pythons, because usually they're so scarce. I reckoned it would make a nice little ecological study if I could ever get the funds," Rick told me when I visited him at the University of Sydney before my trip to the NT.

In late 1986, with money from the Australian Research Council, the project got off to a low-key start. "Over the next few years we would spend a few weeks up there, just catching pythons on the dam wall, scale-clipping and releasing them and then never seeing them again," Rick explained. He initially thought that the pythons were dying or moving away, but after he'd placed radio-transmitters in a few it became evident that the snakes were fine and mostly stayed put.

"That's when I started to contemplate the awful reality that there was this extraordinary abundance," Rick said. He wasn't catching the relatively small number of pythons he'd marked because of the remote chance of finding them again among such a huge population. He realised he needed someone to work regularly at Fogg Dam. Enter Thomas, a Swedish herpetologist who'd studied snakes in Africa. Thomas set up camp at Fogg Dam and began catching, marking and radio-tracking pythons.

Since then, the project has provided an unprecedented insight into this remarkable ecosystem. "It's a beautiful, simple system to study," Thomas told me as we stood on the dam wall. "Lots of people have tried to study ecosystems, and it's hard because there are lots of predators, lots of prey, lots of plants, and so on. Here we have just three species of plant, rainfall, one prey, one predator."

The lack of complexity has helped Thomas and Rick work out why there are so many pythons around Fogg Dam – up to several hundred snakes per hectare. It mostly comes down to the abundance of rats. The rodents feed on the grass that sprouts up on the floodplain after the rains, and in a good year, they'll reproduce for as long as nine months. That adds up to a lot of rats, which means a lot of python food and, ultimately, a multitude of python eggs.

WE WERE BACK at the dam after dark, this time accompanied by Thomas's wife, Bea. Ensconced in their four-wheel-drive, we slowly drove along the dam wall, Thomas and Bea leaning out of their respective windows, methodically painting the grass on either side of the road with spotlights.

"Python." Bea's door was open and she was upon the snake – 1m-long dark squiggle beside the road – before Thomas had completely stopped the car. She quickly grabbed the snake behind the head, and, as she lifted it, it threw coil after coil around her arm. She brought it back to the car, where Thomas had a bag ready. In the torchlight, the snake's olive-green skin seemed almost black, although when the beam reflected just right, it took on an opalescent sheen.

Continuing along the road, Thomas spotted the next snake. Striding over confidently, he reached down and caught it. Just as it was wrapping itself around his arm he spotted another, which he calmly grabbed by the tail, lifting the thrashing serpent into the air. These two were also quickly bagged.

As we made our way along the wall, picking up python after →

When threatened, water pythons exhibit an S-shaped threat display. Although non-venomous, the snake's bite can be very painful.

At Fogg Dam, south-east of Darwin, a 1.5m-long water python sits coiled beside a log. The dam and associated floodplain is home to the largest biomass of predators and prey in the world.

python, Thomas explained that what we were seeing was the low-key beginning of an extraordinary phenomenon. After a few years of python catching, he and Rick had noticed that snake numbers on the dam wall showed a well-defined seasonal pattern. During the Wet, numbers dropped significantly, before rising to a peak in November–December, just before the next Wet. To try to explain this recurring pattern they put radio-transmitters inside a few pythons and followed them over the year.

They discovered that during the Dry, the snakes usually hung around Fogg Dam, living in the soil cracks, where temperatures stay in the mid- to high 20s year-round. Then, just before the first heavy rains of the Wet, the pythons crossed the road and headed for higher ground. A few travelled up into the surrounding woodland but most headed for the Adelaide River, where they spent their time around the raised levee banks, up to 12km from their dry-season haunts.

Now, obviously, water pythons have nothing against water, so if they weren't escaping the flood, why were they heading for high ground? It turned out they were following their floodwater-concentrated food supply. Thomas told me that one python he caught during the migration had 12 rats inside it.

AT THE 'LAB' NEXT MORNING, I'm once again surrounded by pythons – arrayed around me are about 30 squirming bags, the fruits of last night's labours. The makeshift laboratory is in the tiny community of Middle Point, a five-minute drive from Fogg Dam. Thomas and Bea stay next door.

Thomas set about processing the haul. The first snake was a first-timer, and Thomas allocated it a number – 6532 – and began marking and measuring it. Holding the snake firmly by the neck, its tail under his foot, Thomas first made a drawing of its head scales. He then spun the snake around so that its tail was in his hand and its head grasped between his dexterous toes, and took note of the pattern of scales under its tail. And finally, he permanently marked the snake by clipping a small piece from a few of its belly scales. He then measured its length and weight, determined its sex – this one was a female – returned it to its bag and set to work on the next.

This one had some V-shaped marks on its back. "Jabiru," Thomas said. The long-term mark–recapture study that he and Rick have been carrying out has revealed that once the snakes get past about 60cm long, they usually survive to old age. Adult pythons, it seems, don't have many predators and although large birds such as the black-necked stork, or jabiru, might have a go occasionally, they generally aren't very successful, as these scars attest.

IT WAS THE REALISATION that so many of the pythons weren't being eaten by predators, but were instead succumbing to the ravages of old age – disease or parasites – that led to the project's current focus. In water pythons, old age is a relative term – some snakes succumb at 10 years old, others at 30. When Thomas compared the blood-parasite levels of young and old snakes he found lots of variation. "Among the young snakes, 1–2 years old, the parasite levels vary between zero and 40 per cent of the red blood cells infected. And then I have about 10 snakes, some of which are more than 20 years old, that have no parasites."

Tom suspects that this variation in parasite loads is connected to the snakes' genetic make-up, specifically the genes that code for the body's response to the invaders. By comparing the DNA of snakes with high and low parasite levels, he hopes to be able to predict how long a snake will survive.

There's a possible threat to water pythons at Fogg Dam and it's hopping ever closer – the cane toad. It isn't the toads' toxicity that has Thomas worried – the pythons don't eat frogs. Rather, he's scared they'll present the snakes with some unwelcome competition. A nest of baby rats would make a nice meal for a toad, and should the amphibian invaders reach the plague proportions that the perfect conditions presented by the dam suggest they will, they could put a serious dent in the young pythons' food supply. They may even eat the baby snakes themselves.

But for now, Fogg Dam remains a land of plenty for the water python, and continues to provide the setting for what is, without question, the most revealing long-term study ever undertaken of one of Australia's true biological wonders. ■

Bea Madsen extracts blood, which she'll later examine for parasites, from a python's tail, while her husband, Tom, holds the snake. Large pythons have few predators and most will succumb to parasites.

The length of a python's head will determine the size of prey it can eat. This can be catastrophic for young snakes – if the rats on which they feed have finished breeding by the time the snakes hatch, they'll starve because the rats are too big for them.

Perched before the gaze of herpetologist Arthur White, a vivid green and golden bell frog illuminates a sphagnum-filled glass enclosure at Taronga Zoo, Sydney. Like many Australian frogs, the species is undergoing a dramatic decline.

STORY BY **MATTHEW CAWOOD**
PHOTOGRAPHY BY **MIKE LANGFORD** AND **RANDY LARCOMBE**

SPAWN OF AN ERA

Australians are listening to frogs as never before.

Issue 48 ◆ Oct–Dec 1997

WE'RE DISCUSSING FROGS in a remote corner of Sydney's Taronga Zoo when herpetologist Arthur White offers his personal history of green and golden bell frogs. As a boy, he would lurk with his mates in a golf-course swamp at Eastlakes, in Sydney's south, waiting for balls to rocket over a nearby hill so they could pinch them for later resale at the clubhouse. "The bell frogs would be clinging to the stems of the reeds in their dozens, soaking up the heat," he recalls.

That was the early 1960s, a time when green and golden bell frogs were common residents of swamps and scrub between Byron Bay, on the north coast of New South Wales, and Victoria's East Gippsland. But these striking animals had all but disappeared from NSW by 1995 when, as a consultant herpetologist, Arthur could find only 12 wild populations in the state. We'd come to see one of these populations, now caged at Taronga, after their home, a vacant block in Sydney's south, was concreted over for an apartment building.

What perturbs Arthur is that the green and golden bell frog is losing the battle for existence despite its reputation as one of Australia's more robust amphibians. It's highly mobile, eats almost anything, breeds in puddles and lays more eggs than most Australian frogs – up to 9000 in a clutch. Yet Arthur believes it's doomed in the wild. "Give it 50 years," he says, looking at the frog enclosure. The species may survive in urban areas, however, because of its ability to coexist with people. But first, Arthur says, people must be prepared to coexist with frogs.

For the most part, frogs live on the fringes of our lives, their calls speaking of damp places and rainy nights. Occasionally humans and amphibians cross paths. Among Australia's 210 described species are some of the world's most fascinating frogs. There are those that raise tadpoles in their stomachs (southern gastric-brooding frog) or in pouches (pouched frog) and some that hatch straight from the egg as fully developed frogs (moss froglet). Some survive seven-year droughts under →

Wielding a bipolar electrode powered by an instrument similar to those used in acupuncture, Mike Tyler stimulates a green tree frog to release its skin secretions in a University of Adelaide laboratory.

The head-torch beams of technical officer Alison Towerton (at right) and volunteer Jo Green converge on a great barred frog in a forest north of Dorrigo on the Great Dividing Range.

the ground (water-holding frog) while others have taken to rainforest canopies and may be evolving into gliding frogs (red-eyed tree frog). But as scientists fill volumes with frog lore, they're discovering Australia is losing frogs at an alarming rate.

IT'S 9 O'CLOCK ON a brisk November night in dense forest north of Dorrigo, on the Great Dividing Range, 420km north of Sydney. I'm with NSW State Forests herpetologist Frank Lemckert, who's hopeful that Maude, a strapping female great barred frog he has fitted with a radio-transmitter, will be sitting in a small picnic ground.

She isn't, of course. Instead, the electronic "pow...pow...pow" of the radio-tracker places her 50m away, either in impenetrable reeds or the deep moonlit creek that flows around their base. Maude is being tracked as part of a project designed to assess the impact of logging on the tennis-ball-sized great and giant barred frogs, and the smaller stuttering frog. Frank aims to determine how the stream-bank-dwelling creatures fare in the 20m wide unlogged zones left along streams to maintain water quality. He wants to know whether the frogs forage in the logged areas, and if not, how many years must elapse after logging before they do.

It's also important to discover whether there's enough food and shelter in the buffer zones to allow them to reproduce. "If the frogs fail to reproduce successfully before the environment recovers, there'll be no frogs left to repopulate the area when conditions are good again," Frank says.

He's hopeful that one day there'll be an inviolable network of bush corridors running through private lands to connect NSW forests. "If you have four or five isolated forest patches, extinction is likely to occur in each of them," he observes. "There's no opportunity to recolonise."

IT LOOKS LIKE FROG heaven. Indeed, this small reedy pond on the northern outskirts of Adelaide is home to dozens of common froglets and spotted grass frogs. But there's a sinister side to it, exposed when contentedly dishevelled researcher Steve Walker approaches to show me a froglet with a withered hand.

"In national parks we expect about 3 per cent of frogs to have some structural abnormality," Steve says. "Here there's about 25–30 per cent abnormalities, and they're often more pronounced than at other sites – missing legs, missing jaws, things like that."

In this pond, frogs act like miners' canaries, revealing water problems caused by modern life's carelessly discarded by-products. Steve, a University of Adelaide master of science, is investigating the connection between pollution and frog deformities. He expected to find most deformities in agricultural areas, but discovered that local dairy farms yielded fewer abnormalities than national parks. The worst problems were found in some urban ponds.

This pond, bounded by a highway and a railway, and topped up by stormwater from an industrial area, carries a heavy load of zinc and about 1000 times more lead than recommended safe levels. "Pollution doesn't just make water look bad and smell – it has an effect on the animals that live in it as well," he says. "And if we destroy things that live in the water, there's a good chance we'll destroy ourselves."

TWENTY MINUTES north of Bathurst, in central-eastern NSW, I glimpse a platypus breaking the Macquarie River's green surface. A few hundred metres upstream, a small but boisterous group from the city's Kelso High School is exclaiming over a mass of frogspawn and attempting to dig out a pobblebonk frog from beneath river debris.

Science teacher Bronwyn Goble tells me that about 150 of the school's 1000 students are involved in Streamwatch – a program jointly funded by the state and federal governments to monitor environmental changes. Streamwatch kits help participating groups carry out a straightforward assessment of a waterway's physical, chemical and biological state.

"We've got students who are frog mad," Bronwyn tells me ruefully, as the sound of excited frog-hunting drifts up the river. Frogs

Vivien Mitchell looks after the University of Adelaide's research frogs and also keeps more than 80 frogs in glass enclosures in her home. "Frogs are better pets than dogs and cats, because they don't leave hair around the place," she says.

became such a popular aspect of Streamwatch that they spawned their own offshoot – Frogwatch. This program gives students sanction to go frogging, provides them with a frog portrait of their home environment and enriches the information-gathering capabilities of the state herpetological societies.

Programs such as Frogwatch enable school students and community groups to contribute to databases such as that compiled by the Frog and Tadpole Study Group of NSW (FATS). Like its counterparts in every other state and territory, FATS embraces anyone fascinated by frogs and disseminates information and advice to members and schools through newsletters, fact sheets and public meetings.

"We ask people – anyone – that if they are driving around and they cross a water body, to stop the engine and listen for the one, two or three frogs calling," says Lothar Voigt, the group's president, as he shows me around his frog-friendly garden in the Sydney suburb of Rose Bay a few weeks later. "We want them to try to identify the frogs or to make a tape recording and send it to us. We'll identify the species for free and send back a note saying what species they are. And we get another data point for our frog count."

Organisations such as FATS also advise people on how to "frogscape" a garden to attract frogs. As Lothar says: "It may take months, it may take years, but if you make your garden attractive to frogs, one day they will find you."

DURING THE EARLY 1980s up to 2000, green tree frogs were being released each year into Martin and Hilary Boscott's St Lucia garden, in Brisbane. "For a while you couldn't tell whether the plants had leaves or frogs," Martin says. Not surprisingly, the green tree frog's "craaaaawk" remains a familiar sound in St Lucia.

The releases were made as part of the Native Frog Restoration Project, an informal organisation founded by the Boscotts to build up frog numbers against cyclical declines and habitat destruction. Martin estimates that 100,000 people in Queensland and NSW were involved in raising more than 1 million tadpoles for the project. A few years after they began the organisation, the Boscotts' garden also received a welcome invasion of dainty green tree frogs and striped marsh frogs, which were promptly included in the breeding program.

Arthur White would like to see a similar project for the green and golden bell frog. He's already working with a community group in Marrickville, a few kilometres from the centre of Sydney, to create a pond that will house some of the frogs that have been bred at Taronga Zoo. If surrounding householders make their yards frog-friendly by restraining pets, reducing garden chemical usage and leaving areas of unmown lawn or other refuges, the frogs may come to regard the gardens as legitimate habitat. Perhaps the future of this and other frog species lies in suburbia – their habitat a chain of welcoming backyards and vacant blocks.

When I think about the numerous stories that I heard while researching this article, I keep hearing Steve Walker: "There were times when I was in a creek looking for frogs, and people would wonder why I wasn't acting my age. Now they want to know more about what I'm doing."

That's cause for optimism, I think. Because it's important, for their sake and ours, that we start listening to the frogs. ■

CHAPTER EIGHT

INVERTEBRATES

They're the cornerstone of our ecological workforce, tirelessly keeping our ecosystems running, but most of their work is hidden from human eyes.

The indefatigable invertebrates – animals without backbones – toil away behind the scenes, providing services such as nutrient recycling and pollination, while also acting as both predator and prey, keeping pests at bay and feeding the more conspicuous vertebrate animals.

Unlike our plants and vertebrates, which are relatively well known, it's thought that only about one-third of Australia's invertebrates have been formally described – a total of about 100,000 species thus far. About 60 per cent of those are insects, a staggeringly diverse group that includes a range of beautiful and conspicuous species, including metallic-blue butterflies the size of your hand, shiny beetles that look like jewels, pugnacious bulldog ants and rapidly darting dragonflies with vivid-scarlet abdomens.

Two of our best-known insects inhabit different ends of the popularity spectrum. Cicadas are a much-loved fixture of Australian life, providing the soundtrack to our long, hot summers. More than 230 species are found here, all but a handful of which are found nowhere else, and collecting the shells or the adults themselves is akin to a rite of passage, an integral part of growing up in Australia. Male cicadas are the loudest of all singing insects, producing a pulsating curtain of white noise with an intensity that can exceed 120 decibels at close range – about the same as a jet taking off and close to the pain threshold of the human ear.

Significantly less popular are our ubiquitous flies. Recorded complaints about Australia's flies date all the way back to January 1688, when William Dampier, one of the earliest Europeans to set foot on the continent, described how they would "creep into one's nostrils; and mouth too, if the lips are not shut very close". About 7500 species of fly have been described from Australia, but it's thought that there could be as many as 30,000 species in total. However, out of all of them, it's the bushflies that win most of the opprobrium – infuriating little blighters that gather in groups around our eyes and mouth. So annoying are they that over the years, scientists have introduced several species of dung beetle from Africa and Europe to help deal with the oversupply of the cow dung in which the flies breed.

Another invertebrate group that forms a central part of our folklore and our daily lives are the spiders. Australia is home to about 3700 species. Out in the bush, you could expect to find about 700 species living together; that number drops to about 50–100 for bushy suburbs. Although all but one family of spiders has venom, most are harmless to humans. However, in Australia, the exception is particularly deadly.

The Sydney funnel-web is one of the world's most toxic spiders, a creature that inspires both fear and fascination. And it certainly looks the part – big, black with large, prominent fangs from which drops of clear venom can sometimes be seen emerging. Unusually, it's the venom of the male Sydney funnel-web that's the more toxic – and is more than likely responsible for all 13 of the recorded deaths from funnel-web spider bites (the good news is that no fatal bites have been recorded since the development of an anti-venom in 1980). By a strange quirk of evolution, the male's venom contains a unique component that severely affects the nervous systems of humans and other primates, but not of other mammals (with the bizarre exception of baby mice).

At the other end of the popularity spectrum are the jumping spiders. Australia's most diverse spider family, with about 330 described species, they are small – rarely more than 1cm in length – with large forward-facing eyes that give them excellent vision. They're the only spiders that can turn their head, rarely use webs, and are often brightly coloured, none more so than the aptly named peacock spiders. The male's abdomen is covered in bright, iridescent scales whose colours rival those of the gaudiest butterflies and each species has its own unique courtship dance, designed to show of the glory of the male's multi-coloured rear end. ■

Previous page: Having tunnelled to the surface and climbed a tree, a cicada begins the process of emergence. Over the next few hours, it will shed its old skin, unfurl its new wings and, finally, take flight.

With their brightly coloured markings and look-at-me mating dances, Australia's peacock spiders are very aptly named. This individual belongs to the genus *Maratus*.

Funnel-webs

Fearsome but fascinating, the Sydney funnel-web is the best known of the 40-odd funnel-web species – a by-product of Australia's most populous city being smack in the middle of its range.

Story by **Karen McGhee** Photography by **Esther Beaton**

Issue 53 Jan–Mar 1999

THE "FUNNEL-WEB LADY" led me into her spider laboratory at the Australian Reptile Park at Somersby, north of Sydney. Housing up to 600 funnel-webs at a time, it was almost wall-to-wall large black hairy arachnids. Along one side were glass terraria set up with soil and rocks for a breeding program and the wall at the far end was lined halfway to the ceiling with row upon row of glass jars, each containing soil and a female Sydney funnel-web (*Atrax robustus*).

Despite being dubbed the funnel-web lady by everyone from local journalists to her coworkers, Lyn Abra was immaculately groomed, quietly spoken and not at all what you might expect of an enthusiastic spider devotee. Her unusual moniker comes from her occupation: on most Sunday afternoons you'll find Lyn calmly going to work with one of the world's most deadly organisms. A window into the park's spider lab allows visitors to watch her 'milk' funnel-webs for their precious toxin, which Lyn does using a glass pipette attached to a suction pump to agitate adult spiders, sucking up the venom as it emerges from their fangs.

Scanning the rows of captive funnel-webs, Lyn brought down a jar and as I peered inside I felt a sudden fight-or-flight adrenaline surge. Sitting impassively within its glass prison was a spider you couldn't ignore – a truly impressive specimen. At about 35mm long, she was about as large as a Sydney funnel-web gets and when Lyn removed the lid I shuffled back a few paces. "That's one of the biggest fallacies about funnel-webs," she said assuredly. "They don't jump." The other popular myth about them chasing people is also untrue, she added.

It took just the slightest provocation – a pipette touched lightly on her legs – for the spider to rear up and display the excitable and unpredictable nature for which funnel-webs are renowned – front legs raised high, head back, fangs on display. A little more gentle stimulation brought two glistening drops of venom to the ends of her fangs. Then, with remarkable speed, she snapped down on the pipette with a force normally used to drive her fangs through the hard external skeletons of the small invertebrates on which these spiders mostly feed.

Funnel-webs are thought to have a preference for millipedes but their diet also extends to small lizards. They usually feed at night, waiting just inside silk-lined burrows, their webs sometimes more like flattened tubes than funnels. Silk trip-lines radiate outwards and anything of a manageable size that sets them vibrating is ambushed.

Lyn's interest in these deadly creatures began when she was a child and developed further after she joined the reptile park in 1967. The park established its Sydney funnel-web-milking program in the early 1970s after an approach from Dr Struan Sutherland, who was leading research into an antivenom against the spider's toxin at Melbourne's Commonwealth Serum Laboratories (now CSL Ltd). Lyn quickly developed a skill for milking and has been doing it ever since. An antivenom was eventually developed by Struan in 1980 and today the reptile park is the sole supplier of the venom used by CSL to produce the lifesaving pharmaceutical.

That's where the spider lab fits in. Lyn's funnel-webs are brought in mostly by the public, but numbers often fall perilously low. In 1996 shortfalls prompted Lyn to establish the first large funnel-web captive-breeding program, and it's since produced hundreds of spiderlings, each of which could one day provide venom for antivenom production.

THE ARACHNOLOGY DEPARTMENT at the Australian Museum in Sydney evoked a sense of organised chaos. I shuffled past piles of papers, books spilling from shelves, flickering computer screens, researchers with heads down in cramped corners and an aquarium containing several large water spiders, before finally reaching the crowded desk of the department's head, Dr Mike Gray.

Mike has been researching funnel-webs since joining the museum in the late 1970s and is now the country's leading authority. "If you work on spiders in Sydney you're inevitably drawn to funnel-webs," he said nonchalantly. "There's a high level of public interest in them and a high level of medical interest also, especially in the days prior to the antivenom. It was inevitable that someone had to work on funnel-webs in the Sydney region and it just expanded from there."

Official records hold the funnel-web responsible for the deaths of 13 people between 1927 and the release of the antivenom. Mike pointed out, however, that the species' villainous reputation needs qualification. It has as much to do with its distribution and reproductive behaviour as the potency of its venom.

The heart of Sydney funnel-web territory just happens to →

Growing to a length of about 35mm, the jet-black Sydney funnel-web spider is an impressive arachnid. Its venom is also among the most toxic of any spider, responsible for the deaths of 13 people between 1927 and the development of an antivenom in 1980.

The Reptile Park encourages the public to bring captured funnel-webs into collection points at hospitals and police stations. Sometimes places such as Mona Vale Hospital can be overwhelmed. Spiders arrive in a variety of containers, although glass jars furnished with a moistened cotton wool ball are recommended.

sit within the country's most populated city, and the opportunity for human–spider contact is increased by the males' habit of leaving their burrows at the onset of maturity – at about 2–3 years of age – to wander in search of mates, leading to roving males frequently turning up in backyards and homes. This is particularly pertinent because, in an unusual twist for spiders, the wandering male Sydney funnel-web has far more potent venom than the sedentary female.

Funnel-web venom is a cocktail of about 50 different compounds, only one of which – delta-atracotoxin – kills humans. And that particular toxin only affects primates. No other mammals, other than baby mice during the first three days of life, have a serious reaction to funnel-web venom. Why this should be so when primates weren't involved in the venom's evolution remains a bizarre and inexplicable quirk of nature.

The male funnel-web probably doesn't eat after embarking on his reproductive quest and dies 6–12 months later. "It's not known whether it's due to an actual biological clock or if it's simply that they don't feed once they've left the burrow," Mike said. The female can live more than 12 years, rarely venturing more than 1m or so from her lair.

Sydney's best-known spider isn't the only funnel-web. There are another 40 or so species, most of them ground- or log-dwellers, although there are at least two tree-dwelling exceptions. They're all restricted to eastern Australia, from Tasmania to Mossman in northern Queensland, with at least three species in South Australia.

The spiders' modern-day preferences for moist habitats are linked to their evolutionary origins some 50 million years ago, at a time when Australia was covered almost entirely by humid forests. "If you're an ancient forest dweller, the need to have protection against water loss isn't as great as if you evolved in a drier environment," Mike explained. "So they have a poor ability to retain moisture. But in drier areas, like the western slopes of the Flinders Ranges, they can avoid conditions that appear to be against them by simply burrowing deeper, closer to the water table."

THE CURATOR OF arachnids at the Queensland Museum, Dr Robert Raven, has been studying spiders for almost 30 years but time hasn't tempered his reverence for funnel-webs. "I've never encountered an animal that's quite so aggressive. It's so excitable!" he explained. "And the remarkable thing is that when the spider goes into the threat pose it can't see what it's attacking because its head's back...it's responding to vibrations."

Robert's come to understand, however, that these spiders are far more vulnerable than their appearance, aggressive behaviour and potent venom suggest. Flatworms have no problems eating them, velvet worms immobilise them with a sticky spray before consuming them, their preference for humid environments means they're susceptible to fungal infections and large lizards take roaming males.

Centipedes, however, are a particular threat. "They chew and rip through the ground and come in at the bottom of the burrow to take the funnel-web," Robert said. "We've had situations where we've been excavating a burrow and the spider has come racing straight up and out. When we've dug the burrow out there's been a 15–20cm-long centipede at the bottom."

To make matters worse, males have to be careful not to become incidental prey for females when mating. "During courtship, the female goes into the attack pose, legs up, fangs back," Robert said. "The male walks into the burrow front on and has different techniques to ensure he doesn't get killed while mating. The main method is to lock the fangs closed or open and one way he does this is by crossing his front legs in an X-shape over the female's fangs, which then pushes her up with her fangs closed. It's a fairly precarious situation."

I began to feel sympathy for the creatures and felt sure Robert was about to tell me that the funnel-web's deadly reputation was more media hype than reality. But he instead uttered an unnerving warning. "If you get bitten by a funnel-web when you're on your own," he said in quiet reverence, "then my advice is to make your peace with God first and then put on a pressure bandage and get to a hospital." ■

A female funnel-web, disturbed in her burrow, displays the classic pose – front legs raised, head up and back, fangs exposed and drops of venom forming at their tips.

Cicadas

Sound of the Australian summer.

Story by **Densey Clyne**

Issue 56 Oct–Dec 1999

UNDERGROUND, in perpetual darkness, a cicada nymph waits for a sign that it's time to enter the world of light and the companionship of his kind. He has inhabited a confined home of earth and tree roots for several years, feeding on sap, periodically moulting, and enlarging his small air space as he grows. Now his life below ground, safely embraced by walls of clammy clay, is about to end. Soon he'll experience the rhythms of day and night, the freedom of flight and the hazards that freedom brings.

It won't be the first time this cicada has seen the light. Long ago, perhaps seven years ago, he and his siblings hatched from eggs laid in a dead branch of a towering eucalypt, high above his present home. Not much larger than a flea, he took a skydive to the ground and, buoyed by air resistance, landed unharmed on the leaf-litter. Within minutes, he was digging into the soil with his specially adapted front legs, seeking the nearest root for his first taste of gum-tree sap.

And so the long years of secret development continued until a few days ago, when the nymph began to dig laboriously upwards. When his escape tunnel was finished, with only a thin plug of soil separating him from the surface world, he returned to his chamber to wait.

Last night it rained and he remained where he was, but tonight it's warm and dry and he's climbed back to the top of the tunnel. Now he starts demolishing the final barrier to his new life. Perhaps it was the calls of his kind that finally turned his steps upward.

IT'S A STILL, humid night in midsummer and conditions are right for me to find just such a nymph creeping from its burrow, heading for the nearest vertical surface. All day and well into the evening, the air above my Sydney bush garden has vibrated to the strident calls of a multitude of cicadas.

Many of our best-known cicadas feed on the sap of gum trees, but they are selective. A given area of bushland will often support a variety of different kinds of cicada according to its composition. And each species produces its own characteristic call.

Where I live, it's the shrill, uninflected chorus of greengrocers, a large species found in south-eastern Australia, that predominates. Set off by a single singer, the sound builds to a monotonous screech, a pulsing plateau of noise that can continue for hours. But it's a sound that my ears simply adjust to as part of the seasonal ambience, a background to summer living. The cicada is the loudest of all singing insects. In the USA, the intensity of sound recorded 80m from a tree-full of calling males reached 100 decibels – louder than a jackhammer.

My torch beam, sweeping slowly across the leaf-litter under the gum trees, picks up a movement, a slight shifting of the browned and curling gum leaves that carpet the ground. And there it is, a cicada nymph, small, muddy, a miniature ogre clumsily heading in stops and starts for the base of a giant angophora tree. I wait for its climb to begin, and then continue my patrol. In an hour or so, when the cicada has settled, I'll fetch my camera and record yet again an event that still fascinates me, even after half a century of cicada watching. The event is the cicada's coming of age, the rite of passage to its brief period of maturity.

The transformation of a cicada nymph into its adult form isn't the dramatic metamorphosis experienced by butterfly, moth and beetle. The body plan of the nymph and adult cicada remains basically the same, the important changes being the maturing of sexual organs and the development of wings. But there's a special magic about it, perhaps related to the secrecy of its happening, the sense of privilege enjoyed by the watcher in the night.

At about midnight, with my camera set up and several photographs taken, I relax. The cicada has fully emerged. It hangs from the cast skin, the outgrown garment of its immaturity. Often clustered in large numbers around the bases of trees, these cast skins, called exuviae, are more frequently seen than the cicadas themselves.

The cicada's delicate new feet contrast with the broad, spiky digging implements it no longer needs, now merely hollow impressions left in the casing to which it clings. Peering closely I can see broad plates under the crumpled mess of its wings. And on its underside, just behind the legs, are a pair of larger plates. It's a male.

The smaller plates are the covers of the tymbals, the sound-producing organs, which only males have. The larger plates, which are always bigger on males, are called opercula. They cover the tympana, thin membranes that cicadas use to hear. His ears and the source of the

raucous racket he produces are right next to each other and I wonder how he manages not to deafen himself.

It turns out that when they're calling, male cicadas relax their tympana, so that they're considerably less sensitive. This is certainly a good thing, as a cicada's ears are tuned to be especially sensitive to the main frequency of the song of its own species, filtering out other frequencies and thereby making the cicada virtually deaf to other sounds.

For us humans, with our ears tuned to a wide range of frequencies, cicada song is an unavoidable accompaniment to daily life during summer – a throbbing, tangible presence. If a heatwave had a sound, this would be it. There are days when schoolteachers in suburban classrooms must raise their voices to compete, others when conversation around the weekend barbecue is almost impossible.

Despite this love–hate relationship we've developed a special proprietary feeling about our cicadas. We boast about them to overseas visitors. And we've given them names we might give to our pets: floury baker, cherrynose, black prince, razor grinder, greengrocer, yellow Monday. I doubt that any other group of insects has been given such evocative names.

THE UNFURLING of the newly emerged cicada's milky blue wings holds my attention. They curl slowly downwards as the cicada pumps its watery green blood, known as haemolymph, into the network of veins, expanding and straightening the wings. Later tonight they'll lose their blue colour and opacity, eventually coming to resemble miniature stained-glass windows. By morning, the haemolymph will have been withdrawn and the wings will be dry and rigid enough to lift this fully adult male greengrocer in flight to a new life.

It will be a life full of hazards. Plump and defenceless, cicadas are much sought after, both by tree-climbing children and by a variety of insectivorous predators. Many take a trip to school in a little boy's pocket or rattling around in a shoe box, while many, many more end up as food.

The deadliest of the cicada's insect enemies, because it's totally geared to one kind of prey, is the female cicada-killer wasp. This large and colourful predator seeks out a cicada in a tree and paralyses it

A cicada nymph transforms into a winged adult. Pumping air through its sides, it split its tough outer casing, before head and thorax emerge, releasing the crumpled wings, into which blood is then pumped.

with her sting. Dropping with it from the tree, she drags it into her burrow, lays an egg on it and flies off to find more victims. In one season a cicada-killer can fill several such burrows with cicadas, alive but helpless, preserved as a lifetime of meals for her grubs.

But cicadas' most visible enemies are the keen-eyed birds that share the treetops with them. Although most cicadas are well camouflaged while feeding, the sites where they feed may be exposed and camouflage often isn't enough: cicadas make a lot of noise and birds have sensitive ears. In flight they are at their most vulnerable. Quite clumsy fliers, cicadas on the wing are like biplanes going up against jet fighters. Many's the time I've winced on hearing the protesting squawk of a cicada as it's carried off in the beak of a currawong or other large insectivorous bird.

Even before they've reached adulthood, cicadas face a multitude of dangers. Underground they can be flooded or dried out, parasitised by beetle larvae or attacked by fungi. During their vulnerable few hours of emergence, predatory insects can attack them or heavy rain or strong wind may detach them from their support. Ants, efficient scavengers and garbage disposers, will immediately attack a daylight-emerging cicada that falls to the ground, and any dead or dying cicada is soon dragged away as food for the ant larvae in the nest.

The odds against survival seem great, but cicadas are still around after several million years of coexistence with those that feed on them. The balance of nature prevails and our sizzling summers happily continue to reverberate with the irritating, raucous, repetitive, deafening but somehow endearing choral performances of greengrocers, cherrynoses, double drummers, razor grinders, *et al.*

As I pack up my photographic equipment I wish the cicada, still hanging motionless from his cast skin, the best of luck. I hope he'll survive the night to join his brothers, adding one more voice to the theme song of a long, hot Australian summer. ■

STORY BY **NATSUMI PENBERTHY** PHOTOGRAPHY BY **JÜRGEN OTTO**

TINY DANCER

Modern camera technology has captured male peacock spiders' miniature courtship dances, revealing that – with bodies that rival butterflies in colour – these Aussie natives can really flaunt it.

Issue 123 ◆ Nov–Dec 2014

IN A SUNLIT ROOM, in the bushland-fringed Sydney suburb of St Ives, photographer Dr Jürgen Otto examines a plastic sample vial. He unscrews the lid, and, tilting the cylinder, gently taps it with his finger. A puff of soil particles and a flash of brilliant blue tumble out and settle on a bush-floor diorama.

Jürgen's German accent is little diluted by the several decades he's spent in Australia. "Come on, there she is," he mutters, eyeballing a teeny Harris's peacock spider. His finger gently shepherds it towards a plain brown female already on set. The furry blue flap curled around the male's pencil tip-sized abdomen is studded with dots and stripes and flanked by leaf-green panels. "Here we go. He sees her," Jürgen whispers, glancing at me.

Two of the male's furry legs rise like poles at a 75° angle and the iridescent, blue-green flap unfurls and pops up. Jiggling the flap frenetically between the V of his upright legs, the spider waggles about with the high-octane energy of a fly.

Seconds later, the female, looking uninterested, turns the cold shoulder on him. The male continues to jiggle and showboat, in a last-ditch attempt to capture her attention, so Jürgen plonks in a finger and hooks him out. "Just in case she eats him," he says wryly, returning the male to its vial.

AUSTRALIA'S 29 peacock spider species are the most attractive of the world's more than 5000 species of jumping spider. At a tiny 4–6mm long, they stand out because of their small size, their relatively large eyes and, of course, the male's dazzling opisthosomal fan. This is a flap on the →

It was originally thought that "flying" peacock spiders used their opisthosomal fans (the large flap) to fly through the air, not to woo the ladies.

A male Harris's peacock spider pats the head of a potential mate – she usually allows this before copulation.

abdomen covered in bright iridescent scales, which makes it appear similar to a butterfly wing. The fans are bold in themselves but it's the male's unique courtship dance that has caught people's attention, especially online.

Jürgen's YouTube channel has attracted more than 3.6 million views. In a mash-up of his footage by another user, one male's acrobatic legs make traffic-controller-like gestures to the rhythm of *Y.M.C.A.* by the Village People; and footage of a coastal peacock spider is slowed as it does a sort of peculiar overhead clap. Each species has its own unique choreography. Most begin by waving their legs to get the female's attention, then follow with a dance using their third legs and opisthosomal fans. They also use rotating appendages called spinnerets (which other spider species use to spin webs) and vibrate their abdomens. The dance can last anywhere from 10 seconds to two hours.

Today, the spiders' fame has spread well beyond YouTube. Last year Jürgen's videos were on show at the Museum of Contemporary Art in Sydney; peacock spider-inspired handbags and shoes have been shown on Bangkok catwalks; and their dance was even the inspiration for a performance by Harvard University students in 2012. Recently, the American Museum of Natural History, in New York, used Jürgen's footage and images for a spider exhibit, as has the Natural History Museum of Denmark in Copenhagen.

DESPITE THE MALES' COLOURFUL harlequinesque get-ups, peacock spiders were largely overlooked by science before Jürgen first pointed his lens at them almost a decade ago. Since then, the number of described Australian species has jumped from seven to 29 – 12 of which were named by Jürgen and his American collaborator, David Hill. "Peacock spiders are really extreme, even in the jumping-spider world," says Maddie Girard, at the University of California, Berkeley. She's midway through a PhD study of the group, despite living on the other side of the world.

For her research, Maddie amplifies the vibrations coming off surfaces around the spiders in order to listen to the complex soundtrack they create by whacking their abdomens on the ground, or vibrating their legs. "I can identify a dud male... just based on sounds a lot of the time," she says.

It's thought that the female doesn't hear this drumming, but feels it through her legs. "You get a male who's older and seemingly weaker, and his sounds are a lot more muddled," Maddie adds. In short, the performance is about the females selecting the males with the best genes, she says.

Jürgen, a sandy-haired 49-year-old, is actually an acarologist. In other words, he's a mite specialist, and his day job involves looking for even tinier creatures for the Department of Agriculture, Fisheries

One of Jürgen's many undescribed spider species, readily identifiable as a peacock spider by its large eyes and large patterned flap, known as an opisthosomal fan.

and Forestry. "It's probably one reason I find looking for spiders quite easy," he says. "A 4mm spider – that's a huge thing for me."

JÜRGEN'S ST IVES HOME is a stone's throw from Sydney's Ku-ring-gai Chase National Park. This is one of the locations where you can find *Maratus volans*, commonly known as the flying spider. Jürgen's very first peacock spider encounter was with a specimen of this spectacular orange-and-turquoise species.

He says that, almost a decade ago, he was a frustrated semi-professional wildlife photographer. He had been scrabbling for subject matter on the east coast after working with tropical wildlife subjects in Townsville for nine years. "I eventually started to photograph flowers," he says. Then, while out on a bushwalk, he spotted something jumping in the leaf-litter.

The flying spider was named in 1874, says Jürgen. But, "strangely enough, the person who first caught it, Henry Bradley, made up the story [about flying]". Jürgen explains that Bradley told his story to the leading arachnid expert in England at the time, who wrote the first record of the spider. The flight myth followed the spiders around for the next 130 years.

The truth is they're nimble, but the physics are all off, says Julianne Waldock, a technical officer at the Western Australian Museum in Perth, who devotes some of her spare time to researching these engaging little spiders. In 2007 she presented a paper that pointed out that there's little evidence that these creatures glide. It wasn't until 2008, when Jürgen captured images of the dance of *M. volans* for the first time, that people came to know more about their miniature performances.

Their internet stardom has had a knock-on effect scientifically. Jürgen's computer is full of files labelled, for example, 'orange blotches' or 'blue face' – temporary names for undescribed species, a few sent to him by photographers around the country.

Indeed, the Harris's peacock spider I watched dance was named after Canberra vineyard worker Stuart Harris, who tramped through the bush for more than 150 hours to find another example of the then-unnamed species after Jürgen commented on a picture he'd posted online.

"There are no scientists working professionally in this field – we're all amateurs," Jürgen says. "We wouldn't know about most of these species if it wasn't for amateurs." They're certainly less well known than mites, he says, maybe because they're not pests.

"Macro photography is really huge now," he says, "and people think of these spiders as the Holy Grail… I think one day they will be as famous as kangaroos and koalas. I really do." ■

Fear and loathing and flies

Our murderous relationship with the summer's inescapable, infuriating irritators.

Story by **Jack Rozycki**

Issue 81 Jan–Mar 2006

Australian Geographic writer Matthew Cawood is beset by bushflies as he explores the Flinders Ranges in SA on assignment during the height of summer.

THERE WAS a buzz of anxiety about the possibility of flies alighting on the Queen during her visit to Australia in 1963 and the CSIRO was charged with the urgent task of finding a way to keep the dirty, disrespectful insects off Her Majesty during an upcoming garden party at Yarralumla. Two entomologists, Doug Waterhouse and Dick Norris, got to work and created a Royal spray from a non-toxic repellent chemical, di-N-propyl isocinchomeronate, they found in a US Army survival manual. It was a brilliant success and after the Royal visit the formula was handed over to Samuel Taylor (the owner of the Mortein brand) for the asking – at that time, CSIRO policy was to make its discoveries freely available because they'd been developed with public funding. Today, the product, named Aerogard, is a major brand worth many millions of dollars.

Until Aerogard and its imitators came along to keep the annoying flies at bay, we used pump sprays, and before that, it was pretty much down to the Barcoo salute outdoors, and flyscreens at home. That much-overused Aussie bush image, the hat with the dangling corks, seems to be more cartoon shorthand than fact – it would have been ineffective and the ever-practical bushies wouldn't have persevered with a remedy that didn't work.

There are 20–30,000 species of fly in Australia (out of some 250,000 species in the world), although the biggest problem for us, out in the paddock, has always been the bushfly. One of the earliest Europeans to have set foot in this country, William Dampier, wrote in January 1688, after his observation of this persistent and annoying creature, "The inhabitants of the Country are the miserablest people in the World...their eye lids are always half closed to keep the flies out of their eyes; they being so troublesome here that no fanning will keep them from coming to one's face; and without the assistance of both hands to keep them off, they will creep into one's nostrils, and mouth too if the lips are not shut very close..."

A century and a half later, the bush fly problem was as unpleasant as ever: "...sleep after sunrise was impossible, on account of the number of flies which kept buzzing around the face... Into the eyes, when unclosed they soon found their way...neither were the nostrils safe from their attacks, which were made simultaneously on all points, and in multitudes," wrote explorer Sir George Grey in December 1837 about his flyridden journey through north-western Australia. The flies clearly bothered Europeans more than Aboriginals. Long-time CSIRO entomologist Don Colless, now in his 80s, reckons the bushfly came to Australia with people, but its population exploded with European colonisation.

"Before humans came, the opportunity for breeding wasn't there. The flies breed in excrement and the kangaroo faeces are too hard," he said. "But when human beings came they brought dogs with them, and dog and human poo are a perfect breeding medium." With the advent of cattle and sheep grazing the problem grew exponentially. To keep flies out of the home – particularly blowies, which have a strong attraction to raw flesh (meat) as a breeding ground, the flyscreen was introduced. It's worth remembering that on stations and country properties, a fair amount of home slaughtering went on and killing rooms, and meat houses, would have been particularly vulnerable to blowfly strike. Before refrigeration, meat was stored in meat safes – metal boxes with perforated sides that allowed ventilation but with the holes too small for flies.

THOSE UNABLE to afford flyscreens often hung strips of hessian over doorways. In theory, they'd brush the flies off one's back.

A popular and inexpensive breakthrough came with flypaper, which became available from 1885 onwards. The sticky, resin-coated strips of paper or film, which also contained a sweet attractant such as molasses, trapped the flies as they landed on it. Flypaper was quite effective against houseflies, albeit the method relied on the insects cooperating in their own demise.

Surprisingly, Mortein, Australia's best-known insecticide, initially made as a powder from crushed chrysanthemum flowers to produce a pyrethrum extract, preceded flypaper by about 10 years. Mortein's inventor, J. Hagemann, a German immigrant, named it by combining the French word for dead, *mort*, and the German term for one, *ein*. When in the 1920s a liquid version of Mortein appeared, it could be dispensed by a pump-spray atomiser and our war against the fly took a quantum leap. Mortein's distributor, Samuel Taylor, purchased the rights to the product and in 1953 introduced the first aerosol can (called Pressure Pak).

On the sun-scorched plains of Brunette Downs cattle station on the Barkly Tableland, NT, flies are a serious pest for man and beast alike.

These days, we use about 6.7 million cans of flyspray and about 3 million containers of personal insect repellent each year.

While the housefly and the bushfly annoyed, the most troublesome fly, in terms of economic damage rather than simply inconvenience or aggravation, has been the sheep blowfly, which probably arrived in Australia from South Africa towards the latter part of the 19th century.

The sheep blowfly continues to create serious strife for Australia's woolgrowers. To prevent blowflies laying maggots under the skin of the sheep's nether regions, some graziers have been 'mulesing' their flocks – a practice that involves flaying the skin around the sheep's rear end. But mulesing has been condemned by some as cruel, and a US-based animal rights group, People for the Ethical Treatment of Animals, once convinced some of our high-value wool customers to boycott Australian wool in protest.

Sadly, no acceptable chemical fly repellent has as yet been found to be effective against the sheep blowfly.

THE CSIRO was also involved in the dung-beetle program, which helped to bring under control the bovine-dung breeding buffalo fly. The organisation's Dr George Bornemissza worked on the project during the 1970s and eventually 50 species were imported to help our native beetles, which weren't coping with dissipating the huge quantities of cattle droppings.

As Australia's population grew, and gravitated to towns and cities, the flies followed, especially the bushflies and houseflies, and bred happily in the streets' plentiful horse manure. In response, we turned on the flies with murderous hatred – if advertising of the period is anything to go by – and the "deadly" housefly was accused of being a "Slayer of Men", a "Champion Killer of Babies" and the "Greatest Peril to the Health of the Home".

To defeat this deadly peril, there was even a serious suggestion from a Tasmanian parliamentarian to spray rubbish tips and manure heaps with a solution of arsenic, although, in the end, the plan was sensibly shelved when it was pointed out that mass poisonings would result.

But other dangerous chemicals, such as the organochlorin pesticides aldrin and its sister chemical, dieldrin, were used extensively in Australia to defeat fly infestations from World War II until the 1980s, resulting in significant environmental damage.

Organochlorin pesticides are now banned in Australia. While the natural chemical pyrethrum is still the main ingredient in some fly sprays, and growing the daisies is a thriving industry in Tasmania, most fly sprays and repellents are made up of synthetic chemicals, and there's understandable anxiety among some Australian consumers after our experience with organochlorins.

A growing segment of the personal insect repellent market is using natural chemicals – produced by plants as their own anti-insect defences. Plants don't seem to 'mind' if insects crawl all over them, as long as they don't eat them. To survive, they exude oils and resins that flies find distasteful. By rubbing such oil concentrates onto ourselves – in the main, lemony oils such as citral and citronellal, provided by Australian lemon myrtle and lemon-scented gum – we can stop flies biting us.

These solutions are most effective against biting insects such as bushflies, sandflies, ants and mosquitoes. But against annoying houseflies and blowflies, such repellents still have a way to go, although research into natural products is accelerating.

Since white colonisation, Australia's had a morbid fascination with flies that has at times bordered on the pathological. Advertising of various means of defeating flies played up that fear and loathing. At the same time, somewhat ambivalently, the fly entered our popular culture and became part of our vernacular, particularly the blowfly, which with its affectionate diminutive of "blowie", appears in countless sayings, jokes, cartoons and songs, such as the 1972 Top-40 hit for Frankie Davidson, *50 Million Blowflies Can't be Wrong*. ■

Jewels of the trees

Story by **Steve Wilson**

Issue 65 Jan–Mar 2002

Temognatha carpentariae Many of the 85 Australian jewel beetle species currently in the genus *Temognatha* are conspicuous insects because of their large size and eye-catching colours and patterns.

I'LL NEVER FORGET that hot January afternoon, as I stood beneath a flowering mallee tree near Jerramungup in the south-west of Western Australia. The still air was thick with the heady aroma of nectar and there was a deep, droning buzz as scores of giant jewel beetles wheeled, soared and crashlanded on the mallee's cream-coloured blossoms. I could see their wing cases glinting metallic green and purple as they blundered and jostled, eager to reach the flowers' sweet resources.

Events like this unfold throughout Australia during the warmer months. There are some 1500 species of jewel beetle here, ranging in length from a few millimetres to 7cm. Yet few Australians have heard of them, much less seen them, and we still know precious little about their habits.

We do know that many species of jewel beetle are attracted to certain flowers, such as those of eucalypts, angophoras and various tea-trees, and that others are leaf-chewers, with preferences for particular plants, such as wattles, she-oaks and conifers. But because many jewel beetle larvae are wood-boring grubs, their early life-stages are a mystery. We're aware of them only when they emerge briefly into the world of sunlight and nectar.

My memorable encounter at Jerramungup occurred during a bumper year, when a mix of species appeared by the millions. No-one knows how long jewel beetles remain as grubs, nor what causes their synchronised emergence; in some cases, perhaps chemical changes in their host plants are the trigger. If the notorious hoop pine jewel beetle is anything to go by, development can take quite some time: this beetle horrifies homeowners by emerging from pine furniture in which it's been living as a grub since before the timber was milled. One report suggests it can be as long as 17 years.

Our largest genus, *Castiarina*, is the least-known group. Of 465 species named so far, full life histories are known for fewer than a dozen. Different species feed on the stems, trunks or roots of various plants according to their type, age, height and thickness, as well as their state of health. Some may even choose their hosts on the basis of different degrees of burning, or length of time since the last fire.

According to Dr Shelley Barker, an honorary research associate at the South Australian Museum in Adelaide, the classification of Australia's jewel beetles is a bit of a minefield. "Many species were named more than once by different people," he told me. "Their specimens have been lodged in museums worldwide, so sorting out what's what can be a problem." In his quest to catalogue our jewel beetles, Shelley has already described and named more than 200 species and has dozens more waiting in the wings.

Thanks to their exquisite beauty, jewel beetles caught the attention of enthusiasts long ago and, like butterflies, they're avidly collected. Collectors in the first few decades of the 20th century may have possessed priceless information about the beetles they caught, but few of their records have survived.

FORTUNATELY, THIS ISN'T true of Horace Brown, who collected in southern WA and central and northern Queensland from just after World War I into the 1940s. Brown recorded dates, localities and the plants on which his beetles were found. His vast collection, under wraps for decades, resurfaced in the early 2000s revealing a hoard of valuable information. Among the rows of specimens in naphthalene-filled boxes are species not seen since they were first found. Many of his field sites were in Queensland's brigalow belt and were cleared 50–60 years ago.

The work of interpreting the collection falls largely to its custodian, Mark Hanlon. Studying Brown's beetles involves following a paper trail of neat, faded, handwritten specimen labels that meanders through museums all over the world. As a result, animals forgotten for 80 or more years are being searched for and rediscovered in the wild, some reduced to tiny populations in remnant thickets of a dozen or so old trees. One such beetle goes by the scientific name of *Melobasis aurocyanea*.

Discovered by Brown in the early 1930s, it was rediscovered in 2001 in a small roadside patch of wattle in southern WA. I'm looking forward to next summer. There's a stand of black wattle near Cecil Plains in southern Queensland where I like to watch the great shiny green beetles with stripes of powdery yellow alight in the trees' crowns, and then rush down the stems like frenetic, gaudy little robots. For creatures that spend so much of their lives in dark obscurity, their emergence into the world of light couldn't be more colourful or dramatic.

Castiarina subtirfasciata With more than 450 species, *Castiarina* is Australia's largest jewel beetle genus. They are small- to medium-sized beetles and are found in all states and on many islands. They can be seen in large numbers on flowering bushes like this melaleuca blossom.

Stigmodera gratiosa Members of the *Stigmodera* genus have such gem-like qualities that they were once widely used for brooches and ornaments. Seven Australian species belong to the genus but the hard shell and everlasting lustre of this WA native were particularly valued by jewellers. Its delicately sculpted carapace with patches of bronze sheen has the appearance of a multifaceted precious gem.

Selected Index

First instances of a particular term in a story are set in non-bold text. Photographs are set in **bold** text.

◆

→

Selected Index

◆

Photography credits

◆

COVER Steve Morenos; 1 Auscape; 2 Jami Tarris; 4 St John Pound/Alamy; 6 Darren Jew; 7 Rod Scott; 8 Mitch Reardon; 10 Theo Allofs/Getty; 13 Cyril Ruoso/Minden Pictures; 14 Theo Allofs/Getty; 16(L) Mitch Reardon; 16(R) Mitch Reardon; 17(L) Mitch Reardon; 17(R) Tier Und Naturfotografie J und C Sohns; 18 Jim Frazier; 19 Jim Frazier; 20 Jim Frazier; 21 Jim Frazier; 22 Roland Seitre/Minden Pictures; 24 Jason Edwards; 25(T) Bill Bachman; 25(B) Robin Smith; 27 Mitch Reardon; 28 Bill Hatcher; 30(L) Peter Schouten; 30(R) Bill Hatcher; 31 Bill Hatcher; 32 Bill Hatcher; 33 Bill Hatcher; 34 Jane Hammond; 35 Robert McLean; 37 Jason Edwards; 38 Jason Edwards; 39 Jason Edwards; 40 D. Parer & E. Parer-Cook/ Minden Pictures; 42(L) Ian Connellan; 42(R) Ian Connellan; 43 Jason Edwards; 44 Ofer Levy; 46(L) Grahame McConnell; 46(R) Grahame McConnell; 47 David Hancock; 48 Mitch Reardon; 50 Mitch Reardon; 51 Mitch Reardon; 52 Andrew Gregory; 55 D. Parer & E. Parer-Cook/Minden Pictures; 56 Vanessa Mylett; 58(L) Mitch Reardon; 58(R) Mitch Reardon; 59 Mitch Reardon; 60 Mitch Reardon; 61 Mitch Reardon; 63 Christina N. Zdenek; 64 Bill Bachman; 66(L) Bill Bachman; 66(R) Bill Bachman; 67 Bill Bachman; 68 Matthew Newton; 69 Matthew Newton; 70 Jiri Lochman; 72(L) Jiri Lochman; 72(R) Jiri Lochman; 73 Jiri Lochman; 75 Esther Beaton; 76 Alexander Safonov; 79 Phillip Colla/SeaPics.com; 80 Tobias Bernhard; 82 Giordano Cipriani; 83 Migration Media - Underwater Imaging; 84 Micheline Jenner; 85 Norbert Wu; 86 Darren Jew; 87 Darren Jew; 88 Darren Jew; 89(L) Darren Jew; 89(R) Darren Jew; 90 Kevin Deacon; 91(T) Kevin Deacon; 91(B) Kevin Deacon; 92 Kevin Deacon; 93 Kevin Deacon; 94 Darren Jew; 96(L) Darren Jew; 96(R) Townsville Maritime Museum; 97 Darren Jew; 99 Kelvin Aitken; 100 Darren Jew; 102 Darren Jew; 103 Darren Jew; 104 Luis Javier Sandoval; 106 Steve Woods Photography; 108 Tony Karacsonyi; 109 Tony Karacsonyi; 110 Tony Karacsonyi; 111(T) Tony Karacsonyi; 111(B) Tony Karacsonyi; 112 Darren Jew; 114(L) Roy Hunt; 114(R) Darren Jew; 115 Darren Jew; 116 Esther Beaton; 119 Chrissie Goldrick; 121 Jason Edwards; 122(L) Jason Edwards; 122(R) Jason Edwards; 123 Jason Edwards; 124 Image courtesy of the Western Australian Museum; 125 Steve Murphy; 126 Chris Lane/Fairfax; 128 John Gould; 129 Collection of the Queen Victoria Museum and Art Gallery, Launceston, Tasmania; 130 Esther Beaton; 131 Esther Beaton; 132 Chrissie Goldrick; 134 Chrissie Goldrick; 135 Chrissie Goldrick; 136 Jason Edwards; 139 Auscape; 140 Esther Beaton; 141(L) Esther Beaton; 141(R) Esther Beaton; 142 Jason Edwards; 144 Jason Edwards; 145(L) Jason Edwards; 145(R) Jason Edwards; 146 David Hancock; 147 David Hancock; 148 Jason Edwards; 150 Jason Edwards; 151 Jason Edwards; 152 One Shot/PNZ/Miz Watanabe; 153 BIOSPHOTO/ Alamy Stock Photo; 154 Frans Lanting; 157 Nick Rains; 158 Tim Laman; 160 Conrad Hoskins; 161 Conrad Hoskins; 163 Nick Rains; 164 Bill Bachman; 165 Steve Wilson; 166 Auscape/Contributor; 167(L) Auscape/UIG; 167(R) Nick Rains; 168 Julian Finn/Museums Victoria; 170(L) Peter Batson/Deep sea photography; 170(R) Peter Batson/Deep sea photography; 171 Peter Batson/Deep sea photography; 173 Gary Bell/OceanwideImages.com; 174 Steve Wilson; 177 Esther Beaton; 178 Doug Perrine/SeaPics.com; 180 Doug Perrine/SeaPics.com; 181 Doug Perrine/SeaPics.com; 183 Steve Wilson; 184 Steve Wilson; 185 Steve Wilson; 186 Russell Shakespeare; 188(L) Chrissie Goldrick; 188(R) Russell Shakespeare; 189 Russell Shakespeare; 191 Steve Wilson; 193 David Hancock; 194 David Hancock; 195(T) David Hancock; 195(B) David Hancock; 196 Mike Langford; 198(R) Mike Langford; 198(L) Randy Larcombe; 199 Randy Larcombe; 200 Holly Michele; 203 Jürgen Otto; 205 Esther Beaton; 206 Esther Beaton; 207 Esther Beaton; 208 Topic Images Inc.; 210 Jürgen Otto; 212 Jürgen Otto; 213 Jürgen Otto; 214 Randy Larcombe; 215 Dean Saffron; 216 Steve K Wilson; 217 (T) Jiri Lochman, Lochman Transparencies; 217 (B) Jiri Lochman, Lochman Transparencies; 223 Matthew Newton; back cover Steve Morenos.

Photography Index

◆

The shy albatrosses of Albatross Island, Tasmania. See p 68.

Writer Index

◆

Acknowledgements

◆

First published in 2017
Bauer Media Ltd, 54 Park Street, Sydney, NSW 2000.
Telephone (02) 9263 9813 Fax (02) 8116 9377 Email editorial@ausgeo.com.au
www.australiangeographic.com.au

Book editors Chrissie Goldrick, Joanna Hartman and Geordie Torr
Book design Mike Ellott
Chapter introductions Geordie Torr
Sub editor Geordie Torr
Editorial assistance and image management Rebecca Cotton and Jess Teideman
Proofreader Susan McCreery

Managing editor Australian Geographic commercial Lauren Smith
Australian Geographic Editor in chief Chrissie Goldrick
Publisher Jo Runciman
Bauer Media Chief Executive Officer Paul Dykzeul

Printed in China through Leo Paper Products

National Library of Australia Cataloguing-in-Publication entry
Title: Australia gone wild / edited by Chrissie Goldrick, Joanna Hartmann, Geordie Torr; Mike Ellott (designer).

ISBN: 9781925694505 (hardback)

Notes: Includes index.

Subjects: Wildlife photography--Australia.
Nature photography--Australia.
Animals--Australia--History.
Plants--Australia--History.

Other Creators/Contributors: Goldrick, Chrissie, editor. Hartmann, Joanna, editor. Torr, Geordie, editor. Ellott, Mike, book designer.

Australian Geographic Pty. Ltd., issuing body.

On the cover

In Australia, we can enjoy a wide variety of native wildlife in our own backyards, from parrots and songbirds to bandicoots and possums. The familiar common ringtail possum (*Pseudocheirus peregrinus*) uses its white-tipped prehensile tail to hold onto things, and when not in use, will curl it into a spiral – the source of its common name.

Back cover: a pair of Tasmanian devils

Photography by Steve Morenos

www.stevemorenos.com

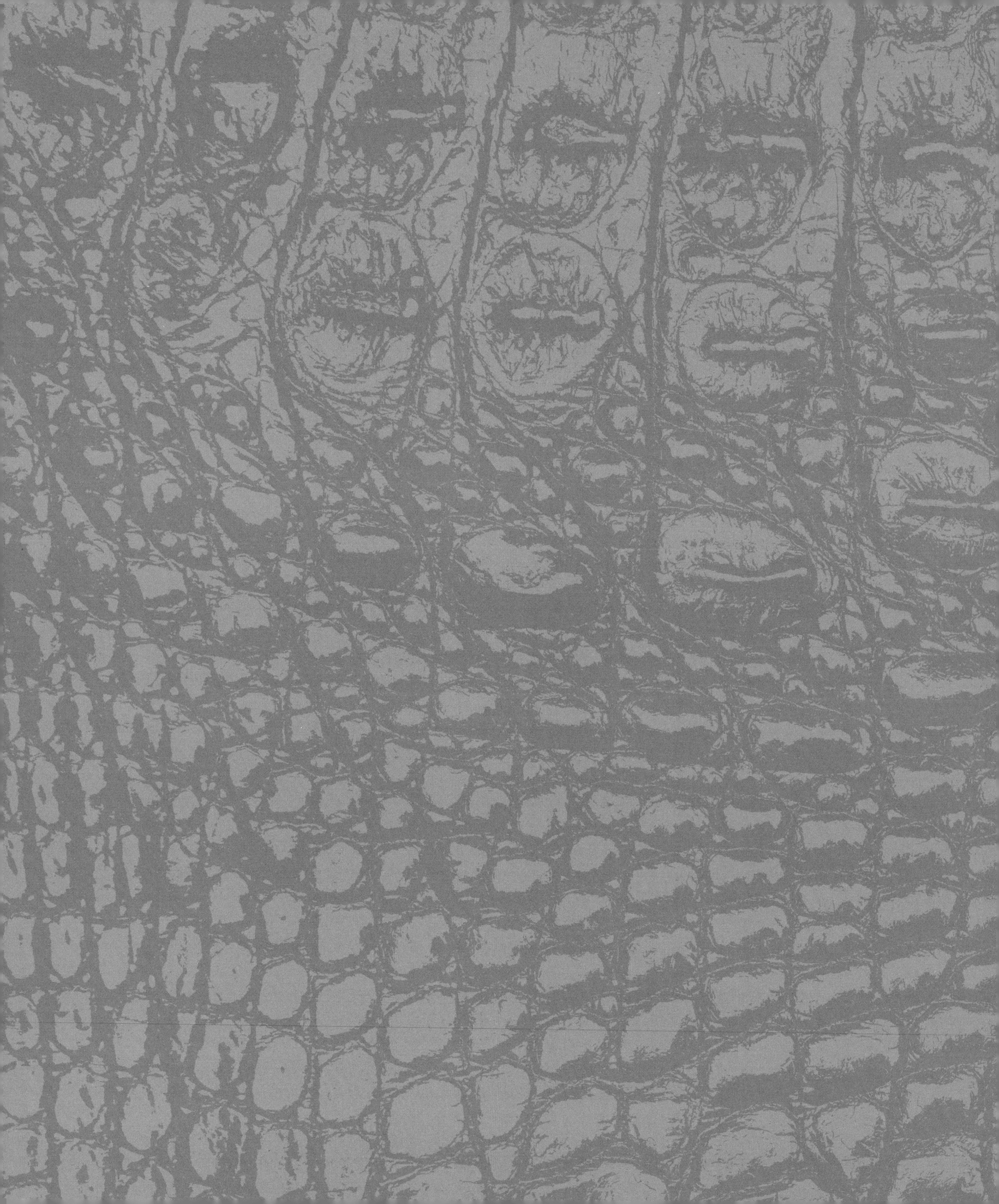